Sing unto the Lord, O ye saints of his, and give thanks at the remembrance of his holiness (Psalms 30:4).

The Christian dispensation was ushered in with a song when an angel chorus broke the midnight stillness over the hills of Judea with "Glory to God in the highest, and on earth peace, good will toward men."

Singing was inherent in the worship of the Early Church. The Apostle Paul, writing to the Ephesian church and again to the Colossians, exhorts that "psalms and hymns and spiritual songs" be used for mutual encouragement and edification. The apostle set an example by joining with Silas in midnight songs of praise in circumstances not conducive to rejoicing, in the Philippian jail.

In Old Testament times worship and song were inseparable. Moses' "Sing ye to the Lord, for he hath triumphed gloriously" in a sense set the pace for the children of Israel in expressing their praise and thanksgiving. King David's psalms, themselves hymns of praise and petition, abound in encouragement to "come before his presence with singing."

What fortitude Martin Luther inspired during the Reformation by his hymns, among them the immortal "A Mighty Fortress Is Our God"! And the Wesleys! Who can measure the impact of their hymns on the Wesleyan revival in England?

Worship in song. Yesterday, today, and throughout eternity: "And they sung as it were a new song before the throne" (Revelation 14:3). Meanwhile: "Make a joyful noise unto God, all ye lands: sing forth the honour of his name: make his praise glorious" (Psalms 66:1-2).

May the Church of Jesus Christ carry on in the tradition of the Lord's redeemed. And may this hymnal be used of God as we respond to the call: "O come, let us sing unto the Lord: let us make a joyful noise to the rock of our salvation" (Psalms 95:1).

WORSHIP IN SONG

HYMNAL

Let the word of Christ dwell in you richly in all wisdom; teaching and admonishing one another in psalms and hymns and spiritual songs, singing with grace in your hearts to the Lord.

Colossians 3:16

LILLENAS PUBLISHING COMPANY
KANSAS CITY, MISSOURI

Contents

The numbers indicate general classifications. Since hymns vary in length, some hymns have had to be placed in a different classification in order to complete a page. Also, many hymns apply to more than one topic. Please refer to the Topical Index in the back of the hymnal for a complete listing of all hymns in each of the above and other topics.

1 How Firm a Foundation

FOUNDATION

"K" in Rippon's "A Selection of Hymns," 1787　　　Early American Melody

1. How firm a foun - da - tion, ye saints of the Lord,
2. Fear not; I am with thee. Oh, be not dis - mayed,
3. When thro' the deep wa - ters I call thee to go,
4. When thro' fie - ry tri - als thy path - way shall lie,
5. E'en down to old age all My peo - ple shall prove
6. The soul that on Je - sus hath leaned for re - pose

Is laid for your faith in His ex - cel - lent Word!
For I am thy God, I will still give thee aid.
The riv - ers of sor - row shall not o - ver - flow;
My grace, all - suf - fi - cient, shall be thy sup - ply.
My sov' - reign, e - ter - nal, un - change - a - ble love;
I will not, I will not de - sert to his foes;

What more can He say than to you He hath said,
I'll strength - en thee, help thee, and cause thee to stand,
For I will be with thee thy tri - als to bless,
The flames shall not hurt thee; I on - ly de - sign
And when hoar - y hairs shall their tem - ples a - dorn,
That soul, tho' all hell should en - deav - or to shake,

To you who for ref - uge to Je - sus have fled?
Up - held by My gra - cious, om - nip - o - tent hand.
And sanc - ti - fy to thee thy deep - est dis - tress.
Thy dross to con - sume and thy gold to re - fine.
Like lambs they shall still in My bos - om be borne.
I'll nev - er, no nev - er, no nev - er for - sake.

2   Joyful, Joyful, We Adore Thee

HYMN TO JOY

Henry van Dyke, 1852-1933   *Arr. from* **Ludwig van Beethoven, 1770-1827**

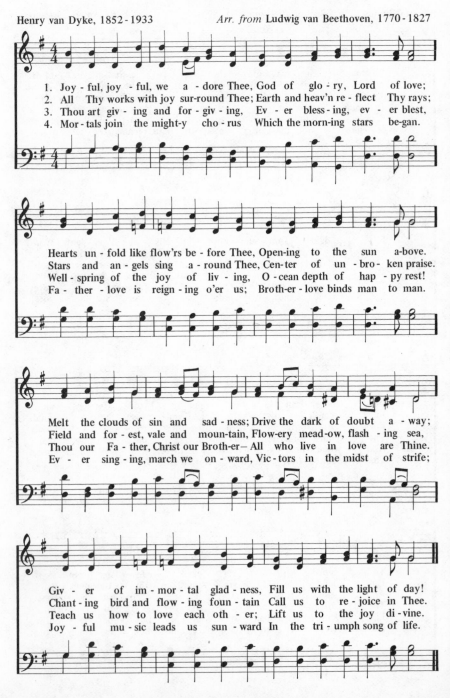

1. Joy - ful, joy - ful, we a - dore Thee, God of glo - ry, Lord of love;
2. All Thy works with joy sur-round Thee; Earth and heav'n re - flect Thy rays;
3. Thou art giv - ing and for - giv - ing, Ev - er bless - ing, ev - er blest,
4. Mor - tals join the might-y cho - rus Which the morn-ing stars be-gan.

Hearts un - fold like flow'rs be - fore Thee, Open-ing to the sun a-bove.
Stars and an - gels sing a - round Thee, Cen- ter of un - bro - ken praise.
Well - spring of the joy of liv - ing, O - cean depth of hap - py rest!
Fa - ther - love is reign - ing o'er us; Broth-er - love binds man to man.

Melt the clouds of sin and sad - ness; Drive the dark of doubt a - way;
Field and for - est, vale and moun-tain, Flow-ery mead-ow, flash - ing sea,
Thou our Fa - ther, Christ our Broth-er— All who live in love are Thine.
Ev - er sing - ing, march we on - ward, Vic-tors in the midst of strife;

Giv - er of im - mor - tal glad - ness, Fill us with the light of day!
Chant - ing bird and flow - ing foun - tain Call us to re - joice in Thee.
Teach us how to love each oth - er; Lift us to the joy di - vine.
Joy - ful mu - sic leads us sun - ward In the tri - umph song of life.

3 To God Be the Glory

Fanny J. Crosby, 1820-1915

W. H. Doane, 1832-1915

1. To God be the glory—great things He hath done. So loved He the world that He
2. O per-fect re-demp-tion, the purchase of blood, To ev-'ry be-liev-er the
3. Great things He hath taught us, great things He hath done, And great our rejoicing thro'

gave us His Son, Who yielded His life an a-tone-ment for sin, And opened the
prom-ise of God! The vil-est of-fend-er who tru-ly believes, That moment from
Je-sus, the Son; But pu-rer, and higher, and greater will be Our won-der, our

REFRAIN

Life-gate that all may go in.
Je-sus a par-don receives. Praise the Lord, praise the Lord, Let the earth hear His
transport, when Je-sus we see.

voice! Praise the Lord, praise the Lord, Let the peo-ple re-joice! O come to the

Fa-ther, thro' Je-sus, the Son, And give Him the glo-ry—great things He hath done.

4   A Mighty Fortress Is Our God

EIN FESTE BURG

Martin Luther, 1483-1546
Tr. by Frederick H. Hedge, 1805-1890

Martin Luther, 1483-1546

1. A might-y For-tress is our God, A Bul-wark nev-er fail - ing;
2. Did we in our own strength con-fide, Our striv-ing would be los - ing,
3. And though this world, with devils filled, Should threaten to un - do us,
4. That word a-bove all earth - ly powers, No thanks to them, a - bid - eth;

Our Help-er He, a - mid the flood Of mor-tal ills pre - vail - ing.
Were not the right Man on our side, The Man of God's own choos - ing.
We will not fear, for God hath willed His truth to tri - umph through us.
The Spir-it and the gifts are ours Through Him who with us sid - eth.

For still our an - cient foe Doth seek to work us woe; His craft and power are
Dost ask who that may be? Christ Je - sus, it is He; Lord Sa - ba -oth, His
The prince of dark-ness grim— We trem-ble not for him. His rage we can en-
Let goods and kin-dred go, This mor-tal life al - so. The bod-y they may

great, And, armed with cru-el hate, On earth is not his e - qual.
name, From age to age the same, And He must win the bat - tle.
dure, For, lo, his doom is sure; One lit - tle word shall fell him.
kill; God's truth a - bid - eth still. His king-dom is for - ev - er.

5 How Great Thou Art!

Carl Boberg, 1859 - 1940
Tr. by Stuart K. Hine, 1899 -

O STORE GUD

Swedish Folk Melody
Arr. by Manna Music, Inc.

1. O Lord, my God! When I in awe-some won-der Con-sid-er
2. When through the woods and for-est glades I wan-der And hear the
3. And when I think that God, His Son not spar-ing, Sent Him to
4. When Christ shall come with shout of ac-cla-ma-tion And take me

all the worlds Thy hands have made, I see the stars, I hear the roll-ing
birds sing sweet-ly in the trees; When I look down from lof-ty mountain
die, I scarce can take it in;— That on the Cross, my bur-den glad-ly
home, what joys shall fill my heart! Then I shall bow in hum-ble ad-o-

REFRAIN

thun-der, Thy pow'r through-out the u-ni-verse dis-played,
gran-deur And hear the brook and feel the gen-tle breeze,
bear-ing, He bled and died to take a-way my sin.—
ra-tion And there pro-claim, my God, how great Thou art! Then sings my

soul, my Saviour God, to Thee. How great Thou art, how great Thou art! Then

sings my soul, my Saviour God, to Thee. How great Thou art, how great Thou art!

*Translator's original words are "works" and "mighty."

6

O Worship the King

LYONS

Robert Grant, 1785-1838

Johann Michael Haydn, 1737-1806

1. O wor-ship the King, all glo-rious a-bove, And grate-ful-ly
2. O tell of His might, and sing of His grace, Whose robe is the
3. Thy boun-ti-ful care, what tongue can re-cite? It breathes in the
4. Frail chil-dren of dust, and fee-ble as frail, In Thee do we

sing His won-der-ful love: Our Shield and De-fend-er, the
light, whose can-o-py space. His char-iots of wrath the deep
air; it shines in the light. It streams from the hills; it de-
trust, nor find Thee to fail. Thy mer-cies how ten-der! how

An-cient of Days, Pa-vil-ioned in splen-dor, and gird-ed with praise.
thun-der-clouds form, And dark is His path on the wings of the storm.
scends to the plain, And sweet-ly dis-tills in the dew and the rain.
firm to the end! Our Mak-er, De-fend-er, Re-deem-er, and Friend!

7

Majestic Sweetness

ORTONVILLE

Samuel Stennett, 1727-1795

Thomas Hastings, 1784-1872

1. Ma-jes-tic sweetness sits enthroned Up-on the Saviour's brow; His head with
2. No mor-tal can with Him compare A-mong the sons of men; Fair-er is
3. He saw me plunged in deep dis-tress, And flew to my re-lief; For me He
4. To Him I owe my life and breath And all the joys I have; He makes me
5. Since from His boun-ty I re-ceive Such proofs of love di-vine, Had I a

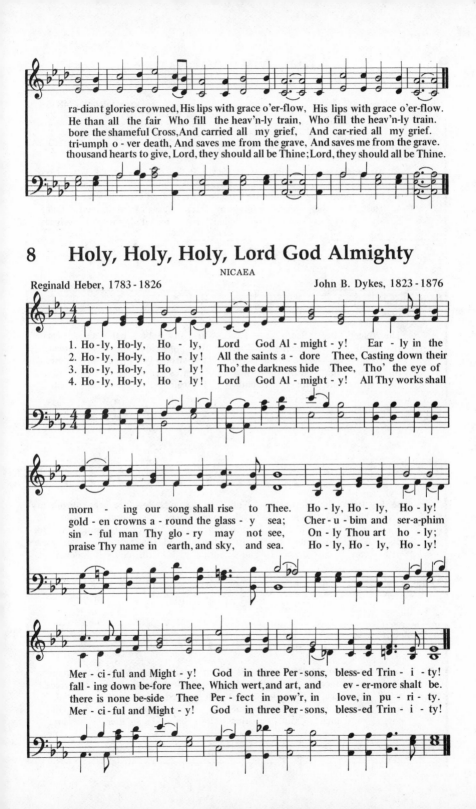

ra-diant glories crowned, His lips with grace o'er-flow, His lips with grace o'er-flow.
He than all the fair Who fill the heav'n-ly train, Who fill the heav'n-ly train.
bore the shameful Cross, And carried all my grief, And car-ried all my grief.
tri-umph o - ver death, And saves me from the grave, And saves me from the grave.
thousand hearts to give, Lord, they should all be Thine; Lord, they should all be Thine.

8 Holy, Holy, Holy, Lord God Almighty

NICAEA

Reginald Heber, 1783-1826

John B. Dykes, 1823-1876

1. Ho-ly, Ho-ly, Ho - ly, Lord God Al - might - y! Ear - ly in the
2. Ho-ly, Ho-ly, Ho - ly! All the saints a - dore Thee, Casting down their
3. Ho-ly, Ho-ly, Ho - ly! Tho' the darkness hide Thee, Tho' the eye of
4. Ho-ly, Ho-ly, Ho - ly! Lord God Al - might - y! All Thy works shall

morn - ing our song shall rise to Thee. Ho - ly, Ho - ly, Ho - ly!
gold - en crowns a - round the glass - y sea; Cher - u - bim and ser-a-phim
sin - ful man Thy glo - ry may not see, On - ly Thou art ho - ly;
praise Thy name in earth, and sky, and sea. Ho - ly, Ho - ly, Ho - ly!

Mer - ci - ful and Might - y! God in three Per - sons, bless-ed Trin - i - ty!
fall - ing down be-fore Thee, Which wert, and art, and ev - er-more shalt be.
there is none be-side Thee Per - fect in pow'r, in love, in pu - ri - ty.
Mer - ci - ful and Might - y! God in three Per - sons, bless-ed Trin - i - ty!

9 Arise, My Soul, Arise

LENOX

Charles Wesley, 1707-1788

Lewis Edson, 1748-1820

1. A - rise, my soul, a - rise. Shake off thy guilt - y fears.
2. He ev - er lives a - bove For me to in - ter - cede,
3. Five bleed - ing wounds He bears, Re - ceived on Cal - va - ry.
4. The Fa - ther hears Him pray, His dear A - noint - ed One;
5. My God is rec - on - ciled; His par - d'ning voice I hear.

The bleed - ing Sac - ri - fice In my be - half ap - pears.
His all - re - deem - ing love, His pre - cious blood to plead.
They pour ef - fec - tual prayers; They strong - ly plead for me.
He can - not turn a - way The pres - ence of His Son.
He owns me for His child; I can no lon - ger fear.

Be - fore the throne my Sure - ty stands, Be - fore the throne my
His blood a - toned for all our race, His blood a - toned for
"For - give him, oh, for - give," they cry. "For - give him, oh, for -
His Spir - it an - swers to the Blood, His Spir - it an - swers
With con - fi - dence I now draw nigh, With con - fi - dence I

Sure - ty stands; My name is writ - ten on His hands.
all our race, And sprin - kles now the throne of grace.
give," they cry, "Nor let that ran - somed sin - ner die."
to the Blood, And tells me I am born of God.
now draw nigh, And, "Fa - ther, Ab - ba, Fa - ther," cry.

10 All Hail the Power of Jesus' Name

DIADEM

Edward Perronet, 1726 - 1792
Alt. by John Rippon, 1751 - 1836

James Ellor, 1819 - 1899

1. All hail the pow'r of Je - sus' name! Let an - gels prostrate fall,
2. Ye cho - sen seed of Is - rael's race, Ye ransomed from the Fall,
3. Let ev - 'ry kin - dred, ev - 'ry tribe, On this ter - res - trial ball,
4. Oh, that with yon - der sa - cred throng We at His feet may fall,

Let an - gels pros - trate fall. Bring forth the roy - al di - a - dem,
Ye ransomed from the Fall, Hail Him who saves you by His grace,
On this ter - res - trial ball, To Him all maj - es - ty as - cribe,
We at His feet may fall! We'll join the ev - er - last - ing song,

And crown _____ Him, Crown Him,

And crown Him, crown Him, crown Him, crown Him, And crown Him
And crown _____ Him, Crown Him,

And crown Him, crown Him, crown Him, Crown _____

crown Him; crown Him;

Lord of all. Crown Him; And crown Him Lord of all!

crown _____ Him,

_____ Him; And crown Him Lord of all!

11 All Hail the Power of Jesus' Name

CORONATION

Edward Perronet, 1726-1792
Alt. by John Rippon, 1751-1836

Oliver Holden, 1765-1844

1. All hail the pow'r of Je - sus' name! Let an - gels pros - trate fall.
2. Ye cho - sen seed of Is - rael's race, Ye ran-somed from the Fall,
3. Let ev - 'ry kin - dred, ev - 'ry tribe, On this ter - res - trial ball,
4. Oh, that with yon - der sa - cred throng We at His feet may fall!

Bring forth the roy - al di - a - dem, And crown Him Lord of all.
Hail Him who saves you by His grace, And crown Him Lord of all.
To Him all maj - es - ty as - cribe, And crown Him Lord of all.
We'll join the ev - er - last - ing song, And crown Him Lord of all.

Bring forth the roy - al di - a - dem, And crown Him Lord of all.
Hail Him who saves you by His grace, And crown Him Lord of all.
• To Him all maj - es - ty as - cribe, And crown Him Lord of all
We'll join the ev - er - last - ing song, And crown Him Lord of all.

12 O for a Thousand Tongues!

AZMON

Charles Wesley, 1707-1788·

Carl G. Glazer, 1784-1829
Arr. by Lowell Mason, 1792-1872

1. O for a thou - sand tongues to sing My great Re-deem-er's praise,
2. My gra - cious Mas - ter and my God, As - sist me to pro - claim,
3. Je - sus! the name that charms our fears, That bids our sor - rows cease;
4. He breaks the pow'r of can-celed sin; He sets the pris - 'ner free.

The glo-ries of my God and King, The tri-umphs of His grace!
To spread thro' all the earth a-broad, The hon-ors of Thy name.
'Tis mu-sic in the sin-ner's ears; 'Tis life, and health, and peace.
His blood can make the foul-est clean; His blood a-vailed for me.

13   O Thou in Whose Presence

DAVIS (MEDITATION)

Joseph Swain, 1761-1796   Freeman Lewis, 1780-1859

1. O Thou in whose pres - ence my soul takes de - light, On
2. Where dost Thou, dear Shep - herd, re - sort with Thy sheep, To
3. Oh, why should I wan - der, an al - ien from Thee, Or
4. He looks! and ten thou - sands of an - gels re - joice, And
5. Dear Shep - herd! I hear and will fol - low Thy call; I

whom in af - flic - tion I call, My Com - fort by day and my
feed them in pas - tures of love? Say, why in the val - ley of
cry in the des - ert for bread? Thy foes will re - joice when my
myr - i - ads wait for His word. He speaks! and e - ter - ni - ty,
know the sweet sound of Thy voice. Re - store and de - fend me, for

Song in the night, My Hope, my Sal - va - tion, my All!
death should I weep, Or a - lone in this wil - der - ness rove?
sor - rows they see, And smile at the tears I have shed.
filled with His voice, Re - ech - oes the praise of the Lord.
Thou art my all, And in Thee I will ev - er re - joice.

14   O God, Our Help in Ages Past

ST. ANNE

Isaac Watts, 1674 - 1748

William Croft, 1678 - 1727

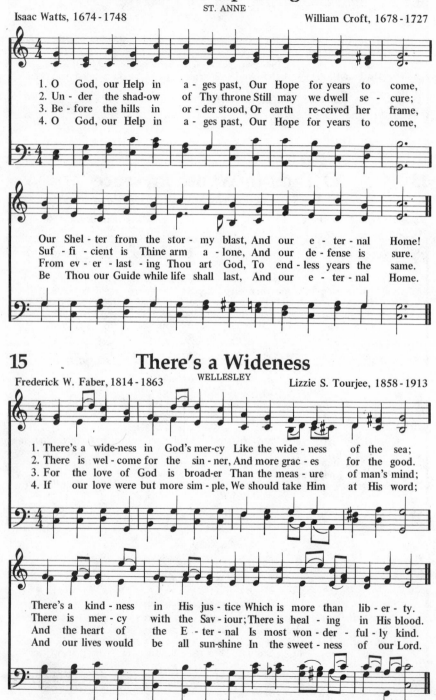

1. O   God, our Help in   a - ges past, Our Hope for years to   come,
2. Un - der   the shad-ow   of Thy throne Still may   we dwell se - cure;
3. Be - fore   the hills in   or - der stood, Or earth   re-ceived her   frame,
4. O   God, our Help in   a - ges past, Our Hope for years to   come,

Our Shel - ter from the stor - my blast, And our   e - ter - nal   Home!
Suf - fi - cient is Thine arm   a - lone, And our   de - fense is   sure.
From ev - er - last - ing Thou art   God, To   end - less years the   same.
Be   Thou our Guide while life shall last, And our   e - ter - nal   Home.

15   .   There's a Wideness

WELLESLEY

Frederick W. Faber, 1814 - 1863

Lizzie S. Tourjee, 1858 - 1913

1. There's a   wide-ness in   God's mer-cy   Like the wide - ness   of the sea;
2. There is wel - come for the   sin - ner, And more grac - es   for the good.
3. For   the love of God is broad - er   Than the meas - ure   of man's mind;
4. If   our love were but more sim - ple, We should take Him   at His word;

There's a   kind - ness   in   His jus - tice Which is more than   lib - er - ty.
There is   mer - cy   with   the Sav - iour; There is heal - ing   in His blood.
And   the heart of   the   E - ter - nal   Is most won - der - ful - ly kind.
And   our lives would   be   all sun-shine   In the sweet - ness   of our Lord.

16 Love Divine, All Loves Excelling

BEECHER

Charles Wesley, 1707-1788

John Zundel, 1815-1882

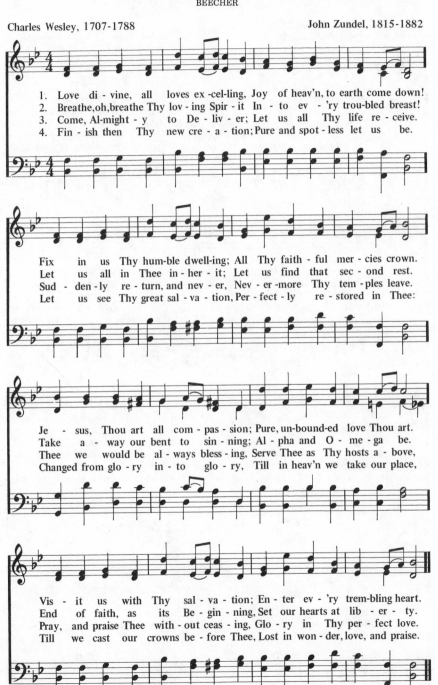

1. Love di - vine, all loves ex -cel-ling, Joy of heav'n, to earth come down!
2. Breathe,oh,breathe Thy lov - ing Spir - it In - to ev - 'ry trou-bled breast!
3. Come, Al-might - y to De - liv - er; Let us all Thy life re - ceive.
4. Fin - ish then Thy new cre - a - tion; Pure and spot - less let us be.

Fix in us Thy hum-ble dwell-ing; All Thy faith - ful mer - cies crown.
Let us all in Thee in - her - it; Let us find that sec - ond rest.
Sud - den-ly re - turn, and nev - er, Nev - er -more Thy tem - ples leave.
Let us see Thy great sal - va - tion, Per - fect - ly re - stored in Thee:

Je - sus, Thou art all com - pas - sion; Pure, un-bound-ed love Thou art.
Take a - way our bent to sin - ning; Al - pha and O - me - ga be.
Thee we would be al - ways bless - ing, Serve Thee as Thy hosts a - bove,
Changed from glo - ry in - to glo - ry, Till in heav'n we take our place,

Vis - it us with Thy sal - va - tion; En - ter ev - 'ry trem-bling heart.
End of faith, as its Be - gin - ning, Set our hearts at lib - er - ty.
Pray, and praise Thee with - out ceas - ing, Glo - ry in Thy per - fect love.
Till we cast our crowns be - fore Thee, Lost in won - der, love, and praise.

17   All Creatures of Our God and King

LASST UNS ERFREUEN

St. Francis of Assisi, 1182-1226
Tr. by William H. Draper, 1855-1933

Melody from
Geistliche Kirchengesäng, 1623
Arr. by Ralph Vaughan Williams, 1872-1958

1. All crea-tures of our God and King, Lift up your voice and with us
2. Thou rush-ing wind that art so strong, Ye clouds that sail in heaven a-
3. Thou flow-ing wa - ter, pure and clear, Make mu - sic for thy Lord to
4. And all ye men of ten - der heart, For - giv - ing oth-ers, take your
5. Let all things their Cre - at - or bless, And wor -ship Him in hum - ble-

sing, Al -le - lu - ia! Al - le -lu - ia! Thou burn-ing sun with gold-en
long, O praise Him! Al - le - lu - ia! Thou ris - ing morn, in praise re-
hear. Al -le - lu - ia! Al - le -lu - ia! Thou fire so mas-ter -ful and
part. O sing ye! Al - le - lu - ia! Ye who long pain and sor -row
ness. O praise Him! Al -le - lu - ia! Praise, praise the Fa - ther, praise the

beam, Thou sil - ver moon with soft-er gleam! O praise Him, O
joice; Ye lights of eve- ning, find a voice! O praise Him, O
bright, Thou giv - est man both warmth and light! O praise Him, O
bear, Praise God and on Him cast your care! O praise Him, O
Son, And praise the Spir-it, Three in One! O praise Him, O

praise Him! Al -le - lu - ia! Al - le -lu - ia! Al-le -lu - ia!

Arrangement used by permission of Oxford University Press.

18 This Is My Father's World

TERRA BEATA

Maltbie D. Babcock, 1858-1901

Franklin L. Sheppard, 1852-1930

1. This is my Fa - ther's world, And to my lis - t'ning ears All
2. This is my Fa - ther's world. The birds their car - ols raise; The
3. This is my Fa - ther's world. Oh, let me ne'er for - get That

na - ture sings, and round me rings The mu - sic of the spheres.
morn- ing light, the lil - y white De - clare their Mak - er's praise.
though the wrong seems oft so strong, God is the Rul - er yet.

This is my Fa-ther's world; I rest me in the thought Of
This is my Fa-ther's world. He shines in all that's fair; In the
This is my Fa-ther's world. The bat - tle is not done; Je -

rocks and trees, of skies and seas—His hand the won - ders wrought.
rus - tling grass I hear Him pass; He speaks to me ev - 'ry - where.
sus, who died, shall be sat - is - fied, And earth and heav'n be one.

19 All Glory, Laud, and Honor

ST. THEODULPH

Theodulph of Orleans, ?-821
Tr. by John M. Neale, 1818-1866

Melchior Teschner, 16th or 17th century

1. All glo - ry, laud, and hon - or To Thee, Re - deem-er, King,
2. The com - pa - ny of an - gels Are prais - ing Thee on high,
3. To Thee, be - fore Thy pas - sion, They sang their hymns of praise;

To whom the lips of chil - dren Made sweet ho - san - nas ring.
And mor - tal men and all things Cre - a - ted make re - ply.
To Thee, now high ex - alt - ed, Our mel - o - dy we raise.

Thou art the King of Is - ra - el, Thou Da - vid's roy - al Son,
The peo - ple of the He - brews With palms be - fore Thee went;
Thou didst ac - cept their prais - es; Ac - cept the praise we bring,

Who in the Lord's name com - est, The King and Bless-ed One.
Our praise and prayer and an - thems Be - fore Thee we pre - sent.
Who in all good de - light - est, Thou good and gra-cious King.

20 Eternal Father, Strong to Save

MELITA

William Whiting, 1825 - 1878

John B. Dykes, 1823 - 1876

1. E - ter - nal Fa - ther, strong to save, Whose arm hath bound the
2. O Christ, whose voice the wa - ters heard, And hushed their rag - ing
3. O Ho - ly Spir - it, who didst brood Up - on the wa - ters
4. O Trin - i - ty of love and power, Our breth - ren shield in

rest - less wave, Who bidd'st the might - y o - cean deep
at Thy word; Who walk - edst on the foam - ing deep
dark and rude, And bid their an - gry tu - mult cease,
dan - ger's hour; From rock and tem - pest, fire and foe,

Its own ap - point - ed lim - its keep: O hear us when we
And calm a - mid the storm didst sleep: O hear us when we
And give, for wild con - fu - sion, peace: O hear us when we
Pro - tect them where - so - e'er they go. Thus ev - er - more shall

cry to Thee For those in per - il on the sea.
cry to Thee For those in per - il on the sea.
cry to Thee For those in per - il on the sea.
rise to Thee Glad hymns of praise from land and sea.

21 Come, Thou Almighty King

ITALIAN HYMN (Trinity)

Anonymous

Felice de Giardini, 1716-1796

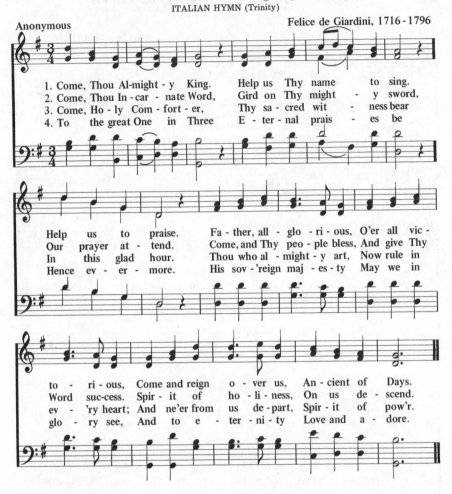

1. Come, Thou Al-might - y King, Help us Thy name to sing,
2. Come, Thou In - car - nate Word, Gird on Thy might - y sword,
3. Come, Ho - ly Com - fort - er, Thy sa - cred wit - ness bear
4. To the great One in Three E - ter - nal prais - es be

Help us to praise. Fa - ther, all - glo - ri - ous, O'er all vic -
Our prayer at - tend. Come, and Thy peo - ple bless, And give Thy
In this glad hour. Thou who al - might - y art, Now rule in
Hence ev - er - more. His sov - 'reign maj - es - ty May we in

to - ri - ous, Come and reign o - ver us, An - cient of Days.
Word suc-cess. Spir - it of ho - li - ness, On us de - scend.
ev - 'ry heart; And ne'er from us de-part, Spir - it of pow'r.
glo - ry see, And to e - ter - ni - ty Love and a - dore.

22 God Moves in a Mysterious Way

MANOAH

William Cowper, 1731-1800

From Greatorex's "Collection," 1851

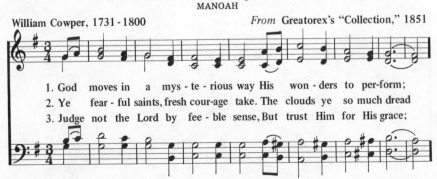

1. God moves in a mys - te - rious way His won - ders to per-form;
2. Ye fear - ful saints, fresh cour-age take. The clouds ye so much dread
3. Judge not the Lord by fee - ble sense, But trust Him for His grace;

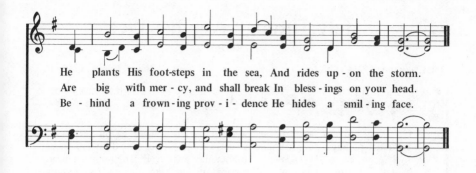

23   # Jesus Shall Reign

DUKE STREET

Isaac Watts, 1674-1748   John Hatton, 1710-1793

24 Safely Through Another Week

SABBATH

John Newton, 1725 - 1807

Lowell Mason, 1792 - 1872

1. Safe-ly through an-oth-er week God has brought us on our way;
2. While we pray for par-d'ning grace, Thro' the dear Re-deem-er's name,
3. Here we come Thy name to praise; May we feel Thy pres-ence near.
4. May Thy gos-pel's joy-ful sound Con-quer sin-ners, comfort saints,

Let us now a bless-ing seek, Wait-ing in His courts to-day.
Show Thy rec-on-cil-ed face, Take a-way our sin and shame.
May Thy glo-ry meet our eyes, While we in Thy house ap-pear.
Make the fruits of grace a-bound, Bring re-lief for all com-plaints.

Day of all the week the best, Em-blem of e-ter-nal rest!
From our world-ly cares set free, May we rest this day in Thee;
Here af-ford us, Lord, a taste Of our ev-er-last-ing feast;
Thus may all our Sab-baths prove, Till we join the Church a-bove;

Day of all the week the best, Em-blem of e-ter-nal rest!
From our world-ly cares set free, May we rest this day in Thee.
Here af-ford us, Lord, a taste Of our ev-er-last-ing feast.
Thus may all our Sab-baths prove, Till we join the Church a-bove.

25　Heavenly Father, King Eternal

L. Harold Johnston, 1924-　　　　　　　　　　　　　　　L. Harold Johnston, 1924-

1. Heav'n-ly Fa - ther, King E - ter - nal,　Lead-ing on to vic - to - ry,
2. Thro' the val - ley, o'er the sum - mit,　Dark-est night and bright-est day,
3. Fa - ther, hear our sup - pli - ca - tion　As we bow our hearts to Thee.
4. Sing! Oh, sing, ye pure and spot - less,　For this day art thou made whole.

Thro' the din and strife of bat - tle　Con-querors by Thy side are we.
Wa - ters deep and stor - my plac - es,　Still Thou lead - est all the way.
Fill us with Thy Ho - ly Spir - it;　For like Thee, Lord, we would be.
Let the rocks and rills pro-claim it:　Love hath cleansed yet one more soul.

Powers of Sa - tan can - not harm us;　E - vil can - not long en - dure.
Flash of light-ning, crash of thun - der,　Rest-less wave, I shall not fear;
May Thy blood which flowed from Cal-v'ry　Sin and guile this day e - rase.
Praise His name for full sal - va - tion;　Give Him praise for-ev - er - more.

March - ing 'neath Thy might - y ban - ner,　We do sure-ly feel se - cure.
For the path - way straight be-fore me　Is not long when Thou art near.
From our pres - ent low - ly sta - tion　El - e - vate us by Thy grace.
Glad - ly take the cross of Je - sus;　Fol-low as He leads be-fore.

26 For the Beauty of the Earth

DIX

Folliott S. Pierpoint, 1835-1917

Conrad Kocher, 1786-1872

1. For the beau-ty of the earth, For the glo-ry of the skies,
2. For the won-der of each hour Of the day and of the night,
3. For the joy of hu-man love, Broth-er, sis-ter, par-ent, child;
4. For Thy Church that ev-er-more Lift-eth ho-ly hands a-bove,

For the love which from our birth O-ver and a-round us lies,
Hill and vale, and tree and flower, Sun and moon, and stars of light,
Friends on earth, and friends a-bove; For all gen-tle thoughts and mild;
Of-fering up on ev-'ry shore Her pure sac-ri-fice of love,

Lord of all, to Thee we raise This our hymn of grate-ful praise.

27 Sun of My Soul

HURSLEY

John Keble, 1792-1866

Adapt. from "Katholisches Gesangbuch," Vienna, 1774

1. Sun of my soul! Thou Sav-iour dear, It is not night if Thou be near.
2. When the soft dews of kind-ly sleep My wea-ry eye-lids gent-ly steep,
3. A-bide with me from morn till eve, For with-out Thee I can-not live.
4. Be near to bless me when I wake, Ere thro' the world my way I take.

Oh, may no earth-born cloud a - rise To hide Thee from Thy ser - vant's eyes!
Be my last tho't—How sweet to rest For-ev - er on my Saviour's breast!
A-bide with me when night is nigh, For with-out Thee I dare not die.
A-bide with me till in Thy love I lose my - self in heav'n a - bove.

28 Lead On, O King Eternal

LANCASHIRE

Ernest W. Shurtleff, 1862 - 1917   Henry Smart, 1813 - 1879

1. Lead on, O King E - ter - nal. The day of march has come;
2. Lead on, O King E - ter - nal, Till sin's fierce war shall cease,
3. Lead on, O King E - ter - nal. We fol - low, not with fears;

Hence - forth in fields of con - quest Thy tents shall be our home.
And ho - li - ness shall whis - per The sweet A - men of peace.
For glad - ness breaks like morn - ing Wher-e'er Thy face ap - pears.

Thro' days of prep - a - ra - tion Thy grace has made us strong;
For not with swords' loud clash - ing, Nor roll of stir - ring drums;
Thy cross is lift - ed o'er us; We jour - ney in its light.

And now, O King E - ter - nal, We lift our bat - tle song.
With deeds of love and mer - cy, The heav'n - ly King-dom comes.
The crown a - waits the con - quest; Lead on, O God of might.

29 Immortal, Invisible

JOANNA

Walter C. Smith, 1824 - 1908

Welsh Melody, 1839

1. Im - mor - tal, in - vis - i - ble, God on - ly wise,
2. Un - rest - ing, un - hast - ing, and si - lent as light,
3. To all, life Thou giv - est, to both great and small;
4. Great Fa - ther of Glo - ry, pure Fa - ther of Light,

In light in - ac - ces - si - ble hid from our eyes,
Nor want - ing, nor wast - ing, Thou rul - est in might;
In all life Thou liv - est, the true Life of all;
Thine an - gels a - dore Thee, all veil - ing their sight.

Most bless - ed, most glo - rious, the An - cient of Days,
Thy jus - tice like moun-tains high soar - ing a - bove
Thy wis - dom so bound-less, Thy mer - cy so free,
All laud we would ren - der. O help us to see

Al - might - y, vic - to - rious, Thy great name we praise.
Thy clouds which are foun-tains of good - ness and love.
E - ter - nal Thy good - ness, for naught chang-eth Thee.
'Tis on - ly the splen - dor of light hid - eth Thee.

30

God of Our Fathers

NATIONAL HYMN

Daniel C. Roberts, 1841 - 1907

George W. Warren, 1828 - 1902

Trumpets, before each stanza

1. God of our fa - thers, whose al - might - y hand Leads forth in beau - ty all the star - ry band Of shin - ing worlds in splen - dor thro' the skies, Our grate - ful songs be - fore Thy throne a - rise.

2. Thy love di - vine hath led us in the past. In this free land by Thee our lot is cast. Be Thou our Rul - er, Guard - ian, Guide, and Stay, Thy Word our law, Thy paths our cho - sen way.

3. From war's a - larms, from dead - ly pes - ti - lence, Be Thy strong arm our ev - er sure de - fense. Thy true re - lig - ion in our hearts in - crease; Thy bount-eous good - ness nour - ish us in peace.

4. Re - fresh Thy peo - ple on their toil - some way. Lead us from night to nev - er end - ing day. Fill all our lives with love and grace di - vine; And glo - ry, laud, and praise be ev - er Thine.

31

O Could I Speak

ARIEL

Samuel Medley, 1738-1799

Arr. by Lowell Mason, 1792-1872

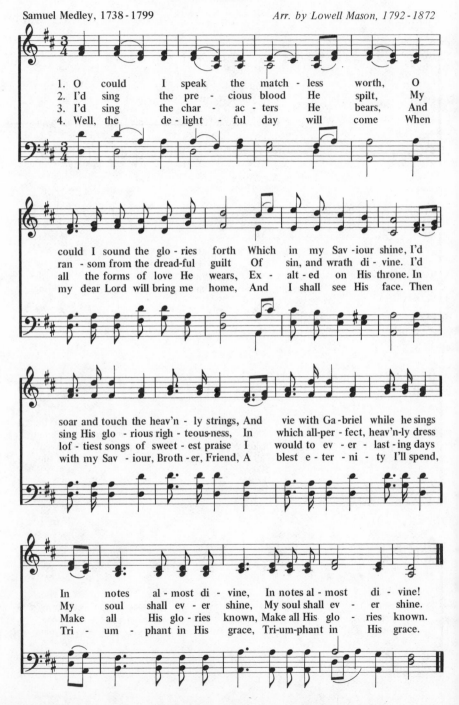

1. O could I speak the match - less worth, O could I sound the glo - ries forth Which in my Sav - iour shine, I'd soar and touch the heav'n - ly strings, And vie with Ga - briel while he sings In notes al - most di - vine, In notes al - most di - vine!

2. I'd sing the pre - cious blood He spilt, My ran - som from the dread-ful guilt Of sin, and wrath di - vine. I'd sing His glo - rious righ - teous-ness, In which all-per - fect, heav'n-ly dress My soul shall ev - er shine, My soul shall ev - er shine.

3. I'd sing the char - ac - ters He bears, And all the forms of love He wears, Ex - alt - ed on His throne. In lof - tiest songs of sweet - est praise I would to ev - er - last-ing days Make all His glo - ries known, Make all His glo - ries known.

4. Well, the de - light - ful day will come When my dear Lord will bring me home, And I shall see His face. Then with my Sav - iour, Broth - er, Friend, A blest e - ter - ni - ty I'll spend, Tri - um - phant in His grace, Tri-um-phant in His grace.

32   Nearer, My God, to Thee

BETHANY

Sarah F. Adams, 1805-1848

Lowell Mason, 1792-1872

1. Near - er, my God, to Thee, Near - er to Thee,
2. Though like the wan - der - er, The sun gone down,
3. There let the way ap - pear, Steps un - to heaven;
4. Then, with my wak - ing thoughts Bright with Thy praise,
5. Or if, on joy - ful wing Cleav - ing the sky,

E'en though it be a cross That rais - eth me!
Dark - ness be o - ver me, My rest a stone;
All that Thou send - est me, In mer - cy given;
Out of my ston - y griefs Beth - el I'll raise;
Sun, moon, and stars for - got, Up - ward I fly,

Still all my song shall be, Near - er, my God, to Thee;
Yet in my dreams I'd be Near - er, my God, to Thee;
An - gels to beck - on me Near - er, my God, to Thee;
So by my woes to be Near - er, my God, to Thee;
Still all my song shall be, Near - er, my God, to Thee;

Near - er, my God, to Thee, Near - er to Thee!
Near - er, my God, to Thee, Near - er to Thee!
Near - er, my God, to Thee, Near - er to Thee!
Near - er, my God, to Thee, Near - er to Thee!
Near - er, my God, to Thee, Near - er to Thee!

33 Take Time to Be Holy

HOLINESS

William D. Longstaff, 1822-1894

George C. Stebbins, 1846-1945

1. Take time to be ho-ly. Speak oft with thy Lord; A-bide in Him
2. Take time to be ho-ly. The world rush-es on; Spend much time in
3. Take time to be ho-ly. Let Him be thy Guide; And run not be-

al-ways, And feed on His Word. Make friends with God's chil-dren; Help
se-cret With Je-sus a-lone. By look-ing to Je-sus, Like
fore Him, What-ev-er be-tide. In joy or in sor-row, Still

those who are weak, For-get-ting in noth-ing His bless-ing to seek.
Him thou shalt be; Thy friends in thy con-duct His likeness shall see.
fol-low thy Lord And, look-ing to Je-sus, Still trust in His Word.

34 My Soul, Be on Thy Guard

LABAN

George Heath, 1750-1822

Lowell Mason, 1792-1872

1. My soul, be on thy guard; Ten thou-sand foes a-rise;
2. Oh, watch, and fight, and pray; The bat-tle ne'er give o'er.
3. Ne'er think the vic-t'ry won, Nor lay thine ar-mor down;
4. Fight on, my soul, till death Shall bring thee to thy God;

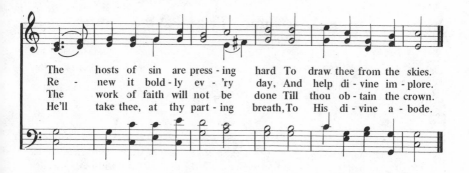

The | hosts of sin are press-ing | hard To | draw thee from the skies.
Re - | new it bold-ly ev - 'ry | day, And | help di - vine im - plore.
The | work of faith will not be | done Till | thou ob - tain the crown.
He'll | take thee, at thy part - ing | breath, To | His di - vine a - bode.

35 O Love That Wilt Not Let Me Go

ST. MARGARET

George Matheson, 1842 - 1906

Albert L. Peace, 1844 - 1912

1. O Love that wilt not let me go, I rest my wea - ry soul in Thee. I give Thee back the life I owe, That in Thine o-cean depths its flow May rich - er, full - er be.
2. O Light that fol - lowest all my way, I yield my flick-'ring torch to Thee. My heart re - stores its bor-rowed ray, That in Thy sun-shine's blaze its day May bright-er, fair - er be.
3. O Joy that seek-est me through pain, I can - not close my heart to Thee. I trace the rain-bow through the rain, And feel the prom-ise is not vain That morn shall tear - less be.
4. O Cross that lift - est up my head, I dare not ask to fly from Thee. I lay in dust life's glo - ry dead, And from the ground there blos-soms red Life that shall end - less be.

36 Open My Eyes, That I May See

Clara H. Scott, 1841 - 1897

Clara H. Scott, 1841 - 1897

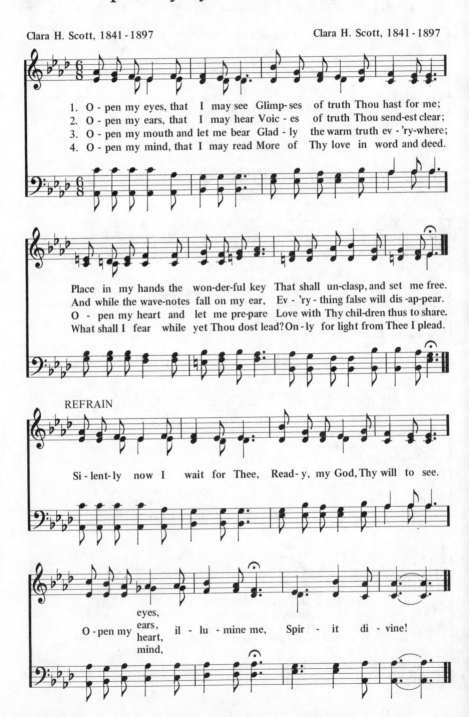

1. O - pen my eyes, that I may see Glimp- ses of truth Thou hast for me;
2. O - pen my ears, that I may hear Voic - es of truth Thou send-est clear;
3. O - pen my mouth and let me bear Glad - ly the warm truth ev - 'ry-where;
4. O - pen my mind, that I may read More of Thy love in word and deed.

Place in my hands the won-der-ful key That shall un-clasp, and set me free.
And while the wave-notes fall on my ear, Ev - 'ry - thing false will dis -ap-pear.
O - pen my heart and let me pre-pare Love with Thy chil-dren thus to share.
What shall I fear while yet Thou dost lead? On - ly for light from Thee I plead.

REFRAIN

Si - lent-ly now I wait for Thee, Read- y, my God, Thy will to see.

O - pen my eyes,
ears,
heart,
mind, il - lu - mine me, Spir - it di - vine!

37   Jesus, Lover of My Soul

MARTYN

Charles Wesley, 1707-1788   Simeon B. Marsh, 1798-1875

1. Je - sus, Lov - er of my soul,   Let me to Thy bos - om fly,
2. Oth - er ref - uge have I none;   Hangs my help-less soul on Thee.
3. Thou, O Christ, art all I want;   More than all in Thee I find.
4. Plen-teous grace with Thee is found,   Grace to cov - er all my sin.

While the near - er wa - ters roll,   While the tem - pest still is high!
Leave, ah, leave me not a - lone;   Still sup-port and com - fort me!
Raise the fall - en, cheer the faint,   Heal the sick, and lead the blind.
Let the heal - ing streams a-bound;   Make and keep me pure with - in.

Hide me, O my Sav - iour, hide,   Till the storm of life is past.
All my trust on Thee is stayed;   All my help from Thee I bring.
Just and ho - ly is Thy name;   I am all un - righ-teous-ness.
Thou of life the Foun-tain art;   Free - ly let me take of Thee.

Safe in - to the ha - ven guide.   Oh, re - ceive my soul at last!
Cov - er my de - fense-less head   With the shad-ow of Thy wing.
False and full of sin I am;   Thou art full of truth and grace.
Spring Thou up with - in my heart;   Rise to all e - ter - ni - ty.

A Closer Walk with Thee

Haldor Lillenas, 1885 - 1959   Haldor Lillenas, 1885 - 1959

1. Lord, I am plead - ing; hear Thou my prayer. Let me Thy bless - ed
2. Voic - es of earth un - num-bered I hear; Cares and per - plex - ing
3. Strong are the foes that con - quer I must. Long is the way, but
4. Glo - ri - ous Mas - ter, King of my soul, On Thee my bur - dens

fel - low - ship share. From day to day Thy serv - ant I'd be.
prob-lems are near. Trust-ing in Thee, my soul shall be free.
in Thee I trust. In my own strength but weak -ness I see.
glad - ly I roll. Thou art my por - tion e - ter - nal - ly.

REFRAIN

Grant me a clos - er walk with Thee. Oh, for a clos - er

walk with Thee! Near to Thy side I ev - er would be. Shield me and

hide me; Con-stant-ly guide me In - to a clos - er walk with Thee.

39   More Love to Thee

Elizabeth Prentiss, 1818 - 1878   William H. Doane, 1832 - 1915

1. More love to Thee, O Christ, More love to Thee! Hear Thou the
2. Once earth - ly joy I craved, Sought peace and rest. Now Thee a-
3. Then shall my lat - est breath Whis - per Thy praise. This be the

prayer I make On bend-ed knee. This is my ear - nest plea:
lone I seek; Give what is best. This all my prayer shall be:
part - ing cry My heart shall raise; This still my prayer shall be:

More love, O Christ, to Thee; More love to Thee, More love to Thee!

40   I Want to Be like Jesus

Thomas O. Chisholm, 1866 - 1960   David Livingstone Ives, 1921 -

1. I have one deep, su - preme de - sire, That I may be like Je - sus.
2. He spent His life in do - ing good; I want to be like Je - sus.
3. A ho - ly, harm - less life He led; I want to be like Je - sus.
4. Oh, per - fect life of Christ, my Lord! I want to be like Je - sus.

To this I fer - vent - ly as - pire, That I may be like Je - sus.
In low - ly paths of ser - vice trod; I want to be like Je - sus.
The Fa - ther's will, His drink and bread; I want to be like Je - sus.
My rec - om - pense and my re - ward, That I may be like Je - sus.

I want my heart His throne to be, So that a watch - ing world may
He sym - pa - thized with hearts dis - tressed; He spoke the words that cheered and
And when at last He comes to die, "For - give them, Fa - ther," hear Him
His Spir - it fill my hun - g'ring soul, His pow - er all my life con -

see His like - ness shin - ing forth in me. I want to be like Je - sus.
blessed; He welcomed sinners to His breast. I want to be like Je - sus.
cry For those who taunt and cru - ci - fy. I want to be like Je - sus.
trol; My deepest pray'r, my high - est goal, That I may be like Je - sus.

41

Be Still, My Soul

FINLANDIA

Katharina von Schlegel, 1697-?
Trans. by Jane L. Borthwick, 1813-1897

Jean Sibelius, 1865-1957

1. Be still, my soul; the Lord is on thy side. Bear patient-
2. Be still, my soul; thy God doth un - der-take To guide the
3. Be still, my soul; the hour is has - t'ning on When we shall

ly the cross of grief or pain; Leave to thy God to
fu - ture as He has the past. Thy hope, thy con - fi-
be for - ev - er with the Lord, When dis - ap - point - ment,

or - der and pro - vide. In ev - 'ry change He faith - ful will re-
dence let noth-ing shake; All now mys - te - rious shall be bright at
grief, and fear are gone, Sor - row for - got, love's pur-est joys re-

main. Be still, my soul; thy best, thy heav'n - ly Friend
last. Be still, my soul; the waves and winds still know
stored. Be still, my soul; when change and tears are past,

Thro' thor - ny ways leads to a joy - ful end.
His voice who ruled them while He dwelt be - low.
All safe and bless - ed we shall meet at last.

42 Close to Thee

Fanny J. Crosby, 1820 - 1915

Silas J. Vail, 1818 - 1884

1. Thou, my ev - er - last - ing por - tion, More than friend or life to me,
2. Not for ease or world-ly pleas-ure Nor for fame my prayer shall be.
3. Lead me thro' the vale of shad - ows; Bear me o'er life's fit - ful sea;

Fine

D.S.—All a - long my pil - grim jour - ney, Sav - iour, let me walk with Thee.
D.S.—Glad-ly will I toil and suf - fer; On - ly let me walk with Thee.
D.S.—Then the gate of life e - ter - nal May I en - ter, Lord, with Thee.

REFRAIN

D.S.

Close to Thee, close to Thee, Close to Thee, close to Thee;

43 O Master, Let Me Walk with Thee

MARYTON

Washington Gladden, 1836 - 1918

H. Percy Smith, 1825 - 1898

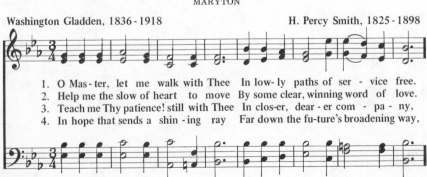

1. O Mas - ter, let me walk with Thee In low- ly paths of ser - vice free.
2. Help me the slow of heart to move By some clear, winning word of love.
3. Teach me Thy patience! still with Thee In clos-er, dear - er com - pa - ny,
4. In hope that sends a shin - ing ray Far down the fu-ture's broadening way,

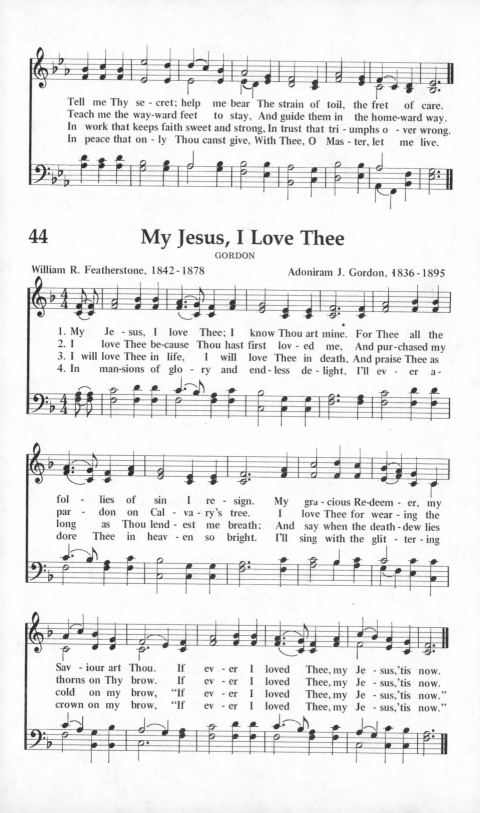

Tell me Thy se - cret; help me bear The strain of toil, the fret of care.
Teach me the way-ward feet to stay, And guide them in the home-ward way.
In work that keeps faith sweet and strong, In trust that tri - umphs o - ver wrong.
In peace that on - ly Thou canst give, With Thee, O Mas - ter, let me live.

44 My Jesus, I Love Thee

GORDON

William R. Featherstone, 1842 - 1878

Adoniram J. Gordon, 1836 - 1895

1. My Je - sus, I love Thee; I know Thou art mine. For Thee all the
2. I love Thee be-cause Thou hast first lov - ed me, And pur-chased my
3. I will love Thee in life, I will love Thee in death, And praise Thee as
4. In man-sions of glo - ry and end-less de - light, I'll ev - er a-

fol - lies of sin I re - sign. My gra - cious Re-deem - er, my
par - don on Cal - va - ry's tree. I love Thee for wear - ing the
long as Thou lend - est me breath; And say when the death - dew lies
dore Thee in heav - en so bright. I'll sing with the glit - ter - ing

Sav - iour art Thou. If ev - er I loved Thee, my Je - sus, 'tis now.
thorns on Thy brow. If ev - er I loved Thee, my Je - sus, 'tis now.
cold on my brow, "If ev - er I loved Thee, my Je - sus, 'tis now."
crown on my brow, "If ev - er I loved Thee, my Je - sus, 'tis now."

45 In Heavenly Love Abiding

SEASONS

Anna L. Waring, 1823-1910

Felix Mendelssohn, 1809-1847

1. In heav'n-ly love a-bid-ing, No change my heart shall fear;
2. Wher-ev-er He may guide me, No want shall turn me back;
3. Green pas-tures are be-fore me, Which yet I have not seen;

And safe is such con-fid-ing, For noth-ing chan-ges here.
My Shep-herd is be-side me, And noth-ing can I lack.
Bright skies will soon be o'er me, Where dark-est clouds have been.

The storm may roar with-out me, My heart may low be laid,
His wis-dom ev-er wak-eth; His sight is nev-er dim.
My hope I can-not meas-ure; My path to life is free;

But God is round a-bout me, And can I be dis-mayed?
He knows the way He tak-eth, And I will walk with Him.
My Sav-iour has my treas-ure, And He will walk with me.

46 He Hideth My Soul

KIRKPATRICK

Fanny J. Crosby, 1820-1915

William J. Kirkpatrick, 1838-1921

1. A won-der-ful Sav-iour is Je-sus, my Lord, A won-der-ful
2. A won-der-ful Sav-iour is Je-sus, my Lord. He tak-eth my
3. With num-ber-less bless-ings each mo-ment He crowns; And, filled with His
4. When, clothed in His brightness, trans-port-ed, I rise To meet Him in

Sav-iour to me. He hid-eth my soul in the cleft of the rock, Where
bur-den a-way. He hold-eth me up, and I shall not be moved. He
full-ness di-vine, I sing in my rap-ture, "Oh, glo-ry to God For
clouds of the sky, His per-fect sal-va-tion, His won-der-ful love I'll

REFRAIN

riv-ers of pleas-ure I see.
giv-eth me strength as my day.
such a Re-deem-er as mine!" He hid-eth my soul in the cleft of the rock
shout with the millions on high.

That shadows a dry, thir-sty land. He hid-eth my life in the depths of His love,

And cov-ers me there with His hand, And cov-ers me there with His hand.

47 Rock of Ages

TOPLADY

Augustus M. Toplady, 1740-1778

Thomas Hastings, 1784-1872

1. Rock of A - ges, cleft for me, Let me hide my - self in Thee.
2. Could my tears for - ev - er flow, Could my zeal no lan - guor know,
3. While I draw this fleet - ing breath, When my eyes shall close in death,

Let the wa - ter and the blood, From Thy wound-ed side which flowed,
These for sin could not a - tone; Thou must save, and Thou a - lone.
When I rise to worlds un-known, And be - hold Thee on Thy throne,

Be of sin the dou - ble cure, Save from wrath and make me pure.
In my hand no price I bring; Sim - ply to Thy cross I cling.
Rock of A - ges, cleft for me, Let me hide my - self in Thee.

48 Immortal Love, Forever Full

SERENITY

John Greenleaf Whittier, 1807-1892

William V. Wallace, 1814-1865

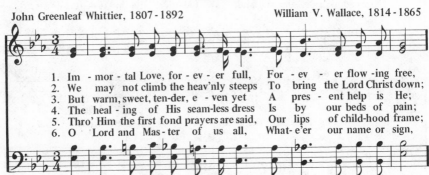

1. Im - mor - tal Love, for - ev - er full, For - ev - er flow -ing free,
2. We may not climb the heav'nly steeps To bring the Lord Christ down;
3. But warm, sweet, ten-der, e - ven yet A pres - ent help is He;
4. The heal - ing of His seam-less dress Is by our beds of pain;
5. Thro' Him the first fond prayers are said, Our lips of child-hood frame;
6. O Lord and Mas - ter of us all, What-e'er our name or sign,

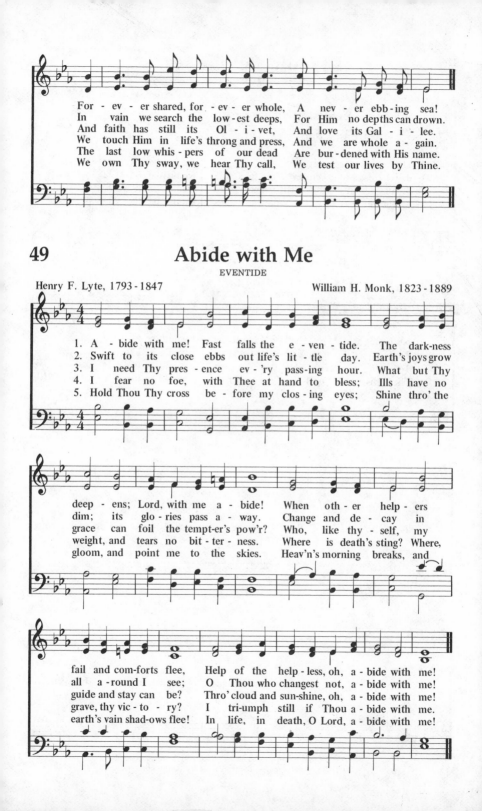

For - ev - er shared, for - ev - er whole, A nev - er ebb - ing sea!
In vain we search the low - est deeps, For Him no depths can drown.
And faith has still its Ol - i - vet, And love its Gal - i - lee.
We touch Him in life's throng and press, And we are whole a - gain.
The last low whis - pers of our dead Are bur - dened with His name.
We own Thy sway, we hear Thy call, We test our lives by Thine.

49

Abide with Me

EVENTIDE

Henry F. Lyte, 1793 - 1847 — William H. Monk, 1823 - 1889

1. A - bide with me! Fast falls the e - ven - tide. The dark-ness
2. Swift to its close ebbs out life's lit - tle day. Earth's joys grow
3. I need Thy pres - ence ev - 'ry pass-ing hour. What but Thy
4. I fear no foe, with Thee at hand to bless; Ills have no
5. Hold Thou Thy cross be - fore my clos - ing eyes; Shine thro' the

deep - ens; Lord, with me a - bide! When oth - er help - ers
dim; its glo - ries pass a - way. Change and de - cay in
grace can foil the tempt-er's pow'r? Who, like thy - self, my
weight, and tears no bit - ter - ness. Where is death's sting? Where,
gloom, and point me to the skies. Heav'n's morning breaks, and

fail and com-forts flee, Help of the help - less, oh, a - bide with me!
all a - round I see; O Thou who changest not, a - bide with me!
guide and stay can be? Thro' cloud and sun-shine, oh, a - bide with me!
grave, thy vic - to - ry? I tri-umph still if Thou a - bide with me.
earth's vain shad-ows flee! In life, in death, O Lord, a - bide with me!

50 I Would Be like Jesus

James Rowe, 1865-1933   Bentley D. Ackley, 1872-1958

1. Earth-ly pleas-ures vain-ly call me; I would be like Je - sus;
2. He has bro-ken ev-'ry fet-ter, I would be like Je - sus;
3. All the way from earth to glo-ry, I would be like Je - sus;
4. That in heav-en He may meet me, I would be like Je - sus;
   would be like Je - sus;

Noth-ing world-ly shall en-thrall me; I would be like Je - sus.
That my soul may serve Him bet-ter, I would be like Je - sus.
Tell-ing o'er and o'er the sto-ry, I would be like Je - sus.
That His words,"Well done,"may greet me, I would be like Je - sus.
   would be like Je - sus.

REFRAIN

Be like Je-sus, this my song, In the home and in the throng;

Be like Je-sus, all day long! I would be like Je - sus.

51 In the Garden

C. Austin Miles, 1868 - 1946   C. Austin Miles, 1868 - 1946

1. I come to the gar - den a - lone, While the dew is still on the
2. He speaks, and the sound of His voice Is so sweet the birds hush their
3. I'd stay in the gar - den with Him Tho' the night a-round me be

ros - es; And the voice I hear, Fall-ing on my ear, The
sing - ing, And the mel - o - dy That He gave to me With-
fall - ing, But He bids me go; Thru the voice of woe, His

REFRAIN

Son of God dis - clos - es.
in my heart is ring - ing. And He walks with me, and He
voice to me is call - ing.

talks with me, And He tells me I am His own; And the

joy we share as we tar - ry there, None oth-er has ev - er known.

Unsearchable Riches

Fanny J. Crosby, 1820 - 1915

John R. Sweney, 1837 - 1899

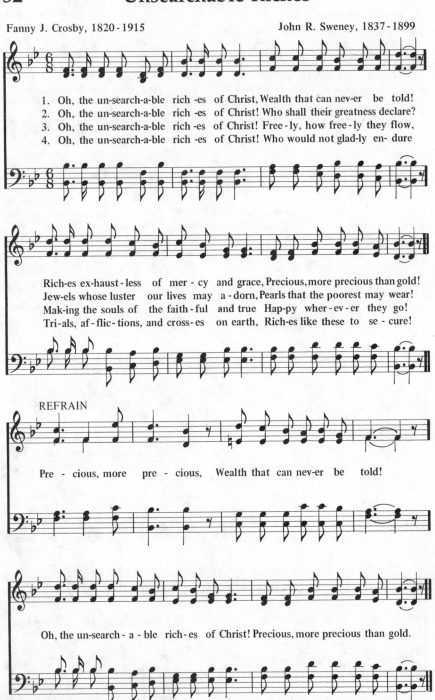

1. Oh, the un-search-a-ble rich-es of Christ, Wealth that can nev-er be told!
2. Oh, the un-search-a-ble rich-es of Christ! Who shall their greatness declare?
3. Oh, the un-search-a-ble rich-es of Christ! Free-ly, how free-ly they flow,
4. Oh, the un-search-a-ble rich-es of Christ! Who would not glad-ly en-dure

Rich-es ex-haust-less of mer-cy and grace, Precious, more precious than gold!
Jew-els whose luster our lives may a-dorn, Pearls that the poorest may wear!
Mak-ing the souls of the faith-ful and true Hap-py wher-ev-er they go!
Tri-als, af-flic-tions, and cross-es on earth, Rich-es like these to se-cure!

REFRAIN

Pre-cious, more pre-cious, Wealth that can nev-er be told!

Oh, the un-search-a-ble rich-es of Christ! Precious, more precious than gold.

53 O Jesus, I Have Promised

ANGEL'S STORY

John E. Bode, 1816-1874

Arthur H. Mann, 1850-1929

1. O Je - sus, I have prom - ised To serve Thee to the end;
2. O let me feel Thee near me! The world is ev - er near.
3. O Je - sus, Thou hast prom - ised To all who fol - low Thee

Be Thou for - ev - er near me, My Mas - ter and my Friend.
I see the sights that daz - zle; The tempt - ing sounds I hear.
That where Thou art in glo - ry There shall Thy ser - vant be.

I shall not fear the bat - tle If Thou art by my side,
My foes are ev - er near me, A - round me and with - in;
And, Je - sus, I have prom - ised To serve Thee to the end.

Nor wan - der from the path - way If Thou wilt be my Guide.
But, Je - sus, draw Thou near - er, And shield my soul from sin.
O give me grace to fol - low, My Mas - ter and my Friend.

54 My Faith Looks Up to Thee

OLIVET

Ray Palmer, 1808-1887

Lowell Mason, 1792-1872

1. My faith looks up to Thee, Thou Lamb of Cal - va - ry,
2. May Thy rich grace im-part Strength to my faint - ing heart,
3. While life's dark maze I tread, And griefs a - round me spread,
4. When ends life's tran - sient dream, When death's cold, sul - len stream

Sav - iour di - vine! Now hear me while I pray; Take all my
My zeal in - spire. As Thou hast died for me, Oh, may my
Be Thou my Guide. Bid dark - ness turn to day; Wipe sor - row's
Shall o'er me roll, Blest Sav - iour, then in love Fear and dis -

guilt a - way. Oh, let me from this day Be whol - ly Thine!
love to Thee Pure, warm, and change-less be, A liv - ing fire!
tears a - way; Nor let me ev - er stray From Thee a - side!
trust re - move. Oh, bear me safe a - bove, A ran - somed soul!

55 Come, Holy Ghost, Our Hearts Inspire

WINCHESTER OLD

Charles Wesley, 1707-1788

From "Este's Psalter," 1592

1. Come, Ho - ly Ghost, our hearts in - spire; Let us Thine in-fluence prove:
2. Come, Ho - ly Ghost, for moved by Thee The proph-ets wrote and spoke.
3. Ex - pand Thy wings, ce - les - tial Dove; Brood o'er our na - ture's night;
4. God, through him-self, we then shall know If Thou with-in us shine,

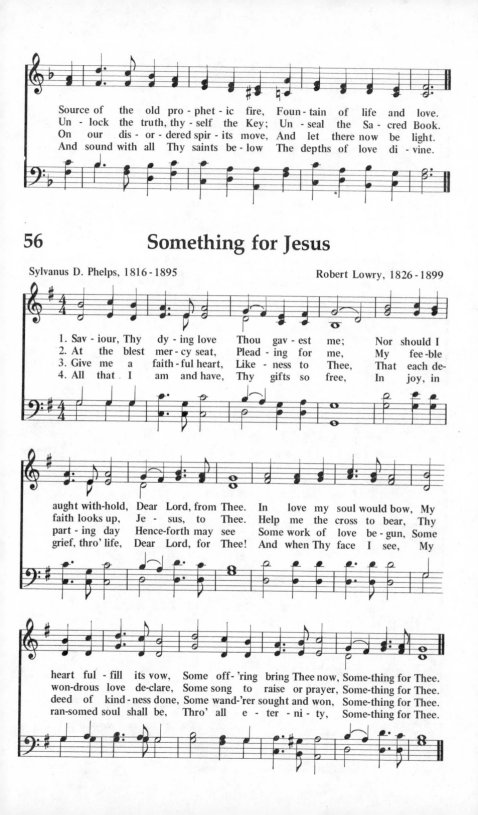

Source of the old pro - phet - ic fire, Foun - tain of life and love.
Un - lock the truth, thy - self the Key; Un - seal the Sa - cred Book.
On our dis - or - dered spir - its move, And let there now be light.
And sound with all Thy saints be - low The depths of love di - vine.

56 Something for Jesus

Sylvanus D. Phelps, 1816 - 1895

Robert Lowry, 1826 - 1899

1. Sav - iour, Thy dy - ing love Thou gav - est me; Nor should I
2. At the blest mer - cy seat, Plead - ing for me, My fee - ble
3. Give me a faith - ful heart, Like - ness to Thee, That each de -
4. All that I am and have, Thy gifts so free, In joy, in

aught with-hold, Dear Lord, from Thee. In love my soul would bow, My
faith looks up, Je - sus, to Thee. Help me the cross to bear, Thy
part - ing day Hence-forth may see Some work of love be - gun, Some
grief, thro' life, Dear Lord, for Thee! And when Thy face I see, My

heart ful - fill its vow, Some off - 'ring bring Thee now, Some-thing for Thee.
won-drous love de-clare, Some song to raise or prayer, Some-thing for Thee.
deed of kind - ness done, Some wand-'rer sought and won, Some-thing for Thee.
ran-somed soul shall be, Thro' all e - ter - ni - ty, Some-thing for Thee.

57 Trust in the Lord

Thomas O. Chisholm, 1866 - 1960

Wendell P. Loveless, 1892 -

1. "Trust in the Lord with all thine heart," This is God's gra-cious com-mand;
2. "Trust in the Lord," who rul - eth all, Se - eth all things as they are,
3. "Trust in the Lord" and peace-ful be; Fret not thy spir - it in vain.
4. "Trust in the Lord"—His eye will guide All thro' the path-way a - head.

"In all thy ways ac-knowl-edge Him, So shalt thou dwell in the land."
Be it a bird - ling in its nest Or yon-der ut - ter-most star.
What tho' the an - swer tar - ries long, Still shalt thou praise Him a-gain.
He hath re-deemed and He will keep; Trust Him and be not a - fraid.

REFRAIN

"Trust in the Lord," O trou-bled soul; Rest in the arms of His care. What-
care, of His care.

ev - er thy lot, it mat-ter-eth not, For noth-ing can trou-ble thee there.

"Trust in the Lord," O trou-bled soul; Noth-ing can trou-ble thee there.

58

I Lay My Sins on Jesus

ST. HILDA

Justin H. Knecht, 1752-1817
Edward Husband, 1843-1908

Horatius Bonar, 1808-1889

1. I lay my sins on Je - sus, The spot - less Lamb of God;
2. I lay my wants on Je - sus; All full - ness dwells in Him.
3. I long to be like Je - sus, Meek, lov - ing, low - ly, mild;

He bears them all and frees us From the ac - curs - ed load.
He heal - eth my dis - eas - es; He doth my soul re - deem.
I long to be like Je - sus, The Fa - ther's ho - ly Child.

I bring my guilt to Je - sus, To wash my crim - son stains
I lay my griefs on Je - sus, My bur - dens, and my cares.
I long to be with Je - sus, A - mid the heav'n - ly throng,

White in His blood most pre - cious, Till not a stain re - mains.
He from them all re - leas - es; He all my sor - rows shares.
To sing with saints His prais - es, And learn the an - gels' song.

59   I Heard the Voice of Jesus Say

Horatius Bonar, 1808-1889   Old English Air

1. I heard the voice of Je - sus say, "Come un - to Me and rest.
2. I heard the voice of Je - sus say, "Be - hold, I free - ly give
3. I heard the voice of Je - sus say, "I am this dark world's Light.

Lay down, thou wea - ry one, lay down Thy head up - on My breast!"
The liv - ing wa - ter; thirst - y one, Stoop down, and drink, and live!"
Look un - to Me; thy morn shall rise, And all thy day be bright!"

I came to Je - sus as I was, Wea - ry, and worn, and sad;
I came to Je - sus, and I drank Of that life - giv - ing stream;
I looked to Je - sus, and I found In Him my Star, my Sun;

rit.

I found in Him a rest - ing-place, And He has made me glad.
My thirst was quenched, my soul re - vived, And now I live in Him.
And in that light of life I'll walk Till trav - 'ling days are done.

Sitting at the Feet of Jesus

J. H., 19th Century

Asa Hull, 19th Century

1. Sit - ting at the feet of Je - sus, Oh, what words I hear Him say!
2. Sit - ting at the feet of Je - sus, Where can mor-tal be more blest?
3. Bless me, O my Sav-iour, bless me, As I sit low at Thy feet.

Hap - py place! so near, so pre - cious! May it find me there each day.
There I lay my sins and sor - rows And, when wear-y, find sweet rest.
Oh, look down in love up - on me; Let me see Thy face so sweet.

Sit - ting at the feet of Je - sus, I would look up - on the past;
Sit - ting at the feet of Je - sus, There I love to weep and pray,
Give me, Lord, the mind of Je - sus; Make me ho - ly as He is.

For His love has been so gra - cious, It has won my heart at last.
While I from His full - ness gath - er Grace and com-fort ev - 'ry day.
May I prove I've been with Je - sus, Who is all my righ-teous - ness.

61 Day by Day

AHNFELT

Carolina V. Sandell-Berg, 1832 - 1903
Tr. by A. L. S.

Oskar Ahnfelt, 1813 - 1882

1. Day by day, and with each pass - ing mo - ment, Strength I find to
2. Ev - 'ry day the Lord him - self is near me, With a spe - cial
3. Help me then, in ev - 'ry trib - u - la - tion, So to trust Thy

meet my tri - als here. Trust - ing in my Fa - ther's wise be - stow - ment, I've no
mer - cy for each hour. All my cares He fain would bear and cheer me, He whose
prom - is - es, O Lord, That I lose not faith's sweet con - so - la - tion, Of - fered

cause for wor - ry or for fear. He whose heart is kind beyond all
name is Coun - se - lor and Pow'r. The pro - tec - tion of His child and
me with - in Thy ho - ly Word. Help me, Lord, when toil and trouble

meas - ure Gives un - to each day what He deems best,___ Lov - ing -
treas - ure Is a charge that on him - self He laid. ___ "As thy
meet - ing, E'er to take, as from a Fa - ther's hand,___ One by

ly its part of pain and pleas - ure, Mingling toil with peace and rest.
days, thy strength shall be in meas - ure," This the pledge to me He made.
one, the days, the mo - ments fleet - ing, Till I reach the prom - ised land.

62 Come, Thou Fount

NETTLETON

Robert Robinson, 1735-1790
3rd Stanza Alt. 1931

John Wyeth, 1770-1858

1. Come, Thou Fount of ev-'ry bless-ing, Tune my heart to sing Thy grace.
2. Here I raise my Eb-e-ne-zer; Hith-er by Thy help I'm come.
3. Oh, to grace how great a debt-or Dai-ly I'm constrained to be!

Streams of mer-cy, nev-er ceas-ing, Call for songs of loud-est praise.
And I hope, by Thy good pleas-ure, Safe-ly to ar-rive at home.
Let that grace, now like a fet-ter, Bind my yield-ed heart to Thee.

Teach me some me-lo-dious son-net, Sung by flam-ing tongues a-bove.
Je-sus sought me when a stran-ger, Wan-d'ring from the fold of God;
Let me know Thee in Thy full-ness; Guide me by Thy might-y hand

Praise the mount! I'm fixed up-on it, Mount of God's un-chang-ing love.
He, to res-cue me from dan-ger, In-ter-posed His pre-cious blood.
Till, transformed, in Thine own im-age In Thy pres-ence I shall stand.

63   I Am Thine, O Lord

Fanny J. Crosby, 1820-1915   William H. Doane, 1832-1915

1. I am Thine, O Lord; I have heard Thy voice, And it told Thy
2. Con-se-crate me now to Thy ser-vice, Lord, By the pow'r of
3. Oh, the pure de-light of a sin-gle hour That be-fore Thy
4. There are depths of love that I can-not know Till I cross the

love to me. But I long to rise in the arms of faith, And be
grace di-vine. Let my soul look up with a stead-fast hope, And my
throne I spend, When I kneel in prayer and with Thee, my God, I com-
nar-row sea; There are heights of joy that I may not reach Till I

REFRAIN

clos-er drawn to Thee.
will be lost in Thine.   Draw me near-er,   near-er, bless-ed
mune as friend with friend!   near-er, near-er,
rest in peace with Thee.

Lord, To the Cross where Thou hast died. Draw me near-er, near-er,

near-er, bless-ed Lord, To Thy pre-cious, bleed-ing side.

64 Guide Me, O Thou Great Jehovah

RHONDDA

From the Welsh
William Williams, 1717-1791

Welsh hymn melody
John Hughes, 1873-1932

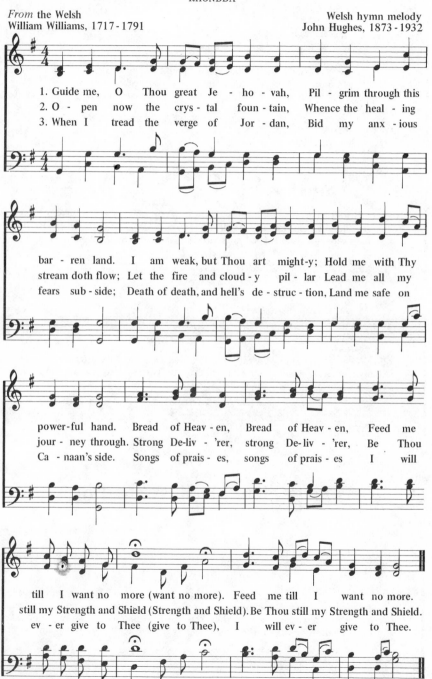

1. Guide me, O Thou great Je - ho - vah, Pil - grim through this bar - ren land. I am weak, but Thou art might-y; Hold me with Thy power-ful hand. Bread of Heav - en, Bread of Heav - en, Feed me till I want no more (want no more). Feed me till I want no more.

2. O - pen now the crys - tal foun - tain, Whence the heal - ing stream doth flow; Let the fire and cloud - y pil - lar Lead me all my jour - ney through. Strong De-liv - 'rer, strong De-liv - 'rer, Be Thou still my Strength and Shield (Strength and Shield). Be Thou still my Strength and Shield.

3. When I tread the verge of Jor - dan, Bid my anx - ious fears sub - side; Death of death, and hell's de - struc - tion, Land me safe on Ca - naan's side. Songs of prais - es, songs of prais - es I will ev - er give to Thee (give to Thee), I will ev - er give to Thee.

65 Guide Me, O Thou Great Jehovah

ZION

William Williams, 1717-1791

Thomas Hastings, 1784-1872

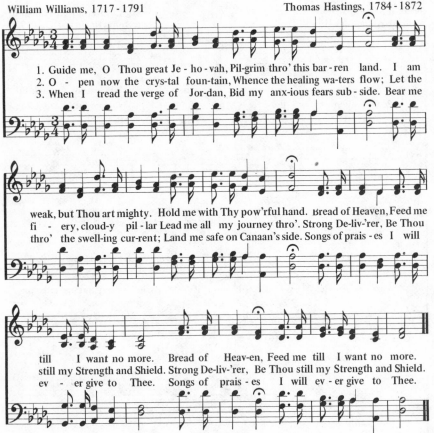

1. Guide me, O Thou great Je - ho - vah, Pil-grim thro' this bar-ren land. I am
2. O - pen now the crys-tal foun-tain, Whence the healing wa-ters flow; Let the
3. When I tread the verge of Jor-dan, Bid my anx-ious fears sub - side. Bear me

weak, but Thou art mighty. Hold me with Thy pow'rful hand. Bread of Heaven, Feed me
fi - ery, cloud-y pil - lar Lead me all my journey thro'. Strong De-liv-'rer, Be Thou
thro' the swell-ing cur-rent; Land me safe on Canaan's side. Songs of prais-es I will

till I want no more. Bread of Heav-en, Feed me till I want no more.
still my Strength and Shield. Strong De-liv-'rer, Be Thou still my Strength and Shield.
ev - er give to Thee. Songs of prais-es I will ev - er give to Thee.

66 Forever Here My Rest Shall Be

MARTYRDOM

Charles Wesley, 1707-1788

Hugh Wilson, 1766-1824

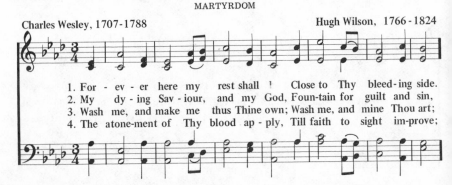

1. For - ev - er here my rest shall ! Close to Thy bleed-ing side.
2. My dy - ing Sav - iour, and my God, Foun-tain for guilt and sin,
3. Wash me, and make me thus Thine own; Wash me, and mine Thou art;
4. The atone-ment of Thy blood ap - ply, Till faith to sight im-prove;

This all my hope, and all my plea, "For me the Sav-iour died."
Sprin-kle me ev-er with Thy blood, And cleanse, and keep me clean.
Wash me, but not my feet a-lone— My hands, my head, my heart.
Till hope in full fru-i-tion die, And all my soul be love.

67   Nearer, Still Nearer

MORRIS

Lelia N. Morris, 1862 - 1929   Lelia N. Morris, 1862 - 1929

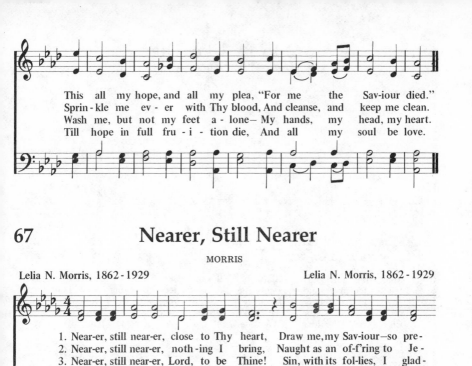

1. Near-er, still near-er, close to Thy heart, Draw me, my Sav-iour—so pre-
2. Near-er, still near-er, noth-ing I bring, Naught as an of-f'ring to Je-
3. Near-er, still near-er, Lord, to be Thine! Sin, with its fol-lies, I glad-
4. Near-er, still near-er, while life shall last, Till safe in glo-ry my an-

cious Thou art! Fold me, oh, fold me close to Thy breast. Shel-ter me safe
sus, my King; On-ly my sin-ful, now contrite heart. Grant me the cleans-
ly re-sign, All of its pleas-ures, pomp and its pride. Give me but Je-
chor is cast; Thro'endless a-ges ev-er to be Near-er, my Sav-

in that "Ha-ven of Rest"; Shel-ter me safe in that "Ha-ven of-Rest."
ing Thy blood doth im-part; Grant me the cleans-ing Thy blood doth impart.
sus, my Lord, cru-ci-fied; Give me but Je-sus, my Lord, cru-ci-fied.
iour, still near-er to Thee; Near-er, my Sav-iour, still near-er to Thee!

68 O to Be like Thee

Thomas O. Chisholm, 1866-1960   CHRISTLIKE   William J. Kirkpatrick, 1838-1921

1. Oh, to be like Thee! bless - ed Re - deem - er, This is my con-stant
2. Oh, to be like Thee! full of com - pas - sion, Lov - ing, for - giv - ing,
3. Oh, to be like Thee! low - ly in spir - it, Ho - ly and harm-less,
4. Oh, to be like Thee! Lord, I am com - ing, Now to re-ceive th'a-
5. Oh, to be like Thee! While I am plead - ing, Pour out Thy Spir - it,

long - ing and prayer. Glad - ly I'll for - feit all of earth's treas-ures,
ten - der and kind, Help - ing the help - less, cheer - ing the faint-ing,
pa - tient and brave; Meek - ly en - dur - ing cru - el re - proach-es,
noint - ing di - vine. All that I am and have I am bring-ing.
fill with Thy love. Make me a tem - ple meet for Thy dwell-ing;

REFRAIN

Je - sus, Thy per' - fect like - ness to wear.
Seek - ing the wan-d'ring sin - ner to find!
Will - ing to suf - fer oth - ers to save.   Oh, to be like Thee!
Lord, from this mo - ment all shall be Thine.
Fit me for life and heav - en a - bove.

Oh, to be like Thee, Bless-ed Re - deem -er, pure as Thou art! Come in Thy

sweet - ness, come in Thy full - ness; Stamp Thine own im-age deep on my heart.

69 The Closer I Walk

Haldor Lillenas, 1885 - 1959

Haldor Lillenas, 1885 - 1959

1. A Sav - iour have I more pre - cious to me Than all of earth's
2. If rug - ged the way that I must pur-sue, If dark be the
3. My heart sings a glad and ju - bi - lant song, As on - ward we
4. I feast on His truth, His rich - es of grace; And dai - ly His

friendships ev - er could be. His rich - es of grace more clear - ly I see
night that I jour - ney thro', My fears all de - part, my tears are but few
go life's path-way a - long. My hope is re - newed, my faith be-comes strong,
count-less mer - cies I trace, Be-hold-ing the glo - ry light of His face,

REFRAIN

The clos - er I walk to Him. The clos - er I walk, the

sweet - er He seems. Much fair - er is He than all of my dreams. His

love lights my way when path - ways are dim, The clos - er I walk to Him.

70 It Is Well with My Soul

VILLE DE HAVRE

Horatio G. Spafford, 1828-1888

Philip P. Bliss, 1838-1876

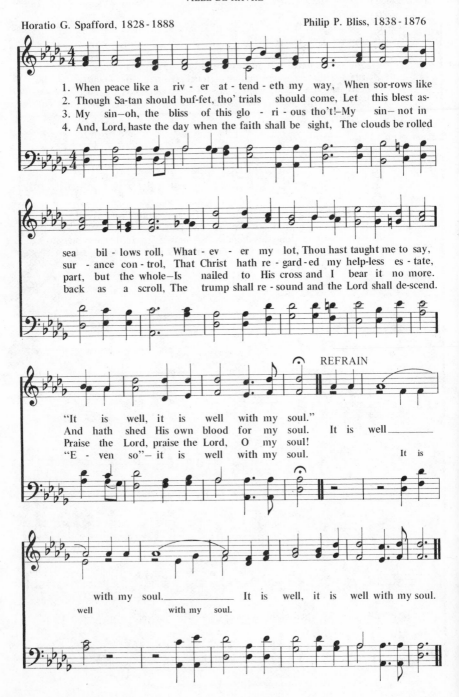

1. When peace like a riv-er at-tend-eth my way, When sor-rows like
2. Though Sa-tan should buf-fet, tho' trials should come, Let this blest as-
3. My sin—oh, the bliss of this glo-ri-ous tho't!—My sin—not in
4. And, Lord, haste the day when the faith shall be sight, The clouds be rolled

sea bil-lows roll, What-ev-er my lot, Thou hast taught me to say,
sur-ance con-trol, That Christ hath re-gard-ed my help-less es-tate,
part, but the whole—Is nailed to His cross and I bear it no more.
back as a scroll, The trump shall re-sound and the Lord shall de-scend.

REFRAIN

"It is well, it is well with my soul."
And hath shed His own blood for my soul. It is well____
Praise the Lord, praise the Lord, O my soul!
"E-ven so"—it is well with my soul. It is

with my soul._____ It is well, it is well with my soul.

well with my soul.

71 I Will Sing of My Redeemer

Philip P. Bliss, 1838-1876

James McGranahan, 1840-1907

1. I will sing of my Re-deem-er And His won-drous love to me;
2. I will tell the won-drous sto-ry, How, my lost es-tate to save,
3. I will praise my dear Re-deem-er; His tri-um-phant pow'r I'll tell,
4. I will sing of my Re-deem-er And His heav'n-ly love to me;

On the cru-el Cross He suf-fered, From the curse to set me free.
In His bound-less love and mer-cy He the ran-som free-ly gave.
How the vic-to-ry He giv-eth O-ver sin, and death, and hell.
He from death to life hath bro't me, Son of God, with Him to be.

REFRAIN

Sing, oh, sing _____ of my Re-deem-er. With His
Sing, oh, sing of my Re-deem-er; Sing, oh, sing of my Redeemer. With His

blood _____ He pur-chased me. _____ On the Cross _____ He
blood He purchased me; With His blood He purchased me. On the Cross He sealed my par-don;

sealed my par-don, Paid the debt _____ and made me free. _____
On the Cross He sealed my pardon, Paid the debt and made me free, and made me free.

I Will Praise Him

Margaret J. Harris, 19th Century

Margaret J. Harris, 19th Century

1. When I saw the cleansing foun-tain O-pen wide for all my sin,
2. Tho' the way seem'd straight and narrow, All I claimed was swept a-way;
3. Then God's fire up-on the al-tar Of my heart was set a-flame.
4. Bless-ed be the name of Je_-sus! I'm so glad He took me in.

I o-beyed the Spir-it's woo-ing When He said,"Wilt thou be clean?"
My am-bi-tions, plans, and wish-es At my feet in ash-es lay.
I shall nev-er cease to praise Him. Glo-ry, glo-ry to His name!
He's for-giv-en my trans-gres-sions; He has cleansed my heart from sin.

REFRAIN

I will praise Him! I will praise Him! Praise the Lamb for sinners slain!

for sinners slain!

Give Him glo-ry, all ye peo-ple, For His blood can wash a-way each stain.

73 Praise Ye the Lord, the Almighty

LOBE DEN HERREN

Joachim Neander, 1650-1680
Tr. by Catherine Winkworth, 1829-1878

"Stralsund Gesangbuch"
From "Praxis Pietatis Melica," 1668

1. Praise ye the Lord, the Al - might - y, the King of cre - a - tion!
2. Praise ye the Lord, who o'er all things so won-drous-ly reign - eth,
3. Praise ye the Lord, who doth pros - per thy work and de - fend thee;
4. Praise ye the Lord, Oh, let all that is in me a - dore Him!

O my soul, praise Him, for He is thy Health and Sal - va - tion!
Shel - ters thee un - der His wings, yea, so gent - ly sus - tain - eth!
Sure - ly His good-ness and mer - cy here dai - ly at - tend thee.
All that hath life and breath, come now with prais-es be - fore Him!

All ye who hear, Now to His tem - ple draw near;
Hast thou not seen How thy de - sires e'er have been
Pon - der a - new What the Al - might - y can do
Let the A - men Sound from His peo - ple a - gain.

Join me in glad ad - o - ra - tion!
Grant - ed in what He or - dain - eth?
If with His love He be - friend thee.
Glad - ly for aye we a - dore Him.

74   Let All the People Praise Thee

Lelia N. Morris, 1862-1929   Lelia N. Morris, 1862-1929

1. Oh, mag - ni - fy the Lord with me, Ye peo - ple of His choice.
2. Oh, praise Him for His ho - li - ness, His wis - dom, and His grace;
3. Had I a thou-sand tongues to sing, The half could ne'er be told

Let all to whom He lend - eth breath Now in His name re - joice.
Sing prais - es for the pre - cious Blood Which ran-somed all our race.
Of love so rich, so full and free; Of bless - ings man - i - fold;

For love's blest rev - e - la - tion, For rest from con-dem - na - tion,
In ten - der-ness He sought us; From depths of sin He brought us;
Of grace that fail - eth nev - er, Peace flow-ing as a riv - er

For ut - ter - most sal - va - tion,
The way of life then taught us. To Him give thanks.
From God, the glo - rious Giv - er. To Him give thanks.

Copyright 1906. Renewed 1934 by Nazarene Publishing House.

REFRAIN

Let all   the peo - ple praise Thee. Let all

let all the peo - ple praise Thee, Lord.

let

all   the peo - ple praise Thee. Let all   the peo - ple

let all

praise Thy name for - ev - er and for - ev - er - more.

75   Come, We That Love the Lord

Isaac Watts, 1674 - 1748   ST. THOMAS   Aaron Williams, 1731 - 1776

1. Come, we that love the Lord, And let our joys be known;
2. Let those re - fuse to sing Who nev - er knew our God;
3. The men of grace have found Glo - ry be - gun be - low;
4. Then let our songs a - bound, And ev - 'ry tear be dry;

Join in a song with sweet ac - cord, And thus sur - round His throne.
But chil - dren of the heaven - ly King May speak their joys a - broad.
Ce - les - tial fruit on earth - ly ground From faith and hope may grow.
We're marching thro' Im - man - uel's ground To fair - er worlds on high.

76 I Will Sing the Wondrous Story

WONDROUS STORY

Francis H. Rowley, 1854 - 1952

Peter P. Bilhorn, 1865 - 1936

1. I will sing the won-drous sto - ry Of the Christ who died for me,
2. I was lost, but Je - sus found me, Found the sheep that went a - stray,
3. I was bruised, but Je - sus healed me; Faint was I from many a fall.
4. Days of dark-ness still come o'er me; Sor-row's paths I of - ten tread.
5. He will keep me till the riv - er Rolls its wa - ters at my feet;

How He left His home in glo - ry For the cross of Cal - va - ry.
Threw His lov - ing arms a - round me, Drew me back in - to His way.
Sight was gone, and fears pos-sessed me, But He freed me from them all.
But the Sav - iour still is with me; By His hand I'm safe - ly led.
Then He'll bear me safe - ly o - ver, Where the loved ones I shall meet.

REFRAIN

Yes, I'll sing the won-drous sto - ry Of the
Yes, I'll sing the won-drous sto - ry

Christ who died for me; Sing it with the saints in
of the Christ who died for me; Sing it with

glo - ry, Gath-ered by the crys-tal sea.
the saints in glo - ry, Gathered by the crys-tal sea.

77 Rejoice, the Lord Is King

DARWALL

Charles Wesley, 1707-1788   John Darwall, 1731-1789

1. Re - joice, the Lord is King; Your Lord and King a - dore!
2. Je - sus, the Sav - iour, reigns, The God of truth and love.
3. His king - dom can - not fail; He rules o'er earth and heaven.

Re - joice, give thanks, and sing, And tri - umph ev - er -
When He had purged our stains, He took His seat a -
The keys of death and hell Are to our Je - sus

more. Lift up your heart; lift up your voice!
bove. Lift up your heart; lift up your voice!
given. Lift up your heart; lift up your voice!

Re - joice; a - gain I say, Re - joice!
Re - joice; a - gain I say, Re - joice!
Re - joice; a - gain I say, Re - joice!

78 Praise Him! Praise Him!

JOYFUL SONG

Fanny J. Crosby, 1820-1915

Chester G. Allen, 1838-1878

1. Praise Him! praise Him! Je-sus, our bless-ed Re - deem-er! Sing, O
2. Praise Him! praise Him! Je-sus, our bless-ed Re - deem-er! For our
3. Praise Him! praise Him! Je-sus, our bless-ed Re - deem-er! Heav'n-ly

Earth, His won-der-ful love pro-claim! Hail Him! hail Him! highest arch-
sins He suffered, and bled, and died. He, our Rock, our Hope of e-
por - tals loud with ho-san - nas ring! Je - sus, Sav - iour, reign-eth for

an - gels in glo - ry; Strength and hon - or give to His ho - ly
ter-nal sal - va - tion— Hail Him! hail Him! Je - sus, the Cru - ci-
ev - er and ev - er. Crown Him! crown Him! Proph-et, and Priest, and

name! Like a shep - herd, Je-sus will guard His chil - dren;
fied! Sound His prais - es! Je-sus, who bore our sor - rows!
King! Christ is com - ing, o - ver the world vic - to - rious;

In His arms He car - ries them all day long.
Love un-bound-ed, won-der-ful, deep, and strong! Praise Him! praise Him!
Pow'r and glo - ry un - to the Lord be - long.

REFRAIN

tell of His ex-cel-lent great-ness. Praise Him! praise Him! ev-er in joy-ful song!

79   Hallelujah! Amen!

Henrietta E. Blair, 19th Century   *Arr. by William J. Kirkpatrick, 1838-1921*

1. How oft in ho-ly con-verse With Christ, my Lord, a-lone,
2. They passed thro' toils and tri-als And, though the strife was long,
3. My soul takes up the cho-rus And, press-ing on my way,
4. Thro' grace I soon shall con-quer, And reach my home on high;

I seem to hear the mil-lions That sing a-round His throne:
They share the vic-tor's con-quest, And sing the vic-tor's song:
Com-mun-ing still with Je-sus, I sing from day to day:
And thro' e-ter-nal a-ges I'll shout be-yond the sky:

REFRAIN

Hal-le-lu-jah! A-men! Hal-le-lu-jah! A-men!

Hal-le-lu-jah! A-men! A-men! A-men!

80 Praise the Lord! Ye Heavens, Adore Him

AUSTRIA

The Foundling Hospital Collection, 1796

Franz Joseph Haydn, 1732-1809

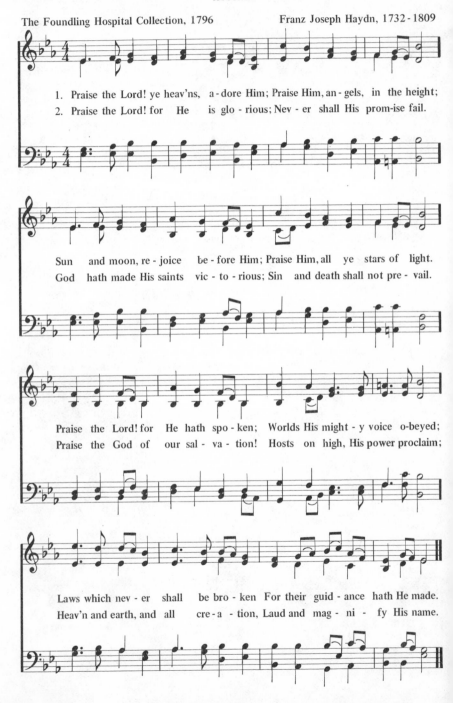

1. Praise the Lord! ye heav'ns, a-dore Him; Praise Him, an-gels, in the height;
2. Praise the Lord! for He is glo-rious; Nev-er shall His prom-ise fail.

Sun and moon, re-joice be-fore Him; Praise Him, all ye stars of light.
God hath made His saints vic-to-rious; Sin and death shall not pre-vail.

Praise the Lord! for He hath spo-ken; Worlds His might-y voice o-beyed;
Praise the God of our sal-va-tion! Hosts on high, His power proclaim;

Laws which nev-er shall be bro-ken For their guid-ance hath He made.
Heav'n and earth, and all cre-a-tion, Laud and mag-ni-fy His name.

81 Glory to His Name

Elisha A. Hoffman, 1839 - 1929

John H. Stockton, 1813 - 1877

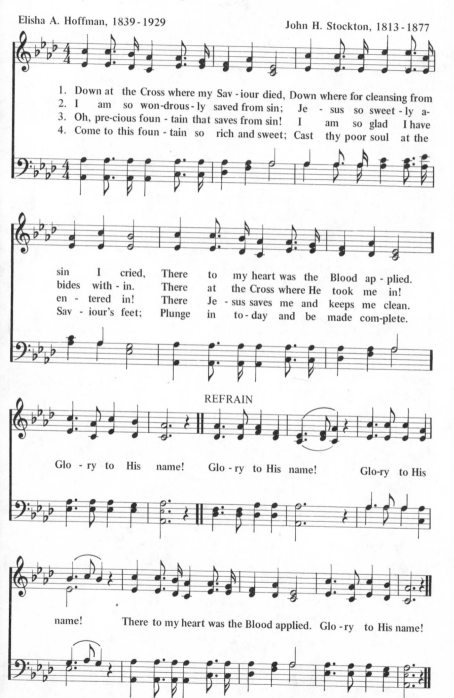

1. Down at the Cross where my Sav-iour died, Down where for cleansing from
2. I am so won-drous-ly saved from sin; Je - sus so sweet-ly a-
3. Oh, pre-cious foun-tain that saves from sin! I am so glad I have
4. Come to this foun-tain so rich and sweet; Cast thy poor soul at the

sin I cried, There to my heart was the Blood ap-plied.
bides with-in. There at the Cross where He took me in!
en - tered in! There Je - sus saves me and keeps me clean.
Sav - iour's feet; Plunge in to-day and be made com-plete.

REFRAIN

Glo - ry to His name! Glo - ry to His name! Glo-ry to His

name! There to my heart was the Blood applied. Glo - ry to His name!

82 Rejoice, Ye Pure in Heart

MARION

Edward H. Plumptre, 1821 - 1891

Arthur M. Messiter, 1834 - 1916

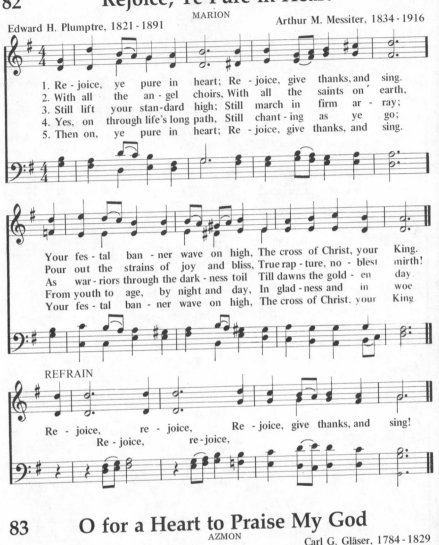

1. Re - joice, ye pure in heart; Re - joice, give thanks, and sing.
2. With all the an - gel choirs, With all the saints on earth,
3. Still lift your stan - dard high; Still march in firm ar - ray;
4. Yes, on through life's long path, Still chant - ing as ye go;
5. Then on, ye pure in heart; Re - joice, give thanks, and sing.

Your fes - tal ban - ner wave on high, The cross of Christ, your King.
Pour out the strains of joy and bliss, True rap - ture, no - blest mirth!
As war - riors through the dark - ness toil Till dawns the gold - en day.
From youth to age, by night and day, In glad - ness and in woe.
Your fes - tal ban - ner wave on high, The cross of Christ, your King

REFRAIN

Re - joice, re - joice, Re - joice, give thanks, and sing!
Re - joice, re - joice,

83 O for a Heart to Praise My God

AZMON

Charles Wesley, 1707 - 1788

Carl G. Gläser, 1784 - 1829
Arr. by Lowell Mason, 1792 - 1872

1. O for a heart to praise my God, A heart from sin set free,
2. A heart re-signed, sub - mis-sive, meek, My great Re - deem - er's throne,
3. Oh, for a low - ly, con-trite heart, Be - liev - ing, true, and clean,
4. A heart in ev - 'ry tho't re-newed, And full of love di - vine;

A heart that al-ways feels Thy blood So free-ly shed for me!
Where on-ly Christ is heard to speak, Where Je-sus reigns a-lone.
Which nei-ther life nor death can part From Him that dwells with-in!
Per-fect, and right, and pure, and good— A cop-y, Lord, of Thine!

84   Blessed Be the Name

Charles Wesley, 1707-1788
Chorus by Ralph E. Hudson, 1843-1901

Ralph E. Hudson, 1843-1901

1. O for a thou-sand tongues to sing, Bless-ed be the name of the Lord!
2. Je-sus, the name that charms our fears, Bless-ed be the name of the Lord!
3. He breaks the pow'r of can-celed sin, Bless-ed be the name of the Lord!

The glo-ries of my God and King, Bless-ed be the name of the Lord!
'Tis mu-sic in the sin-ner's ears, Bless-ed be the name of the Lord!
His blood can make the foul-est clean, Bless-ed be the name of the Lord!

REFRAIN

Bless-ed be the name, Bless-ed be the name, Blessed be the name of the Lord!

Bless-ed be the name, Bless-ed be the name, Blessed be the name of the Lord!

85 We Gather Together

KREMSER

Anonymous
Tr. by Theodore Baker, 1851-1934

Folk Song of the Netherlands
Arr. by Edward Kremser, 1838-1914

1. We gath - er to - geth - er to ask the Lord's bless - ing.
2. Be - side us to guide us, our God with us join - ing,
3. We all do ex - tol Thee, Thou Lead - er tri - um - phant,

He chas - tens and has - tens His will to make known.
Or - dain - ing, main - tain - ing His king - dom di - vine;
And pray that Thou still our De - fend - er wilt be.

The wick - ed op - press - ing now cease from dis - tress - ing.
So from the be - gin - ning the fight we were win -ning.
Let Thy con - gre - ga - tion es - cape trib - u - la - tion.

Sing prais - es to His name; He for - gets not His own.
Thou, Lord, wast at our side— all glo - ry be Thine!
Thy name be ev - er praised. O Lord, make us free!

86 Great Is Thy Faithfulness

FAITHFULNESS

Thomas O. Chisholm, 1866 - 1960

William M. Runyan, 1870 - 1957

1. Great is Thy faith-ful-ness, O God, my Fa - ther; There is no shad-ow of
2. Sum - mer and win - ter, and spring-time and harvest, Sun, moon, and stars in their
3. Par - don for sin and a peace that en - dur - eth, Thy own dear presence to

turn - ing with Thee. Thou chang-est not; Thy com - pas - sions, they fail not;
cours - es a - bove, Join with all na - ture in man - i - fold wit-ness
cheer and to guide; Strength for to - day and bright hope for to - mor-row—

REFRAIN

As Thou hast been Thou for - ev - er wilt be.
To Thy great faith-ful - ness, mer - cy, and love. Great is Thy faith-ful-ness!
Bless-ings all mine, with ten thou-sand be - side!

Great is Thy faithfulness! Morning by morning new mercies I see; All I have

rall.

need - ed Thy hand hath provided. Great is Thy faithfulness, Lord, un-to me!

87 Come, Ye Thankful People, Come

ST. GEORGE'S, WINDSOR

Henry Alford, 1810-1871

George J. Elvey, 1816-1893

1. Come, ye thank-ful peo-ple, come; Raise the song of har-vest home.
2. All the world is God's own field, Fruit un-to His praise to yield;
3. For the Lord our God shall come, And shall take His har-vest home;
4. E-ven so, Lord, quick-ly come To Thy fi-nal har-vest home;

All is safe-ly gath-ered in Ere the win-ter storms be-gin.
Wheat and tares to-geth-er sown, Un-to joy or sor-row grown;
From His field shall in that day All of-fens-es purge a-way;
Gath-er Thou Thy peo-ple in, Free from sor-row, free from sin;

God, our Mak-er, doth pro-vide For our wants to be sup-plied.
First the blade, and then the ear, Then the full corn shall ap-pear.
Give His an-gels charge at last In the fire the tares to cast,
There for-ev-er pu-ri-fied, In Thy pres-ence to a-bide.

Come to God's own tem-ple, come; Raise the song of har-vest home.
Lord of Har-vest, grant that we Whole-some grain and pure may be.
But the fruit-ful ears to store In His gar-ner ev-er-more.
Come, with all Thine an-gels come; Raise the glo-rious har-vest home.

88 Now Thank We All Our God

NUN DANKET

Martin Rinkart, 1586-1649
Tr. by Catherine Winkworth, 1829-1878

Johann Crüger, 1598-1662
Harm. by Felix Mendelssohn, 1809-1847

1. Now thank we all our God With heart and hands and voic - es,
2. Oh, may this boun - teous God Through all our life be near us,
3. All praise and thanks to God The Fa - ther now be giv - en,

Who won-drous things hath done, In whom His world re - joic - es;
With ev - er joy - ful hearts And bless - ed peace to cheer us;
The Son, and Him who reigns With them in high - est heav - en,

Who, from our moth - ers' arms, Hath blessed us on our way
And keep us in His grace, And guide us when per - plexed,
The one e - ter - nal God, Whom earth and heaven a - dore;

With count - less gifts of love, And still is ours to - day.
And free us from all ills In this world and the next.
For thus it was, is now, And shall be ev - er - more.

89 Count Your Blessings

Johnson Oatman, Jr. 1856 - 1922

Edwin O. Excell, 1851 - 1921

1. When up-on life's bil - lows you are tem - pest - tossed, When you are dis-
2. Are you ev - er bur-dened with a load of care? Does the cross seem
3. When you look at oth - ers with their lands and gold, Think that Christ has
4. So a - mid the con-flict, wheth-er great or small, Do not be dis-

cour-aged, think-ing all is lost, Count your man-y bless - ings, name them
heav - y you are called to bear? Count your man-y bless - ings; ev - 'ry
prom-ised you His wealth un - told. Count your man-y bless - ings; mon - ey
cour-aged; God is o - ver all. Count your man-y bless - ings; an - gels

one by one, And it will sur - prise you what the Lord hath done.
doubt will fly, And you will be sing - ing as the days go by.
can - not buy Your re-ward in heav - en nor your home on high.
will at - tend, Help and com-fort give you to your jour - ney's end.

REFRAIN

Count your bless - ings; Name them one by one. Count your
Count your man-y bless - ings; Name them one by one. Count your man-y

bless - ings; See what God hath done. Count your bless-ings;
bless - ings; See what God hath done. Count your many bless-ings;

rit.   *a tempo*

Name them one by one. Count your man-y bless-ings; See what God hath done.

90   Break Thou the Bread of Life

BREAD OF LIFE

Mary A. Lathbury, 1841 - 1913   William F. Sherwin, 1826 - 1888

1. Break Thou the bread of life, Dear Lord, to me, As Thou didst
2. Bless Thou the truth, dear Lord, To me, to me, As Thou didst
3. Teach me to live, dear Lord, On - ly for Thee, As Thy dis -

break the loaves Be - side the sea. Be - yond the sa - cred page
bless the bread By Gal - i - lee. Then shall all bon-dage cease,
ci - ples lived In Gal - i - lee. Then, all my strug-gles o'er,

I seek Thee, Lord; My spir - it pants for Thee, O liv - ing Word!
All fet - ters fall, And I shall find my peace, My All in All.
Then, vic - t'ry won, I shall be - hold Thee, Lord, The Liv - ing One.

91 O Word of God Incarnate

MUNICH

William W. How, 1823 - 1897

Meiningisches Gesangbuch, 1693
Harm. by Felix Mendelssohn, 1809 - 1847

1. O Word of God In-car-nate, O Wis-dom from on high,
2. The Church from Thee, her Mas-ter, Re-ceived the gift di-vine,
3. It float-eth like a ban-ner Be-fore God's host un-furled;
4. O make Thy Church, dear Sav-iour, A lamp of pur-est gold,

O Truth un-changed, un-chang-ing, O Light of our dark sky:
And still that light she lift-eth O'er all the earth to shine.
It shin-eth like a bea-con A-bove the dark-ling world.
To bear be-fore the na-tions Thy true light as of old.

We praise Thee for the ra-diance That from the hal-lowed page,
It is the sa-cred cas-ket Where gems of truth are stored;
It is the Chart and Com-pass That o'er life's surg-ing sea,
O teach Thy wan-d'ring pil-grims By this their path to trace,

A Lan-tern to our foot-steps, Shines on from age to age.
It is the heaven-drawn pic-ture Of Thee, the liv-ing Word.
'Mid mists and rocks and quick-sands, Still guides, O Christ, to Thee.
Till, clouds and dark-ness end-ed, They see Thee face-to-face.

92 The Solid Rock

SOLID ROCK

Edward Mote, 1797 - 1874

William B. Bradbury, 1816 - 1868

1. My hope is built on noth-ing less Than Je-sus' blood and
2. When dark-ness seems to hide His face, I rest on His un-
3. His oath, His cov-e-nant, His blood, Sup-port me in the
4. When He shall come with trum-pet sound, Oh, may I then in

righ-teous-ness. I dare not trust the sweet-est frame, But
chang-ing grace. In ev-'ry high and storm-y gale, My
whelm-ing flood. When all a-round my soul gives way, He
Him be found! Dressed in His righ-teous-ness a-lone, Fault-

REFRAIN

whol-ly lean on Je-sus' name.
an-chor holds with-in the veil.
then is all my Hope and Stay.
less to stand be-fore the throne!

On Christ, the sol-id Rock, I stand; All

oth-er ground is sink-ing sand. All oth-er ground is sink-ing sand.

93 The Name of Jesus

W. C. Martin, 20th Century

Edmund S. Lorenz, 1854 - 1942

1. The name of Je - sus is so sweet, I love its mu - sic
2. I love the name of Him whose heart Knows all my griefs and
3. That name I fond - ly love to hear; It nev - er fails my
4. No word of man can ev - er tell How sweet the name I

to re - peat. It makes my joys full and com - plete, The pre-cious
bears a part, Who bids all anx - ious fears de - part— I love the
heart to cheer; Its mu - sic dries the fall - ing tear. Ex - alt the
love so well. Oh, let its prais - es ev - er swell! Oh, praise the

The

REFRAIN

name of Je - sus! "Je - sus," oh, how sweet the name!
pre-cious name

"Je - sus," ev - 'ry day the same! "Je - sus," let all

saints pro - claim Its wor - thy praise for - ev - er!
Its wor - thy praise

94   All That Thrills My Soul

HARRIS

Thoro Harris, 1874 - 1955   Thoro Harris, 1874 - 1955

1. Who can cheer the heart like Je - sus,   By His pres-ence all di - vine?
2. Love of Christ so free - ly giv - en,   Grace of God be - yond de-gree,
3. Ev - 'ry need His hand sup -ply - ing,   Ev - 'ry good in Him I see;
4. By the crys - tal, flow - ing riv - er   With the ran-somed I will sing,

True and ten - der, pure and pre - cious,   Oh, how blest to call Him mine!
Mer - cy high - er than the heav - en,   Deep - er than the deep-est sea!
On His strength divine re - ly - ing,   He is All in All to me.
And for - ev - er and for - ev - er   Praise and glo - ri - fy the King.

REFRAIN

All that thrills my soul is Je - sus;   He is more than life to me;

to me;

And the fair - est of ten thou-sand   In my bless-ed Lord I see.

95 Sweeter than All

Johnson Oatman, Jr., 1856-1922

J. Howard Entwisle, 20th Century

1. Christ will me His aid af - ford, Nev - er to fall, nev-er to fall,
2. I will fol - low all the way, Hear-ing Him call, hear-ing Him call,
3. Tho' a ves - sel I may be, Bro - ken and small, bro-ken and small,
4. When I reach the crys - tal sea, Voic-es will call, voic-es will call;

While I find my pre - cious Lord Sweet-er than all, sweet-er than all.
Find - ing Him from day to day Sweet-er than all, sweet-er than all.
Yet His bless-ings fall on me, Sweet-er than all, sweet-er than all.
But my Sav-iour's voice will be Sweet-er than all, sweet-er than all.

REFRAIN

Je - sus is now, and ev - er will be, Sweet-er than all the world to me,

Since I heard His lov - ing call— Sweet-er than all, sweet - er than all.

96 The Light of the World Is Jesus

LIGHT OF THE WORLD

Philip P. Bliss, 1838 - 1876

Philip P. Bliss, 1838 - 1876

1. The whole world was lost in the dark-ness of sin; The
2. No dark-ness have we who in Je-sus a-bide; The
3. Ye dwell-ers in dark-ness with sin-blind-ed eyes— The
4. No need of the sun-light in heav-en we're told; The

Light of the world is Je-sus. Like sun-shine at noon-day His
Light of the world is Je-sus. We walk in the Light when we
Light of the world is Je-sus— Go, wash at His bid-ding, and
Light of the world is Je-sus. The Lamb is the Light in the

glo-ry shone in;
fol-low our Guide; The Light of the world is Je-sus.
light will a-rise.
cit-y of gold;

REFRAIN

Come to the Light; 'tis shin-ing for thee. Sweet-ly the Light has dawned upon me.

Once I was blind, but now I can see. The Light of the world is Je-sus.

97 The Unveiled Christ

N. B. Herrell, 1877 - 1954

N. B. Herrell, 1877 - 1954

1. Once our bless-ed Christ of beau-ty Was veiled off from hu-man view;
2. Yes, He is with God, the Fa-ther, In-ter-ced-ing there for you;
3. Ho-ly an-gels bow be-fore Him, Men of earth give prais-es due;

But thro' suf-f'ring, death, and sor-row He has rent the veil in two.
For He is the Well-be-lov-ed Since He rent the veil in two.
For He is the might-y Con-q'ror Since He rent the veil in two.

REFRAIN

Oh, be-hold the Man of Sor-rows! Oh, be-hold Him in plain view!

Lo! He is the might-y Con-q'ror Since He rent the veil in two.

Lo! He is the might-y Con-q'ror Since He rent the veil in two.

98 Our Great Saviour

HYFRYDOL

J. Wilbur Chapman, 1859 - 1918

Rowland W. Prichard, 1811 - 1887
Arr. by Robert Harkness, 1877 - 1961

1. Je - sus! what a Friend for sin - ners! Je - sus! Lov - er of my soul!
2. Je - sus! what a Strength in weak - ness! Let me hide my - self in Him;
3. Je - sus! what a Help in sor - row! While the bil - lows o'er me roll,
4. Je - sus! what a Guide and Keep - er! While the tem - pest still is high,
5. Je - sus! I do now re - ceive Him; More than all in Him I find.

Friends may fail me, foes as - sail me; He, my Sav - ior, makes me whole.
Tempt - ed, tried, and some - times fail - ing, He, my Strength, my vic - t'ry wins.
E - ven when my heart is break - ing, He, my Com - fort, helps my soul.
Storms a - bout me, night o'er - takes me, He, my Pi - lot, hears my cry.
He hath grant - ed me for - give - ness; I am His, and He is mine.

REFRAIN

Hal - le - lu - jah! what a Sav - ior! Hal - le - lu - jah! what a Friend!

Sav - ing, help - ing, keep - ing, lov - ing, He is with me to the end.

99 Fairest Lord Jesus

CRUSADERS' HYMN

From the German, 17th Century

From "Schlesische Volkslieder"
Arr. by Richard S. Willis, 1819-1900

1. Fair - est Lord Je - sus! Rul - er of all na - ture!
2. Fair are the mead - ows; Fair - er still the wood - lands,
3. Fair is the sun - shine, Fair - er still the moon - light,
4. Beau - ti - ful Sav - iour! Lord of all the na - tions!

O Thou of God and man the Son! Thee will I cher - ish,
Robed in the bloom - ing garb of spring. Je - sus is fair - er,
And all the twin - kling star - ry host. Je - sus shines bright - er,
The Son of God and Son of Man! Glo - ry and hon - or,

Thee will I hon - or, Thou, my soul's glo - ry, joy, and crown!
Je - sus is pur - er, Who makes the woe - ful heart to sing!
Je - sus shines pur - er, Than all the an - gels heav'n can boast!
Praise, ad - o - ra - tion, Now and for - ev - er - more be Thine!

100 Jesus, the Very Thought of Thee

ST. AGNES

Bernard of Clairvaux, 12th Century
Trans. by Edward Caswall, 1814-1878

John B. Dykes, 1823-1876

1. Je - sus, the ver - y thought of Thee With sweet-ness fills my breast;
2. No voice can sing, no heart can frame, Nor can the mem - 'ry find
3. O Hope of ev - 'ry con - trite heart, O Joy of all the meek,
4. But what to those who find? Ah, this Nor tongue nor pen can show.

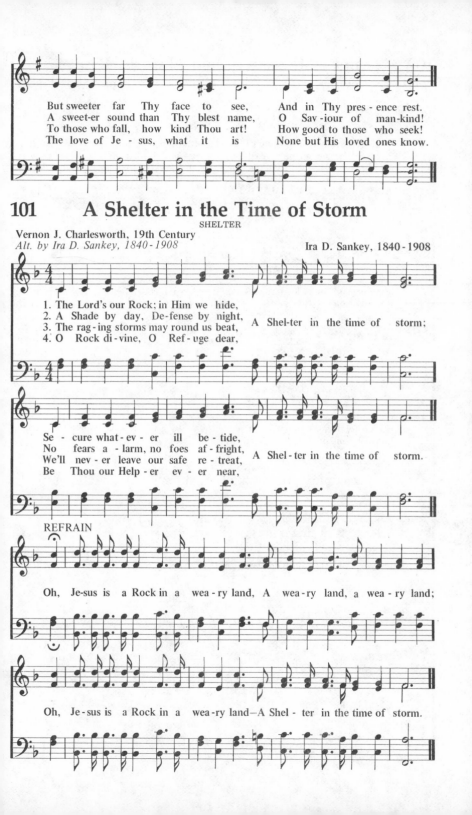

But sweeter far Thy face to see, And in Thy pres-ence rest.
A sweet-er sound than Thy blest name, O Sav-iour of man-kind!
To those who fall, how kind Thou art! How good to those who seek!
The love of Je-sus, what it is None but His loved ones know.

101 A Shelter in the Time of Storm

SHELTER

Vernon J. Charlesworth, 19th Century
Alt. by Ira D. Sankey, 1840-1908

Ira D. Sankey, 1840-1908

1. The Lord's our Rock; in Him we hide,
2. A Shade by day, De-fense by night,
3. The rag-ing storms may round us beat,
4. O Rock di-vine, O Ref-uge dear,

A Shel-ter in the time of storm;

Se - cure what-ev-er ill be-tide,
No fears a-larm, no foes af-fright,
We'll nev-er leave our safe re-treat,
Be Thou our Help-er ev-er near,

A Shel-ter in the time of storm.

REFRAIN

Oh, Je-sus is a Rock in a wea-ry land, A wea-ry land, a wea-ry land;

Oh, Je-sus is a Rock in a wea-ry land—A Shel-ter in the time of storm.

102   Jesus Is the Sweetest Name I Know

Lela Long, 20th Century   Lela Long, 20th Century

1. There have been names that I have loved to hear, But nev-er has there
2. There is no name in earth or heav'n a-bove That we should give such
3. And some-day I shall see Him face-to-face To thank and praise Him

(1) to hear

been a name so dear To this heart of mine As the name di-vine, The
hon-or and such love As the bless-ed name; Let us all acclaim That
for His won-drous grace Which He gave to me When He made me free, The

(1) so dear

REFRAIN

pre-cious, pre-cious name of Je - sus.
wondrous, glorious name of Je - sus.
bless-ed Son of God called Je - sus.   Je - sus is the sweet-est name I

know. And He's just the same as His love-ly name, And that's the rea-son

rall.

why I love Him so. Oh, Je - sus is the sweet-est name I know!

103 · My Wonderful Lord

Haldor Lillenas, 1885 - 1959
Haldor Lillenas, 1885 - 1959

1. I have found a deep peace that I nev-er had known And a joy this world
2. I de - sire that my life shall be or-dered by Thee, That my will be in
3. All the tal - ents I have I have laid at Thy feet; Thy ap-prov - al shall
4. Thou art fair - er to me than the fair-est of earth, Thou om-nip-o-tent,

could not af - ford Since I yield-ed con-trol of my bod - y and soul
per - fect ac - cord With Thine own sov'reign will, Thy de-sires to ful - fill,
be my re - ward. Be my store great or small, I sur - ren - der it all
life - giv - ing Word. O Thou An-cient of Days, Thou art wor - thy all praise,

REFRAIN

To my won - der-ful, won-der-ful Lord.
My won - der-ful, won-der-ful Lord.
To my won - der-ful, won-der-ful Lord.
My won - der-ful, won-der-ful Lord!

My won - der-ful Lord, my
won - der - ful Lord, By an - gels and ser - aphs in heav - en a - dored! I

bow at Thy shrine, my Sav-iour di-vine, My won-der-ful, won-der-ful Lord.

104 Blessed Redeemer

Avis Burgeson Christiansen, 1895—

Harry Dixon Loes, 1892-1965

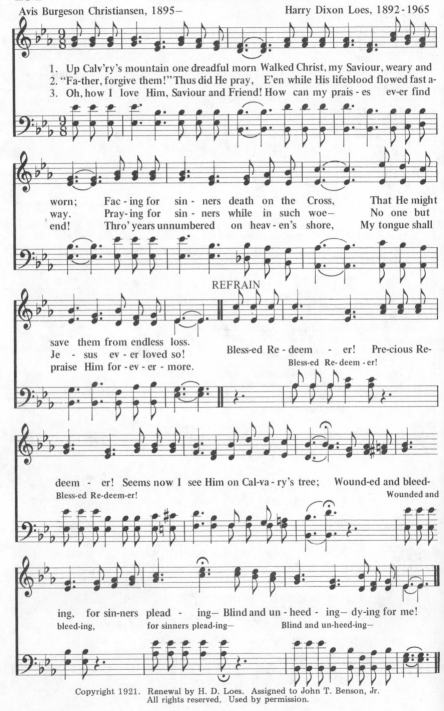

1. Up Calv'ry's mountain one dreadful morn Walked Christ, my Saviour, weary and
2. "Fa-ther, forgive them!" Thus did He pray, E'en while His lifeblood flowed fast a-
3. Oh, how I love Him, Saviour and Friend! How can my prais-es ev-er find

worn; Fac-ing for sin-ners death on the Cross, That He might
way. Pray-ing for sin-ners while in such woe— No one but
end! Thro' years unnumbered on heav-en's shore, My tongue shall

save them from endless loss.
Je-sus ev-er loved so!
praise Him for-ev-er-more.

REFRAIN

Bless-ed Re-deem-er! Precious Re-
Bless-ed Re-deem-er!

deem-er! Seems now I see Him on Cal-va-ry's tree; Wound-ed and bleed-
Bless-ed Re-deem-er! Wounded and

ing, for sin-ners plead-ing— Blind and un-heed-ing— dy-ing for me!
bleed-ing, for sinners plead-ing— Blind and un-heed-ing—

105 Wonderful Saviour

J. M. Harris, 20th Century

J. M. Harris, 20th Century

1. Je - sus, my King, my won-der-ful Sav - iour, All of my life is
2. Freedom from sin, oh, won-der-ful sto - ry! All of its stains washed
3. Je - sus, my Lord, I'll ev - er a - dore Thee, Lay at Thy feet my
4. When in that bright and beau-ti - ful cit - y I shall be - hold Thy

giv - en to Thee. I am re - joic - ing in Thy sal - va - tion.
whit-er than snow! Je -sus has come to live in His tem - ple,
treasures of love. Lead me in ways to show forth Thy glo - ry,
glo - ries un - told, I shall be like Thee, won-der-ful Sav - iour,

REFRAIN

Thy precious blood now mak -eth me free.
And with His love my heart is a - glow.
Ways that will end in heav - en a - bove.
And I will sing while a - ges un - fold.

Won-der-ful Saviour, wonderful

Sav - iour, Thou art so near, so pre - cious to me! Won-der-ful

Sav-iour, won-der-ful Sav - iour, My heart is filled with prais-es to Thee.

106 The Great Physician

William Hunter, 1811-1877

John H. Stockton, 1813-1877

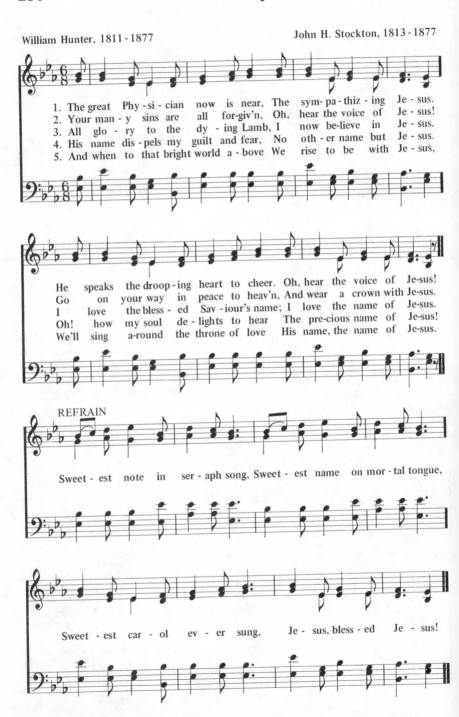

1. The great Phy-si-cian now is near, The sym-pa-thiz-ing Je-sus.
2. Your man-y sins are all for-giv'n, Oh, hear the voice of Je-sus!
3. All glo-ry to the dy-ing Lamb, I now be-lieve in Je-sus.
4. His name dis-pels my guilt and fear, No oth-er name but Je-sus.
5. And when to that bright world a-bove We rise to be with Je-sus,

He speaks the droop-ing heart to cheer. Oh, hear the voice of Je-sus!
Go on your way in peace to heav'n, And wear a crown with Je-sus.
I love the bless-ed Sav-iour's name; I love the name of Je-sus.
Oh! how my soul de-lights to hear The pre-cious name of Je-sus!
We'll sing a-round the throne of love His name, the name of Je-sus.

REFRAIN

Sweet-est note in ser-aph song, Sweet-est name on mor-tal tongue,

Sweet-est car-ol ev-er sung, Je-sus, bless-ed Je-sus!

107 Altogether Lovely

Marie Wolf and
Haldor Lillenas, 1885 - 1959

Haldor Lillenas, 1885 - 1959

1. Since the wondrous grace of my lov-ing Lord Has redeemed and set me free,
2. He has made the des-ert a gar-den fair, Where the fragrant flow-ers grow.
3. He has come to dwell in my in-most self; He's the Bridegroom of my heart.
4. Now the night is gone and the ro-sy dawn Of His love-light shines on me.

All my heart is filled and my soul is thrilled—He is All in All to me.
Ev-'ry cross I bear He will glad-ly share, For I know He loves me so.
What com-mu-nion sweet and what rest complete, Rest that nev-er shall de-part!
Earth has lost its charm; in His might-y arm Sat-is-fied my soul shall be.

REFRAIN

He is al - to-geth-er love-ly, More than
He is al - to-geth-er, al - to-geth-er love-ly,

all the world to me. Fair-er than the
More than all the world to me, to me. Fair-er than the

Rose of Shar - on Is Je-sus, my Sav-iour, to me.
Rose of Shar-on, Rose of Shar-on,

Copyright 1928. Renewed 1956 by Lillenas Publishing Co.

108 All the Way Along

Ada Blenkhorn, 20th Century

Lewis E. Jones, 1865-1936

1. There is One who loves me, One who is my Friend
2. He doth still the tem-pest, bid its tu-mult cease,
3. In my Lord and Sav-iour I will joy-ful be
4. I will sing the prais-es of His won-drous love

All the way a-long,

all the way a-long.

He is ev-er near me, read-y to de-fend.
In the time of troub-le keeps in per-fect peace;
Speak-ing words of com-fort sweet and dear to me,
I will sing more sweet-ly in my home a-bove.

REFRAIN

All the way a-long it is Je - sus. All the way a-long it is

Je - - sus; All the way a-long, bless-ed Je - sus. He's my joy and song

All the way a - long. All the way a - long it is Je - sus.

109 Take the Name of Jesus with You

PRECIOUS NAME

Lydia Baxter, 1809-1874

William H. Doane, 1832-1915

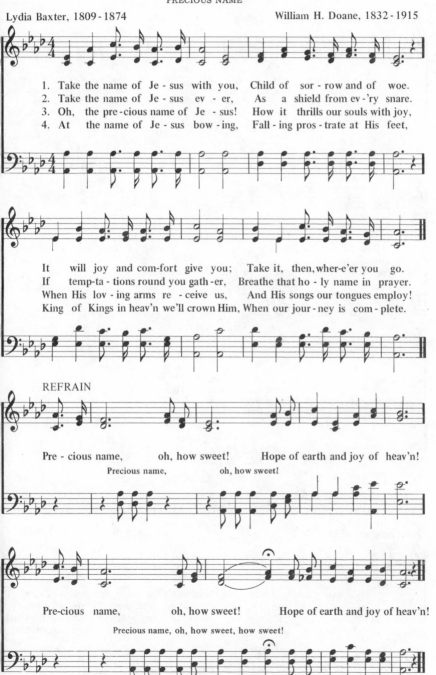

1. Take the name of Je - sus with you, Child of sor - row and of woe.
2. Take the name of Je - sus ev - er, As a shield from ev -'ry snare.
3. Oh, the pre -cious name of Je - sus! How it thrills our souls with joy,
4. At the name of Je - sus bow -ing, Fall - ing pros - trate at His feet,

It will joy and com-fort give you; Take it, then, wher-e'er you go.
If temp-ta - tions round you gath -er, Breathe that ho - ly name in prayer.
When His lov - ing arms re - ceive us, And His songs our tongues employ!
King of Kings in heav'n we'll crown Him, When our jour - ney is com - plete.

REFRAIN

Pre - cious name, oh, how sweet! Hope of earth and joy of heav'n!

Precious name, oh, how sweet!

Pre-cious name, oh, how sweet! Hope of earth and joy of heav'n!

Precious name, oh, how sweet, how sweet!

110   Jesus, Thou Joy of Loving Hearts

SILVER HILL

Bernard of Clairvaux, 1091-1153
Tr. by Ray Palmer, 1808-1887

Source unknown

1. Je - sus, Thou Joy of lov - ing hearts, Thou Fount of
2. Thy truth un - changed hath ev - er stood; Thou sav - est
3. We taste Thee, O Thou liv - ing Bread, And long to
4. Our rest - less spir - its yearn for Thee, Wher - e'er our
5. O Je - sus, ev - er with us stay; Make all our

life, Thou Light of men, From the best bliss that earth im-
those that on Thee call. To them that seek Thee Thou art
feast up - on Thee still. We drink of Thee, the Foun - tain-
change-ful lot is cast, Glad when Thy gra - cious smile we
mo - ments calm and bright. Chase the dark night of sin a-

parts We turn, un - filled, to Thee a - gain.
good; To them that find Thee, All in All.
head, And thirst our souls from Thee to fill.
see, Blest when our faith can hold Thee fast.
way; Shed o'er the world Thy ho - ly light.

111   How Sweet the Name of Jesus Sounds

ST. PETER

John Newton, 1725 - 1807

Alexander R. Reinagle, 1799 - 1877

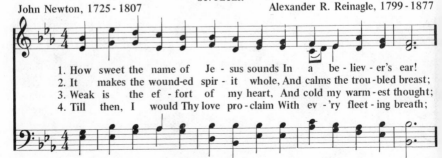

1. How sweet the name of Je - sus sounds In a be - liev - er's ear!
2. It makes the wound-ed spir - it whole, And calms the trou - bled breast;
3. Weak is the ef - fort of my heart, And cold my warm - est thought;
4. Till then, I would Thy love pro - claim With ev - 'ry fleet - ing breath;

It soothes his sor-rows, heals his wounds, And drives a-way his fear.
'Tis man-na to the hun-gry soul, And to the wea-ry, rest.
But when I see Thee as Thou art, I'll praise Thee as I ought.
And may the mu-sic of Thy name Re-fresh my soul in death.

112   My Jesus, as Thou Wilt

JEWETT

Benjamin Schmolck, 1672-1737
Tr. by Jane Borthwick, 1813-1897

Carl M. von Weber, 1786-1826

1. My Je-sus, as Thou wilt. Oh, may Thy will be mine! In-to Thy
2. My Je-sus, as Thou wilt. Tho' seen thro' man-y a-tear, Let not my
3. My Je-sus, as Thou wilt. All shall be well for me; Each changing

hand of love I would my all re-sign. Thro' sor-row or thro' joy,
star of hope Grow dim or dis-ap-pear. Since Thou on earth hast wept
fu-ture scene I glad-ly trust with Thee. Straight to my home a-bove,

Con-duct me as Thine own, And help me still to say, "My Lord, Thy will be done."
And sor-rowed oft a-lone, If I must weep with Thee, "My Lord, Thy will be done."
I trav-el calm-ly on, And sing in life or death, "My Lord, Thy will be done."

113 Give Me Jesus

Fanny J. Crosby, 1820 - 1915

John R. Sweney, 1837 - 1899

1. Take the world, but give me Je - sus. All its joys are but a name;
2. Take the world, but give me Je - sus, Sweet-est com - fort of my soul;
3. Take the world, but give me Je - sus. Let me view His constant smile;
4. Take the world, but give me Je - sus. In His cross my trust shall be,

But His love a - bid - eth ev - er, Thro' e - ter - nal years the same.
With my Sav - iour watch-ing o'er me, I can sing though bil-lows roll.
Then thro'- out my pil - grim jour - ney Light will cheer me all the while.
Till, with clear - er, bright-er vi - sion, Face-to-face my Lord I see.

REFRAIN

Oh, the height and depth of mer - cy! Oh, the length and breadth of love!

Oh, the full - ness of re - demp - tion, Pledge of end - less life a - bove!

114 What a Wonderful Saviour!

BENTON HARBOR

Elisha A. Hoffman, 1839 - 1929

Elisha A. Hoffman, 1839 - 1929

1. Christ has for sin a - tone - ment made.
2. I praise Him for the cleans-ing Blood.
3. He cleansed my heart from all its sin. What a won - der - ful Sav-iour!
4. He gives me o - ver - com - ing pow'r.
5. To Him I've giv - en all my heart.

We are re - deemed; the price is paid.
That rec - on - ciled my soul to God.
And now He reigns and rules there - in. What a won - der - ful Sav-iour!
And tri - umph in each try - ing hour!
The world shall nev - er share a part.

REFRAIN

What a won - der - ful Sav - iour is Je - sus, my Je - sus!

What a won - der - ful Sav - iour is Je - sus, my Lord!

115 My Wonderful Friend

Haldor Lillenas, 1885-1959   Haldor Lillenas, 1885-1959

1. I found such a won-der-ful Sav-iour In Je - sus, my Lord and my King!
2. Sur - pass-ing the love that a moth-er May have for the child of her care;
3. The pleasures the world could af-ford me Are naught to compare with His joy;
4. When sor-row and pain are my por-tion, When tears of bereavement must fall,
5. When tempests around me are sweeping, My Pi - lot and Guide He will be;

Un - dy - ing and true His de - vo - tion; My heart shall His glad praises sing.
The love of a sis - ter or broth-er With His we can nev-er com - pare.
The rap - ture and peace that He gives me, Earth's sorrows can nev-er de-stroy.
My Sav - iour, my Friend, and Companion Will com-fort and keep thro' it all.
And safe is my soul in His keep-ing. My might-y De-liv-'rer is He.

REFRAIN

Oh, what a won-der-ful Sav-iour is He! Con-stant and true is Je - sus.

More than I fan-cied He ev - er could be Is Je-sus, my won-der-ful Friend.

116 Tell Me the Stories of Jesus

STORIES OF JESUS

William H. Parker, 1845 - 1929

Frederic A. Challinor, 1866 - 1952

1. Tell me the sto-ries of Je - sus I love to hear,
2. First let me hear how the chil - dren Stood round His knee;
3. In - to the cit - y I'd fol - low The chil - dren's band,
4. Tell me, in ac-cents of won - der, How rolled the sea,

Things I would ask Him to tell me If He were here:
And I shall fan-cy His bless - ing Rest - ing on me:
Wav - ing a branch of the palm tree High in my hand.
Toss - ing the boat in a tem - pest On Gal - i - lee;

Scenes by the way - side, Tales of the sea—
Words full of kind - ness, Deeds full of grace,
One of His her - alds, Yes, I would sing
And how the Mas - ter, Read - y and kind,

Sto - ries of Je - sus, Tell them to me.
All in the love - light Of Je - sus' face.
Loud - est ho - san - nas! Je - sus is King!
Chid - ed the bil - lows, And hushed the wind.

117 Why Do I Sing About Jesus?

Albert A. Ketchum, 20th Century   Albert A. Ketchum, 20th Century

1. Deep in my heart there's a glad-ness; Je-sus has saved me from
2. On-ly a glimpse of His good-ness, That was suf-fi-cient for
3. He is the fair-est of fair ones; He is the Lil-y, the

sin!   Praise to His name, what a Sav-iour! Cleans-ing with-
me.   On-ly one look at the Sav-iour; Then was my
Rose.   Riv-ers of mer-cy sur-round Him; Grace, love, and

out and with-in!
spir-it set free.   Why do I sing a-bout Je-sus?
pit-y He shows.

Why is He pre-cious to me?   He is my Lord and my

Sav - iour.   Dy-ing, He set me free!
                                         set me free!

118 That Beautiful Name

Jean Perry, alt., 20th Century   Mabel Johnston Camp, 1871-1937

1. I know of a name, A beau-ti-ful name, That an-gels brought
2. I know of a name, A beau-ti-ful name, That un-to a
3. The One of that name My Sav-iour be-came, My Sav-iour of
4. I love that blest name, That won-der-ful name, Made high-er than

down to earth; They whis-pered it low, One night long a-go,
Babe was given. The stars glit-tered bright Through-out that glad night,
Cal-va-ry. My sins nailed Him there; My bur-dens He bare.
all in heaven. 'Twas whis-pered, I know, In my heart long a-go—

REFRAIN

To a maid-en of low-ly birth.
And an-gels praised God in heaven.
He suf-fered all this for me.   That beau-ti-ful name, That
To Je-sus my life I've given.

rit.

beau-ti-ful name From sin has power to free us! That beau-ti-ful

cresc.   *ad lib.*

name, That won-der-ful name, That match-less name is Je-sus!

119 I Love to Walk with Jesus

Charles F. Weigle, 20th Century   Charles F. Weigle, 20th Century

1. Oh, I love to walk with Je - sus, Like the pub - li - cans of old,
2. Oh, I love to walk with Je - sus, Like the man of long a - go
3. Oh, I love to walk with Je - sus All the way to Cal-v'ry's brow,
4. Oh, some - time I'll walk with Je - sus In the land of end-less day,

When He gath-ered them a - bout Him And the bless - ed tid-ings told:
Who had tar - ried by the way-side Near the gates of Jer - i - cho.
Gaze up - on that scene of suf - f'ring While my tears of sor-row flow.
When our jour-ney here is o - ver And we've reached our home to stay.

How He came to bring de - liv - 'rance To the cap-tives in dis - tress,
Je - sus heard his cry for mer - cy, Gave him back his sight that day,
There He tells me how He loves me, Takes my ev - 'ry sin a - way;
Then I'll walk with Him for - ev - er, Sing His prais-es o'er and o'er,

Take a - way our ev - 'ry bur - den, Giv - ing per - fect peace and rest.
And im - me - diate-ly he fol - lowed Je - sus all a - long the way.
So I fol - low Him so glad - ly, Lead me an - y-where He may.
And with all the saints in glo - ry Love, and wor-ship, and a - dore.

REFRAIN

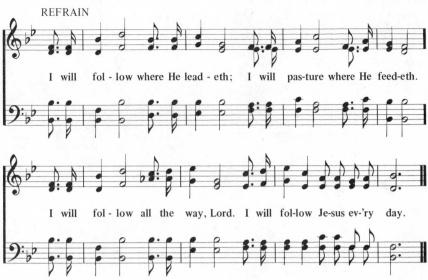

I will fol-low where He lead-eth; I will pas-ture where He feed-eth.

I will fol-low all the way, Lord. I will fol-low Je-sus ev-'ry day.

120   Ride On! Ride On in Majesty

ST. DROSTANE

Henry H. Milman, 1791 - 1868   John B. Dykes, 1823 - 1876

1. Ride on! ride on in maj - es - ty! Hark! all the tribes Ho - san - na cry.
2. Ride on! ride on in maj - es - ty! In low - ly pomp ride on to die.
3. Ride on! ride on in maj - es - ty! The wing-ed squad-rons of the sky
4. Ride on! ride on in maj - es - ty! In low - ly pomp ride on to die.

O Sav - iour meek, pur-sue Thy road With palms and scattered garments strowed.
O Christ, Thy tri-umphs now be - gin O'er cap - tive death and con-quered sin.
Look down with sad and won-d'ring eyes To see th'ap-proach-ing sac - ri - fice.
Bow Thy meek head to mor-tal pain; Then take, O God, Thy pow'r, and reign.

121 Wonderful
(NAME HE BEARS)

Alfred H. Ackley, 1887-1960   Alfred H. Ackley, 1887-1960

1. Won - der - ful birth! To a man-ger He came, Made in the like - ness of
2. Won - der - ful life, full of ser - vice so free! Friend to the poor and the
3. Won - der - ful death, for it meant not de - feat. Cal - va - ry made His great
4. Won - der - ful hope! He is com-ing a - gain, Com - ing as King o'er the

man, to pro-claim God's boundless love for a world sick with sin, Plead-ing
need - y was He; Un - fail - ing good-ness on all He be - stowed; Un - dy -
mis - sion com-plete, Wrought our re-demp-tion, and when He a - rose, Ban-ished
na - tions to reign. Glo - ri - ous prom-ise! His Word can-not fail; His righ-

REFRAIN

with sin - ners to let Him come in.
ing faith in the vil - est He showed.   Won-der-ful name He bears. Won-der-ful
for - ev - er the last of our foes.
teous king-dom at last must pre - vail!

crown He wears. Won-der-ful bless - ings His tri-umphs af - ford.   Won - der - ful

Cal - va - ry! Won-der-ful grace for me! Won-der-ful love of my won-der-ful Lord!

122 More About Jesus

SWENEY

Eliza E. Hewitt, 1851-1920

John R. Sweney, 1837-1899

1. More a-bout Je-sus would I know, More of His grace to oth-ers show;
2. More a-bout Je-sus let me learn, More of His ho-ly will dis-cern;
3. More a-bout Je-sus in His Word, Hold-ing com-mu-nion with my Lord,
4. More a-bout Je-sus on His throne, Rich-es in glo-ry all His own;

More of His sav-ing full-ness see, More of His love who died for me.
Spir-it of God, my Teach-er be, Show-ing the things of Christ to me.
Hear-ing His voice in ev-'ry line, Mak-ing each faith-ful say-ing mine.
More of His king-dom's sure in-crease; More of His com-ing, Prince of Peace.

REFRAIN

More, more a-bout Je-sus; More, more a-bout Je-sus;

More of His sav-ing full-ness see, More of His love who died for me.

123   What a Friend We Have in Jesus

CONVERSE

Joseph M. Scriven, 1820-1886   Charles C. Converse, 1832-1918

1. What a Friend we have in Je-sus,   All   our sins and griefs to bear!
2. Have we tri-als and temp-ta-tions?   Is   there trou-ble an-y-where?
3. Are we weak and heav-y-lad-en,   Cum-bered with a load of care?

What a priv-i-lege to car-ry   Ev-'ry-thing to God in pray'r!
We should nev-er be dis-cour-aged;   Take it to the Lord in pray'r.
Pre-cious Sav-iour, still our Ref-uge!—   Take it to the Lord in pray'r.

Oh, what peace we of-ten for-feit,   Oh, what need-less pain we bear,
Can we find a friend so faith-ful   Who will all our sor-rows share?
Do thy friends despise, for-sake thee?   Take it to the Lord in pray'r.

All be-cause we do not car-ry   Ev-'ry-thing to God in pray'r!
Je-sus knows our ev-'ry weak-ness;   Take it to the Lord in pray'r.
In His arms He'll take and shield thee;   Thou wilt find a sol-ace there.

124 There Is a Fountain

CLEANSING FOUNTAIN

William Cowper, 1731-1800

Early American Melody
Arr. from Lowell Mason, 1792-1872

1. There is a foun-tain filled with blood Drawn from Im-man-uel's veins;
2. The dy-ing thief re-joiced to see That foun-tain in his day;
3. Dear dy-ing Lamb, Thy pre-cious blood Shall nev-er lose its pow'r
4. E'er since, by faith, I saw the stream Thy flow-ing wounds sup-ply,
5. Then in a no-bler, sweet-er song I'll sing Thy pow'r to save,

And sin-ners, plunged be-neath that flood, Lose all their guilt-y stains:
And there may I, though vile as he, Wash all my sins a-way:
Till all the ran-somed Church of God Be saved, to sin no more:
Re-deem-ing love has been my theme And shall be till I die:
When this poor lisp-ing, stamm'ring tongue Lies si-lent in the grave:

Lose all their guilt-y stains, Lose all their guilt-y stains;
Wash all my sins a-way, Wash all my sins a-way;
Be saved, to sin no more, Be saved, to sin no more;
And shall be till I die, And shall be till I die;
Lies si-lent in the grave, Lies si-lent in the grave;

And sin-ners, plunged be-neath that flood, Lose all their guilt-y stains.
And there may I, though vile as he, Wash all my sins a-way.
Till all the ran-somed Church of God Be saved, to sin no more.
Re-deem-ing love has been my theme And shall be till I die.
When this poor lisp-ing, stamm'ring tongue Lies si-lent in the grave.

125 Blessed Be the Fountain

Eden R. Latta, 19th Century

Henry S. Perkins, 19th Century

1. Bless-ed be the foun-tain of Blood, To a world of sin-ners re-vealed.
2. Thor-ny was the crown that He wore, And the Cross His bod-y o'er-came;
3. Fa-ther, I have wandered from Thee; Of-ten has my heart gone a-stray.

Bless-ed be the dear Son of God— On-ly by His stripes we are healed.
Griev-ous were the sor-rows He bore, But He suf-fered thus not in vain.
Crim-son do my sins seem to me— Wa-ter can-not wash them a-way.

Tho' I've wandered far from His fold, Bring-ing to my heart pain and woe,
May I to that foun-tain be led, Made to cleanse my sins here be-low;
Je-sus, to that foun-tain of Thine, Lean-ing on Thy prom-ise I go;

Wash me in the blood of the Lamb,
Wash me in the blood that He shed, And I shall be whit-er than snow.
Cleanse me by Thy wash-ing di-vine,

REFRAIN

Whit - er than the snow,_____ Whit - er
Whit-er than the snow, whit-er than the snow, Whit-er than the snow,

than the snow; ___ Wash me in the blood of the

whit - er than the snow;

Lamb, ___ And I shall be whit - er than snow. ___

of the Lamb,

126 Jesus, Thy Blood and Righteousness

OMBERSLEY

Nicolaus L. Zinzendorf, 1700 - 1760
Tr. by John Wesley, 1703 - 1791

William H. Gladstone, 1840 - 1891

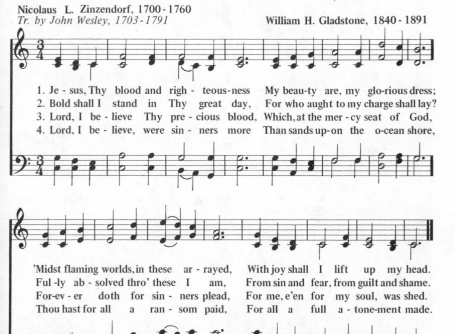

1. Je - sus, Thy blood and righ - teous-ness   My beau-ty are, my glo-rious dress;
2. Bold shall I stand in Thy great day,   For who aught to my charge shall lay?
3. Lord, I be - lieve Thy pre - cious blood,   Which, at the mer - cy seat of God,
4. Lord, I be - lieve, were sin - ners more   Than sands up-on the o-cean shore,

'Midst flaming worlds, in these ar - rayed,   With joy shall I lift up my head.
Ful - ly ab - solved thro' these I   am,   From sin and fear, from guilt and shame.
For-ev - er doth for sin - ners plead,   For me, e'en for my soul, was shed.
Thou hast for all   a ran - som paid,   For all a   full a - tone-ment made.

127 Saved by the Blood

Bertha Mae Lillenas, 1889-1945   Bertha Mae Lillenas, 1889-1945

1. Saved by the blood of the Cru-ci-fied One, Washed and made whiter than snow;
2. Saved by the blood of the Cru-ci-fied One, I am a child of His love;
3. Saved by the blood of the Cru-ci-fied One, Heir to His rich-es of grace;
4. Saved by the blood of the Cru-ci-fied One, Soon I shall look on His face;

Life ev-er-last-ing with-in me be-gun,
Free-ly for-giv-en, my bur-den is gone!   Saved by the blood of the Lamb!
Trust-ing in Him, I find heav-en be-gun,
Meet Him in glo-ry when life's race is run,

REFRAIN

Saved,_____ saved,_____

Saved by the Blood, saved by the Blood, Saved by the blood of the Cru-ci-fied One!
Saved,   saved,   saved,   saved,

Saved,_____ saved,_____

Saved by the Blood, saved by the Blood, Saved by the mer-it of God's on-ly Son!
Saved,   saved,   saved,   saved,

Gone are my burdens and gone are my fears; Gone are the heartaches of many long years.

Sim-ply be-liev-ing, I cast off my fears, Saved by the blood of the Lamb!___

by the blood of the Lamb!

128 He Loves Me

Isaac Watts, 1674-1748

Unknown

1. A - las! and did my Sav-iour bleed? And did my Sov-'reign die?
2. Was it for crimes that I have done He groaned up - on the tree?
3. Well might the sun in dark - ness hide, And shut His glo - ries in,
4. But drops of grief can ne'er re - pay The debt of love I owe.

Would He de - vote that sa - cred head For such a worm as I?
A - maz - ing pit - y! grace un-known! And love be - yond de - gree!
When Christ, the might - y Mak - er, died For man, the crea - ture's, sin.
Here, Lord, I give my - self a - way; 'Tis all that I can do.

REFRAIN

He loves me; He loves me; He loves me, this I know.

I know.

He gave him - self to die for me Be - cause He loves me so!

129 Covered by the Blood

Nellie Edwards, 20th Century

Ran C. Story, 20th Century

1. Once in sin's dark-est night I was wan-d'ring a-lone; A
stran-ger to mer-cy I stood. But the Sav-iour came nigh When He
heard my faint cry, And He put my sins un-der the Blood.

2. From the bur-den I car-ried now I am set free, For
Je-sus has lift-ed my load. Oh, the love and the grace I received in its place When He put my sins un-der the Blood.

3. I can ne'er un-der-stand why He sought e-ven me, Why His
life-blood on Cal-va-ry flowed. But suf-fi-cient for me, Since He
died on the tree, He hath put my sins un-der the Blood.

4. Now He comes to my heart and re-moves ev-'ry care; He
bears all my cum-ber-ing load. In a path-way re-plete With His
love are my feet, Since He put my sins un-der the Blood.

REFRAIN

They are cov-ered by the Blood; they are cov-ered by the Blood. My
sins are all cov-ered by the Blood._____ Mine in-iq-ui-ties so vast
pre-cious Blood.

Have been blot-ted out at last. My sins are all cov-ered by the Blood.___

precious Blood.

130　Nothing but the Blood

Robert Lowry, 1826 - 1899　　　　　　　　Robert Lowry, 1826 - 1899

1. What can wash a - way my sin?
2. For my par - don this I see—
3. Noth-ing can for sin a - tone—
4. This is all my hope and peace—

Noth-ing but the blood of Je - sus.

What can make me whole a - gain?
For my cleans-ing this my plea—
Naught of good that I have done—
This is all my righ-teous-ness—

Noth-ing but the blood of Je - sus.

REFRAIN

Oh, pre - cious is the flow That makes me white as snow.

No oth - er fount I know, Noth-ing but the blood of Je - sus.

131 When I See the Blood

By the Foote Brothers, 19th Century

John G. Foote, 19th Century

1. Christ, our Re-deem - er, died on the Cross; Died for the sin - ner,
2. Chief - est of sin - ners, Je - sus will save; All He has prom-ised,
3. Judg - ment is com - ing; all will be there, Each one re-ceiv - ing
4. Oh, great com-pas - sion! Oh, bound-less love! Oh, lov - ing-kind - ness,

paid all his due. Sprin - kle your soul with the blood of the Lamb,
that will He do. Wash in the foun - tain o - pened for sin,
just - ly his due. Hide in the sav - ing, sin - cleans-ing Blood,
faith - ful and true! Find peace and shel - ter un - der the Blood,

REFRAIN

"And I will pass, will pass o - ver you." "When I see the
"When I

blood, When I see the blood, When I see the
see the blood, When I see the blood, When I

blood, I will pass, I will pass o - ver you."
see the blood, o-ver you."

rit.

132 O Sacred Head, Now Wounded

PASSION CHORALE

From the Latin
Trans. by Paul Gerhardt, 1607-1676
Trans. by James W. Alexander, 1804-1859

Hans Leo Hassler, 1564-1612
Harm. by J. S. Bach, 1685-1750

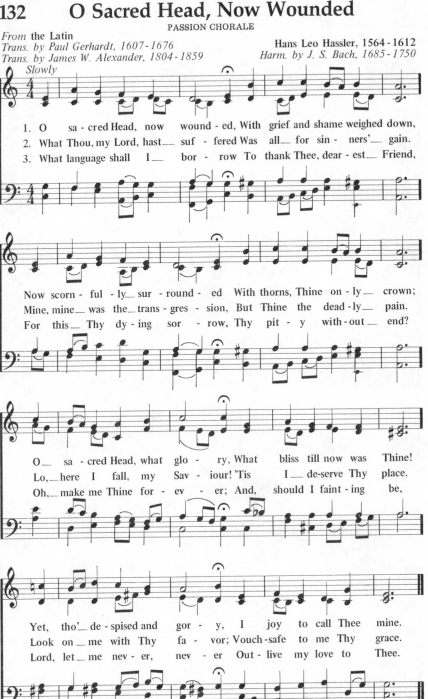

1. O sa-cred Head, now wound-ed, With grief and shame weighed down,
2. What Thou, my Lord, hast suf-fered Was all for sin-ners' gain.
3. What language shall I bor-row To thank Thee, dear-est Friend,

Now scorn-ful-ly sur-round-ed With thorns, Thine on-ly crown;
Mine, mine was the trans-gres-sion, But Thine the dead-ly pain.
For this Thy dy-ing sor-row, Thy pit-y with-out end?

O sa-cred Head, what glo-ry, What bliss till now was Thine!
Lo, here I fall, my Sav-iour! 'Tis I de-serve Thy place.
Oh, make me Thine for-ev-er; And, should I faint-ing be,

Yet, tho' de-spised and gor-y, I joy to call Thee mine.
Look on me with Thy fa-vor; Vouch-safe to me Thy grace.
Lord, let me nev-er, nev-er Out-live my love to Thee.

133 The Blood Will Never Lose Its Power

Civilla D. Martin, 1869-1948

W. Stillman Martin, 1862-1935

1. The blood that Je-sus once shed for me, As my Re-deem-er up-
2. It gives us ac-cess to God on high; From far - off plac-es it
3. It is a shel-ter for rich and poor; It is to heav-en the
4. And when with all the Blood-washed throng We sing in glo-ry re-

on the tree; The Blood that setteth the pris-'ner free Will nev - er lose its
brings us nigh To pre-cious blessings that nev - er die. It will nev - er lose its
o - pen door, The sin - ner's mer-it for - ev - er-more. It will nev - er lose its
demption's song, We'll pass the glo-ri-ous truth a-long; It has nev - er lost its

REFRAIN

pow'r. It will nev- er lose its pow'r.___ It will nev - er lose its pow'r.___
ho - ly pow'r. ho-ly pow'r.

The Blood that cleans -es from all sin Will nev-er lose its pow'r.

134 It Cleanseth Me

F. L. Snyder, 19th Century

A. F. Myers, 19th Century

1. There is a stream that flows from Cal - va - ry, A crim - son tide so
2. Its sav - ing vir - tues ev - er are the same. It cleans-eth still, and
3. No oth - er foun-tain can for sin a - tone But Je - sus' blood, O

deep and wide. It wash - es whit - er than the pur - est snow; It
al - ways will. Poor sin - ners who will seek the Sav-iour's face Shall
pre - cious flood! And who - so - ev - er will may plunge there-in, And

REFRAIN

cleans - eth me, I know.
know His won-drous grace. Hal - le - lu-jah! 'tis His blood that cleanseth
be made free from sin.

me, 'Tis His grace that makes me free. And, my brother, 'tis for thee. Oh, hal - le-

lu - jah! 'tis sal - va-tion full and free; And it cleans-eth, yes, it cleans-eth me.

135 Under the Atoning Blood

Haldor Lillenas, 1885-1959

Haldor Lillenas, 1885-1959

1. I have found a pre - cious rest - ing place, In the shel - ter
2. Where shall I the praise of Christ be - gin? Gone the heav - y
3. E - vil shall not here my soul en - snare; Ten-der - ly I'm
4. Now its heal - ing pow - er makes me whole; Thro' its mer - it

of re - deem-ing grace. Here with joy I see my Sav - iour's face,
bur - den of my sin! Grace has changed the world I'm liv - ing in,
kept with jeal - ous care. Je - sus walks be-side me ev - 'ry - where,
Je - sus saves my soul. Sav-iour, keep me while the a - ges roll

REFRAIN

Un-der the a - ton - ing Blood. Un-der the a - ton - ing blood of the Lamb,

Un - der the a - ton - ing blood of the Lamb; Safe - ly I am

hid - ing, Con-stant-ly a - bid - ing, Un-der the a-ton - ing Blood.

136 There Is Power in the Blood

POWER IN THE BLOOD

Lewis E. Jones, 1865-1936

Lewis E. Jones, 1865-1936

1. Would you be free from your bur - den of sin?
2. Would you be free from your pas - sion and pride?
3. Would you be whit - er, much whit - er than snow?
4. Would you do ser - vice for Je - sus', your King?

There's pow'r in the Blood,

pow'r in the Blood.

Would you o'er e - vil a   vic - to - ry win?
Come for a cleans - ing to   Cal - va - ry's tide.
Sin stains are lost in its   life - giv - ing flow.
Would you live dai - ly His   prais - es to sing?

There's

won-der-ful pow'r in the Blood. There is pow'r, pow'r, won-der-working

There is pow'r,

pow'r In the blood of the Lamb. There is pow'r, pow'r,

in the blood   of the Lamb.   There is pow'r,

won - der - work-ing pow'r In the pre - cious blood of the Lamb.

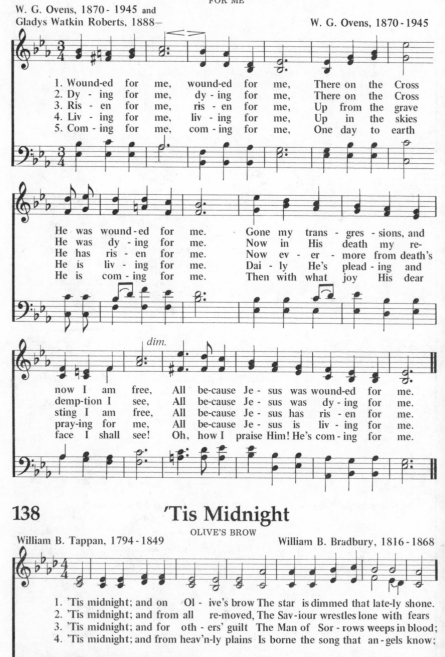

137

Wounded for Me
FOR ME

W. G. Ovens, 1870 - 1945 and
Gladys Watkin Roberts, 1888–

W. G. Ovens, 1870 - 1945

1. Wound-ed for me, wound-ed for me, There on the Cross
2. Dy - ing for me, dy - ing for me, There on the Cross
3. Ris - en for me, ris - en for me, Up from the grave
4. Liv - ing for me, liv - ing for me, Up in the skies
5. Com - ing for me, com - ing for me, One day to earth

He was wound-ed for me. Gone my trans - gres - sions, and
He was dy - ing for me. Now in His death my re-
He has ris - en for me. Now ev - er - more from death's
He is liv - ing for me. Dai - ly He's plead - ing and
He is com - ing for me. Then with what joy His dear

dim.

now I am free, All be-cause Je - sus was wound-ed for me.
demp-tion I see, All be-cause Je - sus was dy - ing for me.
sting I am free, All be-cause Je - sus has ris - en for me.
pray-ing for me, All be-cause Je - sus is liv - ing for me.
face I shall see! Oh, how I praise Him! He's com - ing for me.

138

'Tis Midnight
OLIVE'S BROW

William B. Tappan, 1794 - 1849

William B. Bradbury, 1816 - 1868

1. 'Tis midnight; and on Ol - ive's brow The star is dimmed that late-ly shone.
2. 'Tis midnight; and from all re-moved, The Sav-iour wrestles lone with fears
3. 'Tis midnight; and for oth - ers' guilt The Man of Sor - rows weeps in blood;
4. 'Tis midnight; and from heav'n-ly plains Is borne the song that an-gels know;

'Tis midnight; in the gar - den now The suff'ring Sav-iour prays a - lone.
E'en that dis - ci - ple whom He loved Heeds not his Master's grief and tears.
Yet He that hath in an - guish knelt Is not for-sak-en by His God.
Un - heard by mor- tals are the strains That sweetly soothe the Saviour's woe.

139 Near the Cross

Fanny J. Crosby, 1820 - 1915   William H. Doane, 1832 - 1915

1. Je - sus, keep me near the Cross. There a pre - cious foun-tain,
2. Near the Cross, a trem - bling soul, Love and mer - cy found me;
3. Near the Cross! O Lamb of God, Bring its scenes be - fore me;
4. Near the Cross I'll watch and wait, Hop - ing, trust - ing ev - er,

Free to all, a heal - ing stream, Flows from Cal - v'ry's mountain.
There the Bright and Morn - ing Star Sheds its beams a - round me.
Help me walk from day to day With its shad - ows o'er me.
Till I reach the gold - en strand, Just be - yond the riv - er.

REFRAIN

In the Cross, in the Cross Be my glo - ry ev - er,

Till my rap - tured soul shall find Rest be - yond the riv - er.

140 Lead Me to Calvary

DUNCANNON

Jennie Evelyn Hussey, 1874-1958

William J. Kirkpatrick, 1838-1921

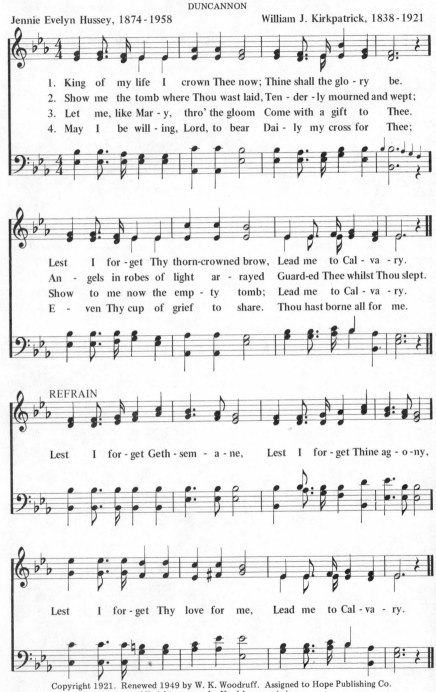

1. King of my life I crown Thee now; Thine shall the glo - ry be.
2. Show me the tomb where Thou wast laid, Ten - der - ly mourned and wept;
3. Let me, like Mar - y, thro' the gloom Come with a gift to Thee.
4. May I be will - ing, Lord, to bear Dai - ly my cross for Thee;

Lest I for - get Thy thorn-crowned brow, Lead me to Cal - va - ry.
An - gels in robes of light ar - rayed Guard-ed Thee whilst Thou slept.
Show to me now the emp - ty tomb; Lead me to Cal - va - ry.
E - ven Thy cup of grief to share. Thou hast borne all for me.

REFRAIN

Lest I for - get Geth - sem - a - ne, Lest I for - get Thine ag - o - ny,

Lest I for - get Thy love for me, Lead me to Cal - va - ry.

141 The Old Rugged Cross

George Bennard, 1873-1958

George Bennard, 1873-1958

1. On a hill far a-way stood an old rug-ged Cross, The em-blem of
2. Oh, the old rug-ged Cross, so de-spised by the world, Has a won-drous at-
3. In the old rug-ged Cross, stained with Blood so divine, A won-drous
4. To the old rug-ged Cross I will ev-er be true, Its shame and re-

suf-f'ring and shame; And I love that old Cross, where the dear-est and best
trac-tion for me; For the dear Lamb of God left His glo-ry a-bove
beau-ty I see; For 'twas on that old Cross Je-sus suf-fered and died
proach gladly bear. Then He'll call me someday to my home far a-way,

REFRAIN

For a world of lost sin-ners was slain.
To bear it to dark Cal-va-ry.   So I'll cher-ish the old rug-ged
To par-don and sanc-ti-fy me.
Where His glo-ry for-ev-er I'll share.
Cross, the

Cross,_____ Till my tro-phies at last I lay down.   I will cling to the
old rug-ged Cross,

old rug-ged Cross,_____ And ex-change it some-day for a crown.
Cross, the old rug-ged Cross,

142 Hallelujah for the Cross

KINSMAN

Horatius Bonar, 1808-1889

James McGranahan, 1840-1907

1. The Cross, it stand-eth fast, Hal-le - lu - jah! Hal-le - lu - jah! De - fy - ing
2. It is the old Cross still, Hal-le - lu - jah! Hal-le - lu - jah! Its tri - umph
3. 'Twas here the debt was paid, Hal-le - lu - jah! Hal-le - lu - jah! Our sins on

ev - 'ry blast, Hal-le - lu - jah! Hal-le - lu - jah! The winds of hell have
let us tell, Hal-le - lu - jah! Hal-le - lu - jah! The grace of God here
Je - sus laid, Hal-le - lu - jah! Hal-le - lu - jah! So round the Cross we

blown, The world its hate hath shown, Yet it is not o-ver-thrown. Hal-le-
shown Through Christ, the bless-ed Son, Who did for sin a - tone. Hal-le-
sing Of Christ, our Of-fer - ing; Of Christ, our liv - ing King. Hal-le-

REFRAIN

lu - jah for the Cross!
lu - jah for the Cross! Hal-le - lu - jah, hal-le - lu - jah, hal-le - lu - jah for the
lu - jah for the Cross!

Cross! Hal - le - lu - jah, hal - le - lu - jah! It shall nev - er suf - fer loss!

143 At the Cross

HUDSON

Isaac Watts, 1674-1748
Refrain by Ralph E. Hudson, 1843-1901

Ralph E. Hudson, 1843-1901

1. A - las! and did my Sav - iour bleed, And did my Sov-'reign
2. Was it for crimes that I have done He groaned up - on the
3. Well might the sun in dark - ness hide, And shut his glo - ries
4. But drops of grief can ne'er re - pay The debt of love I

die? Would He de - vote that sa - cred head For such a worm as I?
tree? A - maz-ing pit - y, grace unknown, And love be-yond de - gree!
in When Christ, the mighty Mak - er, died For man, the creature's, sin.
owe. Here, Lord, I give my - self a - way; 'Tis all that I can do!

REFRAIN

At the Cross, at the Cross, where I first saw the light, And the

bur-den of my heart rolled a - way, rolled a - way. It was there by faith

I re - ceived my sight, And now I am hap - py all the day!

144
When I Survey

HAMBURG

Isaac Watts, 1674-1748

Arr. by Lowell Mason, 1792-1872

1. When I sur - vey the won - drous Cross On which the
2. For - bid it, Lord, that I should boast, Save in the
3. See, from His head, His hands, His feet, Sor - row and
4. Were the whole realm of na - ture mine, That were a

Prince of Glo - ry died, My rich - est gain I
death of Christ, my God. All the vain things that
love flow min - gled down. Did e'er such love and
pres - ent far too small. Love so a - maz - ing,

count but loss, And pour con - tempt on all my pride.
charm me most, I sac - ri - fice them to His blood.
sor - row meet, Or thorns com - pose so rich a crown?
so di - vine, De - mands my soul, my life, my all.

145
When I Survey

EUCHARIST

Isaac Watts, 1674-1748

Isaac B. Woodbury, 1819-1858

1. When I sur - vey the won - drous Cross On which the
2. For - bid it, Lord, that I should boast, Save in the
3. See, from His head, His hands, His feet, Sor - row and
4. Were the whole realm of na - ture mine, That were a

Prince of Glo - ry died, My rich-est gain I
death of Christ, my God. All the vain things that
love flow min - gled down. Did e'er such love and
pres - ent far too small. Love so a - maz - ing,

count but loss, And pour con-tempt on all my pride.
charm me most, I sac - ri - fice them to His blood.
sor - row meet, Or thorns com-pose so rich a crown?
so di - vine, De - mands my soul, my life, my all.

146   Must Jesus Bear the Cross Alone?

MAITLAND

Thomas Shepherd, 1665 - 1739   George N. Allen, 1812 - 1877

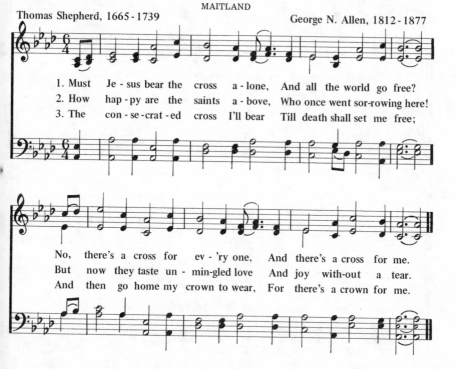

1. Must Je - sus bear the cross a - lone, And all the world go free?
2. How hap - py are the saints a - bove, Who once went sor-rowing here!
3. The con - se - crat - ed cross I'll bear Till death shall set me free;

No, there's a cross for ev - 'ry one, And there's a cross for me.
But now they taste un - min-gled love And joy with-out a tear.
And then go home my crown to wear, For there's a crown for me.

147 In the Cross of Christ

RATHBUN

John Bowring, 1792-1872

Ithamar Conkey, 1815-1867

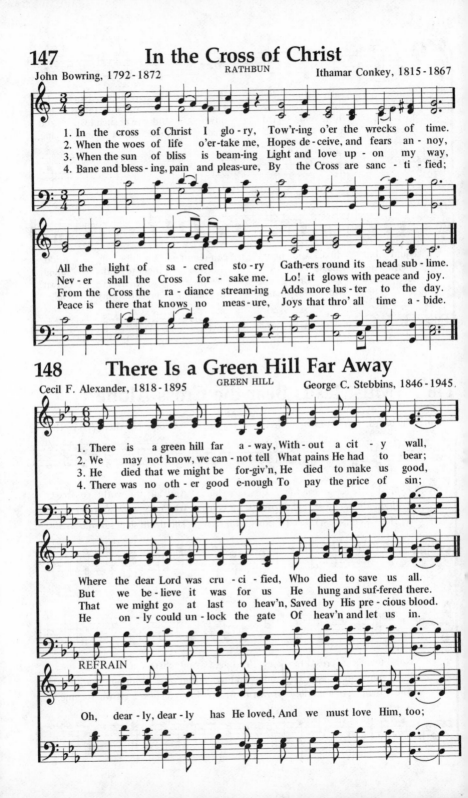

1. In the cross of Christ I glo-ry, Tow'r-ing o'er the wrecks of time.
2. When the woes of life o'er-take me, Hopes de-ceive, and fears an-noy,
3. When the sun of bliss is beam-ing Light and love up-on my way,
4. Bane and bless-ing, pain and pleas-ure, By the Cross are sanc-ti-fied;

All the light of sa-cred sto-ry Gath-ers round its head sub-lime.
Nev-er shall the Cross for-sake me. Lo! it glows with peace and joy.
From the Cross the ra-diance stream-ing Adds more lus-ter to the day.
Peace is there that knows no meas-ure, Joys that thro' all time a-bide.

148 There Is a Green Hill Far Away

GREEN HILL

Cecil F. Alexander, 1818-1895

George C. Stebbins, 1846-1945.

1. There is a green hill far a-way, With-out a cit-y wall,
2. We may not know, we can-not tell What pains He had to bear;
3. He died that we might be for-giv'n, He died to make us good,
4. There was no oth-er good e-nough To pay the price of sin;

Where the dear Lord was cru-ci-fied, Who died to save us all.
But we be-lieve it was for us He hung and suf-fered there.
That we might go at last to heav'n, Saved by His pre-cious blood.
He on-ly could un-lock the gate Of heav'n and let us in.

REFRAIN

Oh, dear-ly, dear-ly has He loved, And we must love Him, too;

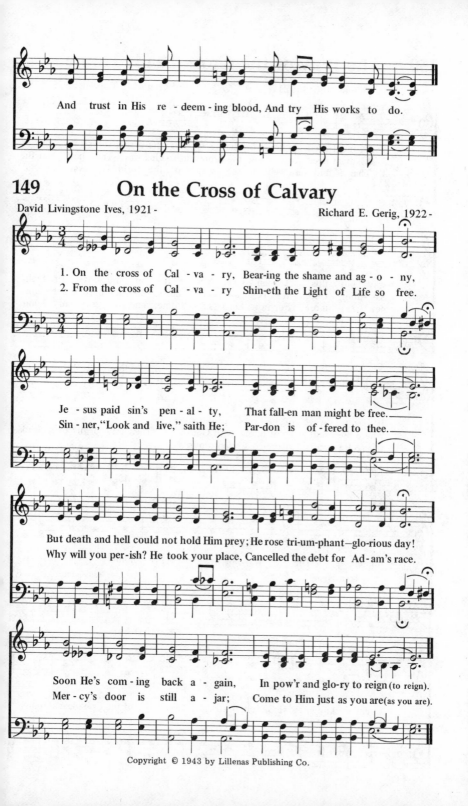

And trust in His re - deem - ing blood, And try His works to do.

149   On the Cross of Calvary

David Livingstone Ives, 1921 -

Richard E. Gerig, 1922 -

1. On the cross of Cal - va - ry, Bear-ing the shame and ag - o - ny,
2. From the cross of Cal - va - ry Shin-eth the Light of Life so free.

Je - sus paid sin's pen - al - ty, That fall-en man might be free.
Sin - ner, "Look and live," saith He; Par-don is of - fered to thee.

But death and hell could not hold Him prey; He rose tri-um-phant—glo-rious day!
Why will you per-ish? He took your place, Cancelled the debt for Ad-am's race.

Soon He's com - ing back a - gain, In pow'r and glo-ry to reign (to reign).
Mer - cy's door is still a - jar; Come to Him just as you are (as you are).

150 The Way of the Cross Leads Home

Jessie Brown Pounds, 1861 - 1921

Charles H. Gabriel, 1856 - 1932

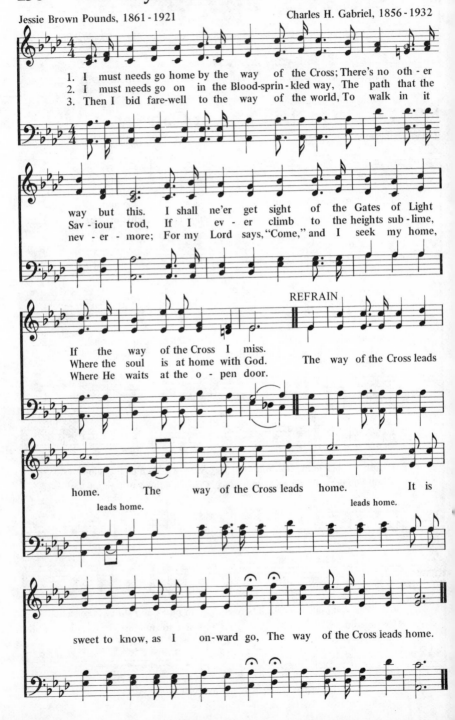

1. I must needs go home by the way of the Cross; There's no oth-er
2. I must needs go on in the Blood-sprin-kled way, The path that the
3. Then I bid fare-well to the way of the world, To walk in it

way but this. I shall ne'er get sight of the Gates of Light
Sav-iour trod, If I ev-er climb to the heights sub-lime,
nev-er-more; For my Lord says, "Come," and I seek my home,

If the way of the Cross I miss.
Where the soul is at home with God.
Where He waits at the o-pen door.

REFRAIN

The way of the Cross leads home. The way of the Cross leads home. It is

leads home.   leads home.

sweet to know, as I on-ward go, The way of the Cross leads home.

151 The Cross Is Not Greater

Ballington Booth, b. 1859

Ballington Booth, b. 1859

1. The cross that He gave may be heav-y, But it ne'er out-weighs His grace.
2. The thorns in my path are not sharp-er Than composed His crown for me;
3. The light of His love shin-eth brighter As it falls on paths of woe.
4. His will I have joy in ful-fill-ing, As I'm walk-ing in His sight.

The storm that I feared may sur-round me, But it ne'er ex-cludes His face.
The cup that I drink, not more bit-ter Than He drank in Geth-sem-a-ne.
The toil of my work grow-eth light-er As I stoop to raise the low.
My all to the Blood I am bring-ing; It a-lone can keep me right.

REFRAIN

The cross is not great-er than His grace. The storm can-not

hide His bless-ed face. I am sat-is-fied to know

That, with Je-sus, here be-low I can con-quer ev-'ry foe.

152 Beneath the Cross of Jesus

ST. CHRISTOPHER

Elizabeth C. Clephane, 1830-1869

Frederick C. Maker, 1844-1927

1. Be -neath the cross of Je - sus I fain would take my stand,
2. Up - on the cross of Je - sus Mine eyes at times can see
3. I take, O Cross, thy shad - ow For my a - bid - ing place.

The shad - ow of a might - y rock With - in a wea - ry land;
The ver - y dy - ing form of One Who suf - fered there for me.
I ask no oth - er sun - shine than The sun - shine of His face;

A home with-in the wil - der - ness; A rest up-on the way,
And from my smit- ten heart, with tears, These won - ders I con - fess:
Con - tent to let the world go by, To know no gain nor loss,

From the burn - ing of the noon-tide heat And the bur - den of the day.
The won - der of His glo -rious love, And my un-wor-thi - ness.
My sin - ful self my on - ly shame, My glo - ry all the Cross.

153 # Calvary Covers It All

Mrs. Walter G. Taylor, 20th Century

Mrs. Walter G. Taylor, 20th Century

1. Far dear - er than all that the world can im - part Was the mes-sage that
2. The stripes that He bore and the thorns that He wore Told His mer-cy and
3. How matchless the grace, when I looked in the face Of this Je - sus, my
4. How bless- ed the tho't that my soul, by Him bought, Shall be His in the

came to my heart (to my heart); How that Je - sus a - lone for my
love ev - er - more (ev - er - more); And my heart bowed in shame as I
cru - ci - fied Lord (of my Lord)! My re - demp-tion com-plete I then
glo - ry on high (His on high), Where with glad - ness and song I'll be

sin did a - tone, And Cal - va - ry cov - ers it all._____
called on His name, And Cal - va - ry cov - ers it all._____
found at His feet, And Cal - va - ry cov - ers it all._____
one of the throng, And Cal - va - ry cov - ers it all!_____
cov-ers it all.

REFRAIN

Cal - va - ry cov - ers it all, My past with its sin and stain. My

guilt and de-spair Je-sus took on Him there, And Cal - va - ry cov - ers it all.

Inspired by the testimony of Charles Crawford, American Bible Society

154   Christ, the Lord, Is Risen Today

EASTER HYMN

Charles Wesley, 1707 - 1788   *From* "Lyra Davidica," 1708

1. Christ, the Lord, is risen to - day.
2. Lives a - gain our glo - rious King.
3. Love's re - deem - ing work is done.
4. Soar we now where Christ has led.

Al - le - lu - ia!

Sons of men and an - gels say:
Where, O death, is now thy sting?
Fought the fight, the bat - tle won.
Fol - lowing our ex - alt - ed Head,

Al - le - lu - ia!

Raise your joys and tri - umphs high.
Dy - ing once, He all doth save.
Death in vain for - bids Him rise.
Made like Him, like Him we rise.

Al - le - lu - ia!

Sing, ye heavens, and, earth, re - ply,
Where thy vic - to - ry, O grave?
Christ has o - pened par - a - dise.
Ours the cross, the grave, the skies.

Al - le - lu - ia!

155 Christ Arose

Robert Lowry, 1826 - 1899   Robert Lowry, 1826 - 1899

1. Low in the grave He lay— Je - sus, my Sav - iour! Wait- ing the coming day—
2. Vain - ly they watch His bed— Je - sus, my Sav - iour! Vain-ly they seal the dead—
3. Death cannot keep his prey— Je - sus, my Sav - iour! He tore the bars a-way—

REFRAIN *faster*

Je - sus, my Lord! Up from the grave He a - rose, With a
He a-rose,

might-y tri - umph o'er His foes. He a - rose a Vic-tor from the
He a-rose!

dark do - main, And He lives for - ev - er with His saints to reign. He a-

rit.

rose! He a - rose! Hal - le - lu -jah! Christ a - rose!
He a-rose! He a-rose!

156   I Know That My Redeemer Liveth

Jessie Brown Pounds, 1861-1921   James H. Fillmore, 1849-1936

1. I know that my Re-deem-er liv - eth, And on the earth
2. I know His prom-ise nev - er fail - eth; The word He speaks,
3. I know my man-sion He pre - par - eth, That where He is

1. And on the earth

a - gain shall stand;   I know e - ter - nal life He
it can - not die.   Tho' cru - el death my flesh as-
there I may be.   Oh, won - drous tho't, for me He

a-gain shall stand;

giv - eth, That grace and pow'r _____ are in His hand.
sail - eth, Yet I shall see _____ Him by and by.
car - eth, And He at last _____ will come for me!

That grace and pow'r are in His hand.

REFRAIN

I know, I know _____ that Je - sus liv - eth, And on the

I know, I know

earth _____ a-gain shall stand; I know, I know _____

And on the earth   I know, I know

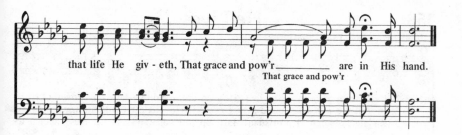

that life He giv - eth, That grace and pow'r_____ are in His hand.
That grace and pow'r

157   The Lord Jehovah Reigns

DARWALL

Isaac Watts, 1674 - 1748   John Darwall, 1731 - 1789

1. The Lord Je - ho - vah reigns; His throne is built on high.
2. The thun - ders of His hand Keep the wide world in awe;
3. Through all His might - y works A - maz - ing wis - dom shines;
4. And will this sov - 'reign King Of glo - ry con - de - scend,

The gar - ments He as - sumes Are light and maj - es - ty. His glo - ries shine
His wrath and jus - tice stand to guard His ho - ly law. And where His love
Sub - dues the pow'rs of hell, Con - founds their dark de - signs. Strong is His arm,
And will He write His name, My Fa - ther and my Friend? I love His name;

with beams so bright, No mor - tal eye can bear the sight.
re - solves to bless, His truth con - firms and seals the grace.
and shall ful - fill His great de - crees and sov - 'reign will.
I love His Word. Join, all my powers, to praise the Lord!

158 He Lives

Alfred H. Ackley, 1887-1960

Alfred H. Ackley, 1887-1960

1. I serve a ris-en Sav-iour; He's in the world to-day. I know that He is
2. In all the world a-round me, I see His lov-ing care, And tho' my heart grows
3. Re-joice, re-joice, O Christian! Lift up your voice and sing E-ter-nal hal-le-

liv-ing, what-ev-er men may say. I see His hand of mer-cy; I
wea-ry I nev-er will de-spair. I know that He is lead-ing, thro'
lu-jahs to Je-sus Christ, the King! The Hope of all who seek Him, the

hear His voice of cheer; And just the time I need Him, He's al-ways near.
all the stor-my blast. The day of His ap-pear-ing will come at last.
Help of all who find, None oth-er is so lov-ing, so good and kind.

REFRAIN *Spirited*

He lives, He lives! Christ Je-sus lives to-day! He walks with me and
He lives, He lives!

talks with me a-long life's nar-row way. He lives, He lives, sal-
He lives, He lives,

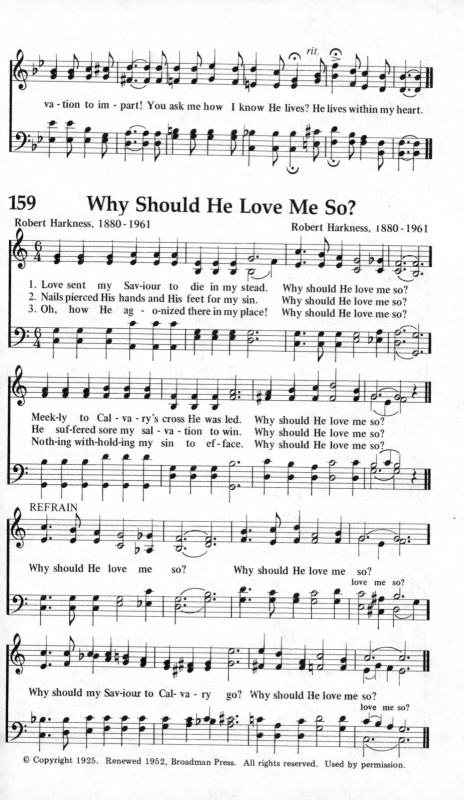

va - tion to im - part! You ask me how I know He lives? He lives within my heart.

159   Why Should He Love Me So?

Robert Harkness, 1880 - 1961   Robert Harkness, 1880 - 1961

1. Love sent my Sav-iour to die in my stead.   Why should He love me so?
2. Nails pierced His hands and His feet for my sin.   Why should He love me so?
3. Oh, how He ag - o-nized there in my place!   Why should He love me so?

Meek-ly to Cal - va - ry's cross He was led.   Why should He love me so?
He suf-fered sore my sal - va - tion to win.   Why should He love me so?
Noth-ing with-hold-ing my sin to ef - face.   Why should He love me so?

REFRAIN

Why should He love me so?   Why should He love me so?
love me so?

Why should my Sav-iour to Cal - va - ry go? Why should He love me so?
love me so?

160 Hallelujah! What a Saviour!

Philip P. Bliss, 1838-1876

Philip P. Bliss, 1838-1876

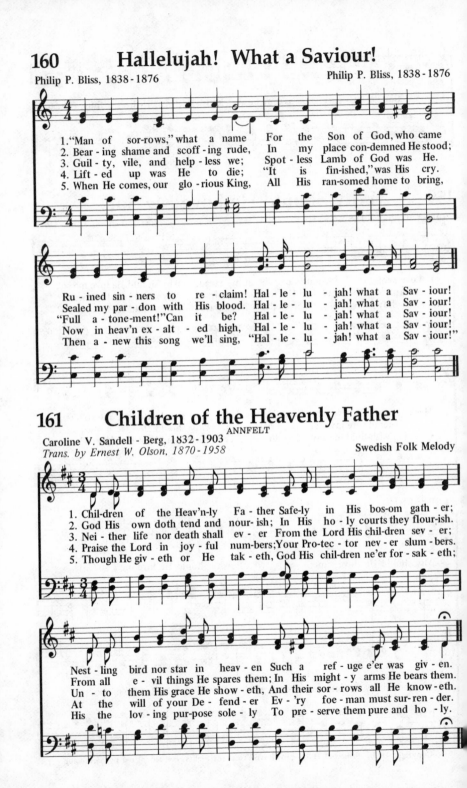

1. "Man of sor-rows," what a name For the Son of God, who came
2. Bear-ing shame and scoff-ing rude, In my place con-demned He stood;
3. Guil-ty, vile, and help-less we; Spot-less Lamb of God was He.
4. Lift-ed up was He to die; "It is fin-ished," was His cry.
5. When He comes, our glo-rious King, All His ran-somed home to bring,

Ru-ined sin-ners to re-claim! Hal-le-lu-jah! what a Sav-iour!
Sealed my par-don with His blood. Hal-le-lu-jah! what a Sav-iour!
"Full a-tone-ment!" Can it be? Hal-le-lu-jah! what a Sav-iour!
Now in heav'n ex-alt-ed high, Hal-le-lu-jah! what a Sav-iour!
Then a-new this song we'll sing, "Hal-le-lu-jah! what a Sav-iour!"

161 Children of the Heavenly Father
ANNFELT

Caroline V. Sandell - Berg, 1832-1903
Trans. by Ernest W. Olson, 1870-1958

Swedish Folk Melody

1. Chil-dren of the Heav'n-ly Fa-ther Safe-ly in His bos-om gath-er;
2. God His own doth tend and nour-ish; In His ho-ly courts they flour-ish.
3. Nei-ther life nor death shall ev-er From the Lord His chil-dren sev-er;
4. Praise the Lord in joy-ful num-bers; Your Pro-tec-tor nev-er slum-bers.
5. Though He giv-eth or He tak-eth, God His chil-dren ne'er for-sak-eth;

Nest-ling bird nor star in heav-en Such a ref-uge e'er was giv-en.
From all e-vil things He spares them; In His might-y arms He bears them.
Un-to them His grace He show-eth, And their sor-rows all He know-eth.
At the will of your De-fend-er Ev-'ry foe-man must sur-ren-der.
His the lov-ing pur-pose sole-ly To pre-serve them pure and ho-ly.

162 Crown Him with Many Crowns

DIADEMATA

Matthew Bridges. 1800 - 1894, and
Godfrey Thring, 1823 - 1903

George J. Elvey, 1816 - 1893

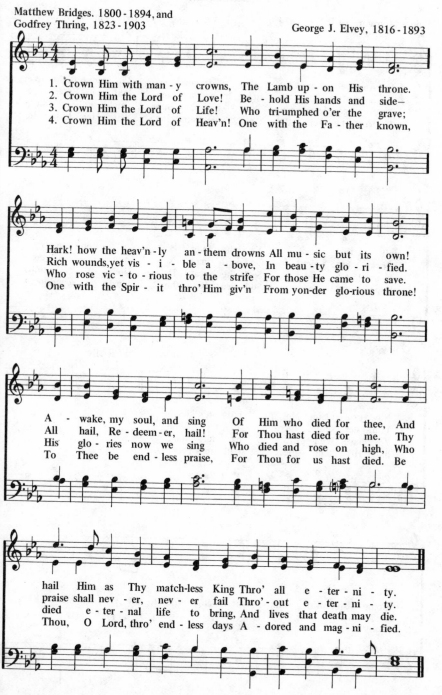

1. Crown Him with man - y crowns, The Lamb up - on His throne.
2. Crown Him the Lord of Love! Be - hold His hands and side—
3. Crown Him the Lord of Life! Who tri - umphed o'er the grave;
4. Crown Him the Lord of Heav'n! One with the Fa - ther known,

Hark! how the heav'n - ly an - them drowns All mu - sic but its own!
Rich wounds, yet vis - i - ble a - bove, In beau - ty glo - ri - fied.
Who rose vic - to - rious to the strife For those He came to save.
One with the Spir - it thro' Him giv'n From yon - der glo - rious throne!

A - wake, my soul, and sing Of Him who died for thee, And
All hail, Re - deem - er, hail! For Thou hast died for me. Thy
His glo - ries now we sing Who died and rose on high, Who
To Thee be end - less praise, For Thou for us hast died. Be

hail Him as Thy match - less King Thro' all e - ter - ni - ty.
praise shall nev - er, nev - er fail Thro' - out e - ter - ni - ty.
died e - ter - nal life to bring, And lives that death may die.
Thou, O Lord, thro' end - less days A - dored and mag - ni - fied.

163 Angels, from the Realms of Glory

REGENT SQUARE

James Montgomery, 1771-1854

Henry Smart, 1813-1879

1. An - gels, from the realms of glo - ry, Wing your flight o'er
2. Shep-herds, in the field a - bid - ing, Watch-ing o'er your
3. Sa - ges, leave your con - tem-pla - tions; Bright - er vi - sions
4. Saints be - fore the al - tar bend-ing, Watch-ing long in

all the earth. Ye who sang cre - a - tion's sto - ry,
flocks by night, God with man is now re - sid - ing;
beam a - far. Seek the great De - sire of Na - tions;
hope and fear, Sud - den - ly the Lord, de - scend-ing,

REFRAIN

Now pro - claim Mes - si - ah's birth.
Yon - der shines the In - fant Light.
Ye have seen His na - tal star. Come and wor - ship.
In His tem - ple shall ap - pear.

Come and wor - ship. Wor - ship Christ, the new - born King.

164 What Child Is This?

GREENSLEEVES

William C. Dix, 1837-1898

Old English Melody

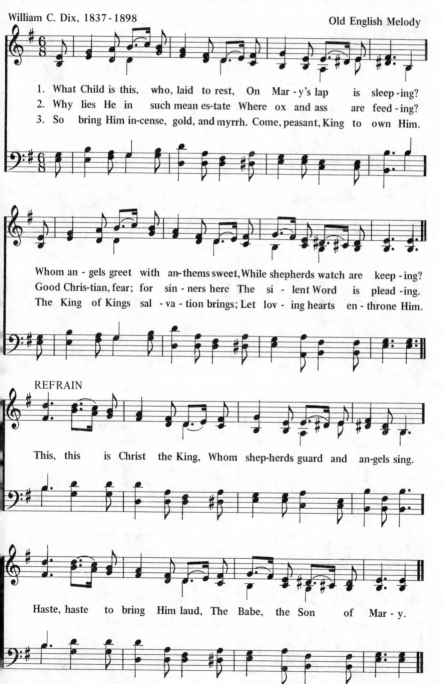

1. What Child is this, who, laid to rest, On Mar-y's lap is sleep-ing?
2. Why lies He in such mean es-tate Where ox and ass are feed-ing?
3. So bring Him in-cense, gold, and myrrh. Come, peasant, King to own Him.

Whom an-gels greet with an-thems sweet, While shepherds watch are keep-ing?
Good Chris-tian, fear; for sin-ners here The si-lent Word is plead-ing.
The King of Kings sal-va-tion brings; Let lov-ing hearts en-throne Him.

REFRAIN

This, this is Christ the King, Whom shep-herds guard and an-gels sing.

Haste, haste to bring Him laud, The Babe, the Son of Mar-y.

165
Silent Night!
STILLE NACHT

Joseph Mohr, 1792-1848

Franz Grüber, 1787-1863

1. Si - lent night! Ho - ly night! All is calm, all is bright
2. Si - lent night! Ho - ly night! Shep-herds quake at the sight!
3. Si - lent night! Ho - ly night! Son of God, love's pure light

Round yon vir - gin moth-er and Child. Ho - ly In -fant, so ten - der and mild,
Glo - ries stream from heav-en a - far; Heav'n-ly hosts sing, Al - le - lu - ia!
Ra - diant beams from Thy ho-ly face, With the dawn of re - deem - ing grace,

Sleep in heav - en - ly peace, Sleep in heav - en - ly peace.
Christ, the Sav - iour, is born! Christ, the Sav - iour, is born!
Je - sus, Lord, at Thy birth; Je - sus, Lord, at Thy birth.

166
Hallelujah! Christ Is Born!

Faith Chambers Wilson, 20th Century

Faith Chambers Wilson, 20th Century

With spirit

Hal - le - lu - jah! Hal - le - lu - jah! Sing this Christ - mas morn.

Hal - le - lu - jah! Hal - le - lu - jah! Christ, the Lord, is born!

167 Thou Didst Leave Thy Throne

MARGARET

Emily E. S. Elliott, 1836-1897

Timothy R. Matthews, 1826-1910

1. Thou didst leave Thy throne and Thy king - ly crown, When Thou
2. Heav-en's arch - es rang when the an - gels sang, Pro -
3. The fox - es found rest, and the birds their nest In the
4. Thou cam'st, O Lord, with the liv - ing word That should
5. When the heav - ens shall ring and her choir shall sing At Thy

cam - est to earth for me; But in Beth-le-hem's home there was
claim - ing Thy roy - al de - gree; But in low - ly birth didst Thou
shade of the for - est tree; But Thy couch was the sod, O Thou
set Thy peo - ple free; But with mock - ing scorn, and with
com - ing to vic - to - ry, Let Thy voice call me home, say - ing,

REFRAIN

found no room For Thy ho - ly Na - tiv - i - ty. 1-4. O
come to earth, And in great hu - mil - i - ty.
Son of God, In the des - erts of Gal - i - lee.
crown of thorn, They bore Thee to Cal - va - ry.
"Yet there is room; There is room at My side for thee!" 5. My

come to my heart, Lord Je - sus; There is room in my heart for Thee.
heart shall re-joice, Lord Je - sus, When Thou com-est and callest for me.

168 Away in a Manger

MUELLER

Stanzas 1 and 2 anonymous
Stanza 3, John T. McFarland, 1851 - 1913

John R. Murray, 1841 - 1905

1. A - way in a man - ger, No crib for a bed, The lit - tle Lord
2. The cat - tle are low - ing; The poor Ba - by wakes, But lit - tle Lord
3. Be near me, Lord Je - sus; I ask Thee to stay Close by me for-

Je - sus Laid down His sweet head. The stars in the sky__ Looked
Je - sus, No cry - ing He makes. I love Thee, Lord Je - sus! Look
ev - er, And love me, I pray. Bless all the dear chil - dren In

down where He lay, The lit - tle Lord Je - sus, A - sleep on the hay.
down from the sky, And stay by my cra - dle To watch lul - la - by.
Thy ten - der care, And take us to heav - en, To live with Thee there.

169 I Heard the Bells on Christmas Day

WALTHAM

Henry W. Longfellow, 1807 - 1882

J. Baptiste Calkin, 1827 - 1905

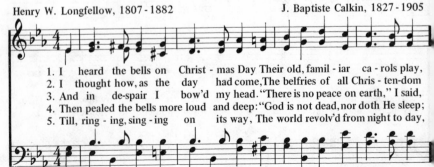

1. I heard the bells on Christ - mas Day Their old, famil - iar ca - rols play,
2. I thought how, as the day had come, The belfries of all Chris - ten - dom
3. And in de - spair I bow'd my head. "There is no peace on earth," I said,
4. Then pealed the bells more loud and deep: "God is not dead, nor doth He sleep;
5. Till, ring - ing, sing - ing on its way, The world revolv'd from night to day,

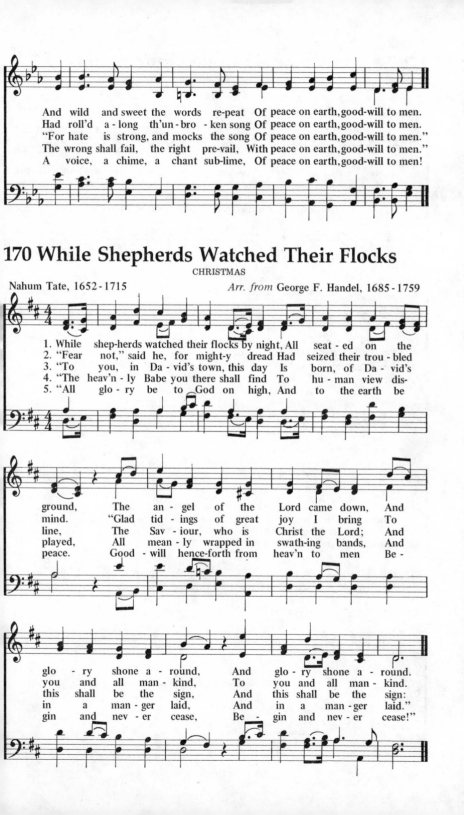

And wild and sweet the words re-peat Of peace on earth, good-will to men.
Had roll'd a - long th'un - bro - ken song Of peace on earth, good-will to men.
"For hate is strong, and mocks the song Of peace on earth, good-will to men."
The wrong shall fail, the right pre-vail, With peace on earth, good-will to men."
A voice, a chime, a chant sub-lime, Of peace on earth, good-will to men!

170 While Shepherds Watched Their Flocks

CHRISTMAS

Nahum Tate, 1652 - 1715   *Arr. from* George F. Handel, 1685 - 1759

1. While shep-herds watched their flocks by night, All seat - ed on the
2. "Fear not," said he, for might-y dread Had seized their trou - bled
3. "To you, in Da - vid's town, this day Is born, of Da - vid's
4. "The heav'n - ly Babe you there shall find To hu - man view dis-
5. "All glo - ry be to God on high, And to the earth be

ground, The an - gel of the Lord came down, And
mind. "Glad tid - ings of great joy I bring To
line, The Sav - iour, who is Christ the Lord; And
played, All mean - ly wrapped in swath-ing bands, And
peace. Good - will hence-forth from heav'n to men Be -

glo - ry shone a - round, And glo - ry shone a - round.
you and all man - kind, To you and all man - kind.
this shall be the sign, And this shall be the sign:
in a man - ger laid, And in a man - ger laid."
gin and nev - er cease, Be - gin and nev - er cease!"

171 O Come, O Come, Emmanuel

VENI EMMANUEL

From the Latin, 12th Century
Stanzas 1, 4 Tr. by John M. Neale, 1818-1866
Stanzas 2-3 Tr. by Henry S. Coffin, 1877-1954

Plainsong, 13th Century

1. O come, O come, Em-man - u - el, And ran - som cap-tive
2. O come, Thou Wis - dom from on high, And or - der all things
3. O come, De - sire of Na - tions; bind All peo - ples in one
4. O come, thou Day - spring, come and cheer Our spir - its by Thine

Is - ra - el, That mourns in lone - ly ex - ile here
far and nigh; To us the path of knowl - edge show,
heart and mind. Bid en - vy, strife, and quar - rels cease;
ad - vent here; Dis - perse the gloom - y clouds of night,

REFRAIN

Un - til the Son of God ap - pear.
And cause us in her ways to go.
Fill the whole world with heav - en's peace.
And death's dark shadows put to flight.

Re - joice! Re - joice! Em-

man - u - el Shall come to thee, O Is - ra - el!

172 Joy to the World

ANTIOCH

Isaac Watts, 1674-1748

Arr. from George F. Handel, 1685-1759

1. Joy to the world! the Lord is come; Let earth re-ceive her King. Let ev-'ry heart pre-pare Him room, And heaven and na-ture sing, And heaven and na-ture sing, And heav-en, and heav-en and na-ture sing.

2. Joy to the world! the Sav-iour reigns; Let men their songs em-ploy; While fields and floods, rocks, hills, and plains Re-peat the sound-ing joy, Re-peat the sound-ing joy, Re-peat, re-peat the sound-ing joy.

3. No more let sin and sor-row grow, Nor thorns in-fest the ground. He comes to make His bless-ings flow Far as the curse is found, Far as the curse is found, Far as, far as the curse is found.

4. He rules the world with truth and grace, And makes the na-tions prove The glo-ries of His righ-teous-ness, And won-ders of His love, And won-ders of His love, And won-ders, won-ders of His love.

(1) And heaven and na-ture sing.

173 As with Gladness Men of Old

DIX

William C. Dix, 1837-1898

Conrad Kocher, 1786-1872

1. As with glad - ness men of old Did the guid - ing
2. As with joy - ous steps they sped To that low - ly
3. As they of - fered gifts most rare At that man - ger
4. Ho - ly Je - sus, ev - 'ry day Keep us in the

star be - hold; As with joy they hailed its light,
man - ger bed, There to bend the knee be - fore
rude and bare, So may we with ho - ly joy,
nar - row way; And, when earth - ly things are past,

Lead - ing on - ward, beam - ing bright; So, most gra - cious
Him whom heaven and earth a - dore, So may we with
Pure, and free from sin's al - loy, All our cost - liest
Bring our ran - somed souls at last Where they need no

Lord, may we Ev - er - more be led to Thee.
will - ing feet Ev - er seek Thy mer - cy seat.
treas - ures bring, Christ, to Thee, our heaven - ly King.
star to guide, Where no clouds Thy glo - ry hide.

174 O Little Town of Bethlehem

ST. LOUIS

Phillips Brooks, 1835 - 1893

Lewis H. Redner, 1831 - 1908

1. O lit - tle town of Beth - le - hem, How still we see thee lie!
2. For Christ is born of Mar - y; And gath-ered all a - bove,
3. How si - lent - ly, how si - lent - ly The won-drous Gift is giv'n!
4. O ho - ly Child of Beth - le - hem, De - scend on us, we pray.

A - bove thy deep and dream-less sleep The si - lent stars go by.
While mor - tals sleep, the an - gels keep Their watch of wond'ring love.
So God im - parts to hu - man hearts The bless-ings of His heav'n.
Cast out our sin, and en - ter in; Be born in us to - day.

Yet in thy dark streets shin - eth The ev - er - last - ing Light;
O morn-ing stars, to - geth - er Pro - claim the ho - ly birth;
No ear may hear His com - ing; But in this world of sin,
We hear the Christ-mas an - gels The great glad tid - ings tell.

The hopes and fears of all the years Are met in thee to - night.
And prais-es sing to God, the King, And peace to men on earth.
Where meek souls will re - ceive Him still, The dear Christ en - ters in.
Oh, come to us, a - bide with us, Our Lord, Em - man - u - el.

175   # Hark! the Herald Angels Sing

MENDELSSOHN

Charles Wesley, 1707-1788
Alt. by George Whitefield, 1714-1770

Felix Mendelssohn, 1809-1847
Adapt. by William H. Cummings, 1831-1915

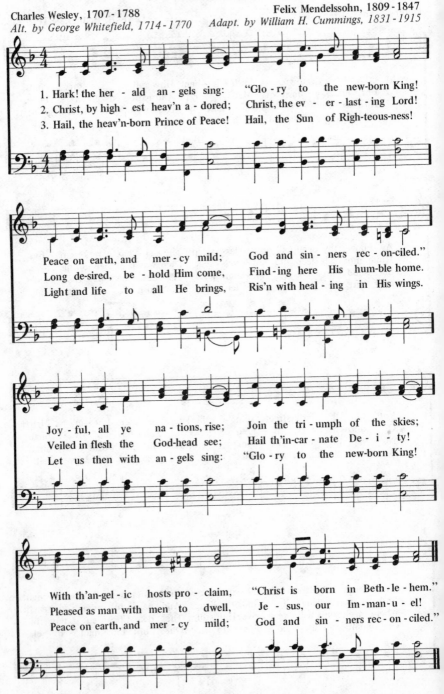

1. Hark! the her - ald an - gels sing: "Glo - ry to the new-born King!
2. Christ, by high - est heav'n a - dored; Christ, the ev - er - last - ing Lord!
3. Hail, the heav'n-born Prince of Peace! Hail, the Sun of Righ-teous-ness!

Peace on earth, and mer - cy mild; God and sin - ners rec - on-ciled."
Long de-sired, be - hold Him come, Find - ing here His hum-ble home.
Light and life to all He brings, Ris'n with heal - ing in His wings.

Joy - ful, all ye na - tions, rise; Join the tri - umph of the skies;
Veiled in flesh the God-head see; Hail th'in-car - nate De - i - ty!
Let us then with an - gels sing: "Glo - ry to the new-born King!

With th'an-gel - ic hosts pro - claim, "Christ is born in Beth-le - hem."
Pleased as man with men to dwell, Je - sus, our Im-man-u - el!
Peace on earth, and mer - cy mild; God and sin - ners rec - on - ciled."

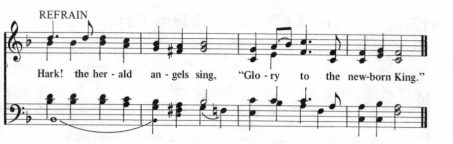

Hark! the her - ald an - gels sing, "Glo - ry to the new-born King."

176   There's a Song in the Air

CHRISTMAS SONG

Josiah G. Holland, 1819 - 1881   Karl P. Harrington, 1861 - 1953

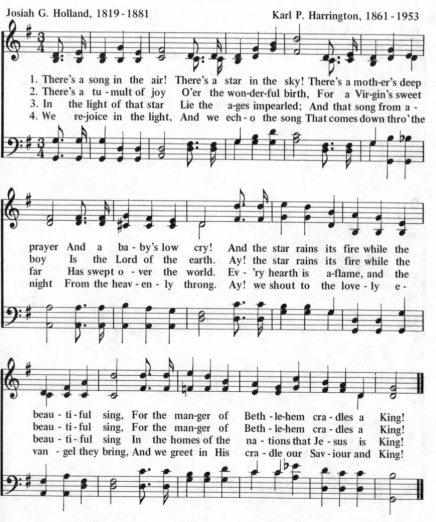

1. There's a song in the air! There's a star in the sky! There's a moth-er's deep
2. There's a tu - mult of joy O'er the won-der-ful birth, For a Vir-gin's sweet
3. In the light of that star Lie the a-ges impearled; And that song from a -
4. We re-joice in the light, And we ech - o the song That comes down thro' the

prayer And a ba - by's low cry! And the star rains its fire while the
boy Is the Lord of the earth. Ay! the star rains its fire while the
far Has swept o - ver the world. Ev - 'ry hearth is a-flame, and the
night From the heav - en - ly throng. Ay! we shout to the love - ly e -

beau - ti - ful sing, For the man-ger of Beth - le-hem cra - dles a King!
beau - ti - ful sing, For the man-ger of Beth - le-hem cra - dles a King!
beau - ti - ful sing In the homes of the na - tions that Je - sus is King!
van - gel they bring, And we greet in His cra - dle our Sav - iour and King!

177 Good Christian Men, Rejoice

IN DULCI JUBILO

From the Latin
Tr. by John M. Neale, 1818-1866

German Melody, 14th Century

mf

1. Good Chris-tian men, re - joice   With heart and soul and voice.
2. Good Chris-tian men, re - joice   With heart and soul and voice.
3. Good Chris-tain men, re - joice   With heart and soul and voice.

Give ye heed to   what we say: News! News! Je - sus Christ is
Now ye hear of   end - less bliss: Joy! Joy! Je - sus Christ was
Now ye need not fear the grave;   Peace! Peace! Je - sus Christ was

born to-day!   Ox and ass be - fore Him bow, And He is in the
born for this.   He hath ope'd the heav'n - ly door, And man is bless - ed
born to save.   Calls you one and calls you all To gain His ev - er -

man-ger now. Christ is born to - day!   Christ is born to - day!
ev - er-more. Christ was born for this!   Christ was born for this!
last-ing hall. Christ was born to   save!   Christ was born to save!

178 O Come, All Ye Faithful

ADESTE FIDELIS

From the Latin, 18th Century
Tr. by Frederick Oakeley, 1802-1880   *From* Wade's "Cantus Diversi," 18th Century

1. O come, all ye faith-ful, joy-ful and tri-um-phant. O come ye, O come ye to Beth-le-hem. Come and be-hold Him, born the King of an-gels.

2. Sing, choirs of an-gels, sing in ex-ul-ta-tion. O sing, all ye bright hosts of heav'n a-bove. Glo-ry to God, all glo-ry in the high-est!

3. Yea, Lord, we greet Thee, born this hap-py morn-ing. O Je-sus, to Thee be all glo-ry giv'n: Word of the Fa-ther, now in flesh ap-pear-ing.

REFRAIN

O come, let us a-dore Him! O come, let us a-dore Him! O come, let us a-dore Him, Christ the Lord!

179 God Rest You Merry, Gentlemen

English Carol, 18th Century

Traditional

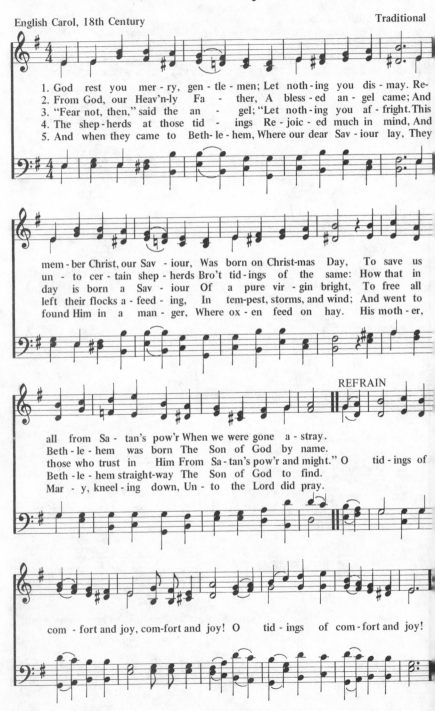

1. God rest you mer - ry, gen - tle - men; Let noth-ing you dis - may. Re-
2. From God, our Heav'n-ly Fa - ther, A bless - ed an - gel came; And
3. "Fear not, then," said the an - gel; "Let noth-ing you af - fright. This
4. The shep - herds at those tid - ings Re - joic - ed much in mind, And
5. And when they came to Beth-le - hem, Where our dear Sav - iour lay, They

mem - ber Christ, our Sav - iour, Was born on Christ-mas Day, To save us
un - to cer - tain shep - herds Bro't tid - ings of the same: How that in
day is born a Sav - iour Of a pure vir - gin bright, To free all
left their flocks a - feed - ing, In tem-pest, storms, and wind; And went to
found Him in a man - ger, Where ox - en feed on hay. His moth - er,

REFRAIN

all from Sa - tan's pow'r When we were gone a - stray.
Beth - le - hem was born The Son of God by name.
those who trust in Him From Sa - tan's pow'r and might." O tid - ings of
Beth - le - hem straight-way The Son of God to find.
Mar - y, kneel - ing down, Un - to the Lord did pray.

com - fort and joy, com-fort and joy! O tid - ings of com-fort and joy!

180 Angels We Have Heard on High

GLORIA

Traditional

French Carol

1. An - gels we have heard on high, Sweet - ly sing - ing o'er the plains,
2. Shepherds, why this ju - bi - lee? Why your joy - ous strains pro-long?
3. Come to Beth - le - hem, and see Him whose birth the an - gels sing;

And the moun-tains in re - ply, Ech - o - ing their joy - ous strains.
What the glad - some tid - ings be Which in - spire your heav'n - ly song?
Come, a - dore on bend - ed knee Christ the Lord, the new-born King.

REFRAIN

Glo - - - - - - ri - a

in ex - cel - sis De - o! Glo - - - -

- - - ri - a in ex - cel - sis De - o!

181   Come, Thou Long-expected Jesus

HYFRYDOL

Charles Wesley, 1707-1788   Rowland H. Prichard, 1811-1887

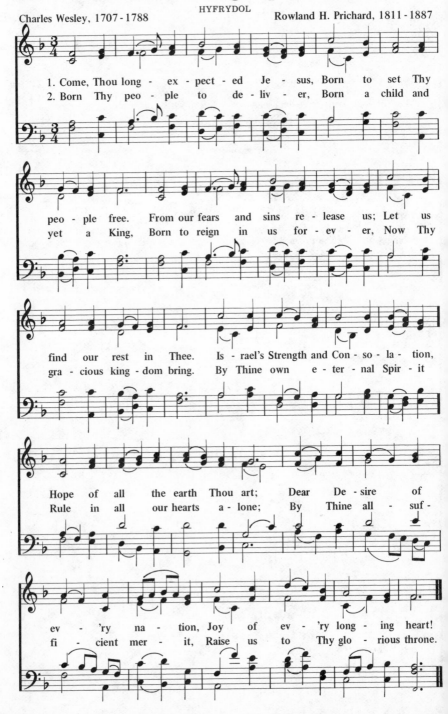

1. Come, Thou long - ex - pect - ed Je - sus, Born to set Thy
2. Born Thy peo - ple to de - liv - er, Born a child and

peo - ple free. From our fears and sins re - lease us; Let us
yet a King, Born to reign in us for - ev - er, Now Thy

find our rest in Thee. Is - rael's Strength and Con - so - la - tion,
gra - cious king - dom bring. By Thine own e - ter - nal Spir - it

Hope of all the earth Thou art; Dear De - sire of
Rule in all our hearts a - lone; By Thine all - suf -

ev - 'ry na - tion, Joy of ev - 'ry long - ing heart!
fi - cient mer - it, Raise us to Thy glo - rious throne.

182 It Came upon the Midnight Clear

CAROL

Edmund H. Sears, 1810-1876

Richard S. Willis, 1819-1900

1. It came up-on the mid-night clear, That glo-rious song of old,
2. Still thro' the clo-ven skies they come, With peace-ful wings un-furled,
3. And ye, be-neath life's crushing load, Whose forms are bend-ing low,
4. For, lo, the days are hast'n-ing on, By proph-et bards fore-told,

From an-gels bend-ing near the earth To touch their harps of gold.
And still their heav'n-ly mu-sic floats O'er all the wea-ry world.
Who toil a-long the climb-ing way With pain-ful step and slow,
When with the ev-er cir-cling years Comes round the age of gold;

"Peace on the earth, good-will to men, From heav'n's all-gra-cious King."
A-bove its sad and low-ly plains They bend on hov'ring wing,
Look up! For glad and gold-en hours Come swift-ly on the wing.
When peace shall o-ver all the earth Its an-cient splen-dors fling,

The world in sol-emn still-ness lay To hear the an-gels sing.
And ev-er o'er its ba-bel sounds The bless-ed an-gels sing.
Oh, rest be-side the wea-ry road And hear the an-gels sing.
And the whole world give back the song Which now the an-gels sing.

183   The First Noel

English Carol, 17th Century

Traditional Melody

1. The first No - el the an-gels did say Was to cer-tain poor
2. They look - ed up and saw a star Bright in the
3. And by the light of that same star Three wise men
4. Then en - tered in those wise men three, Full rev - 'rent-

shep-herds in fields as they lay; In fields where they lay
east be - yond them far, And to the earth it
came from coun - try far; To seek for a King was
ly up - on the knee, And of - fered there, in

keep - ing their sheep, On a cold win-ter's night that was so deep.
gave great light, And so it con-tin-ued both day and night.
their in - tent, And to fol - low the star wher-e'er it went.
His pres - ence, Their gold and myrrh and frank - in - cense.

REFRAIN

No - el, No - el, No - el, No - el, Born is the King of Is - ra - el.

184 Christ Returneth

H. L. Turner, 19th Century

James McGranahan, 1840-1907

1. It may be at morn, when the day is a-wak-ing, When sunlight thro'
2. It may be at mid-day; it may be at twi-light. It may be per-
3. While its hosts cry, "Hosanna!" from heaven de-scend-ing, With glo-ri-fied
4. Oh, joy! oh, de-light! should we go with-out dy-ing, No sick-ness, no

dark-ness and shad-ow is break-ing, That Je-sus will come in the
chance that the blackness of mid-night Will burst in-to light in the
saints and the an-gels at-tend-ing, With grace on His brow, like a
sad-ness, no dread, and no cry-ing! Caught up thro' the clouds with our

full-ness of glo-ry, To re-ceive from the world "His own."
blaze of His glo-ry, When Je-sus re-ceives "His own."
ha-lo of glo-ry, Will Je-sus re-ceive "His own."
Lord in-to glo-ry, When Je-sus re-ceives "His own"!

REFRAIN

O Lord Je-sus, how long, how long Ere we shout the glad song, "Christ re-

rit.

turn-eth! Hal-le-lu-jah! Hal-le-lu-jah! A-men. Hal-le-lu-jah! A-men"?

185 Jesus Is Coming Again

John W. Peterson, 1921 -

John W. Peterson, 1921 -

1. Mar-vel-ous mes-sage we bring;____ Glo-ri-ous car-ol we sing!____
2. For-est and flow-er ex - claim,____ Moun-tain and mead-ow the same,____
3. Stand-ing be-fore Him at last,____ Tri - al and trou-ble all past,____

Won-der-ful word of the King—
All earth and heav-en pro-claim: Je-sus is com-ing a - gain (a-gain)!
Crowns at His feet we will cast.

REFRAIN

Com - ing a - gain,____ Com - ing a - gain;____

May - be morn - ing, may - be noon, May - be evening and may-be soon!

Com - ing a - gain,____ Com - ing a - gain!____

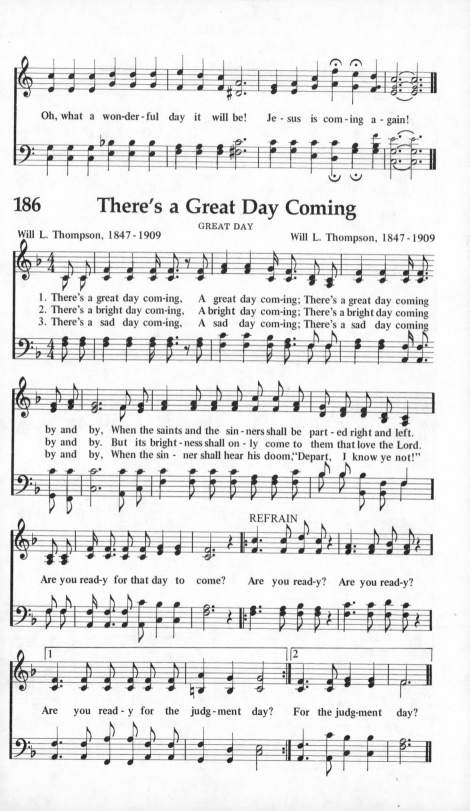

Oh, what a won-der-ful day it will be! Je - sus is com-ing a - gain!

186   There's a Great Day Coming

GREAT DAY

Will L. Thompson, 1847 - 1909   Will L. Thompson, 1847 - 1909

1. There's a great day com-ing, A great day com-ing; There's a great day coming
2. There's a bright day com-ing, A bright day com-ing; There's a bright day coming
3. There's a sad day com-ing, A sad day com-ing; There's a sad day coming

by and by, When the saints and the sin-ners shall be part-ed right and left.
by and by. But its bright-ness shall on-ly come to them that love the Lord.
by and by, When the sin-ner shall hear his doom,"Depart, I know ye not!"

REFRAIN

Are you read-y for that day to come? Are you read-y? Are you read-y?

1

2

Are you read-y for the judg-ment day? For the judg-ment day?

187 Will Jesus Find Us Watching?

Fanny J. Crosby, 1820-1915

William H. Doane, 1832-1915

1. When Je - sus comes to re - ward His ser-vants, Wheth-er it be
2. If at the dawn of the ear - ly morn-ing He shall call us
3. Have we been true to the trust He left us? Do we seek to
4. Bless - ed are those whom the Lord finds watch-ing; In His glo - ry

noon or night, Faith - ful to Him, will He find us watch-ing,
one by one, When to the Lord we re - store our tal - ents,
do our best? If in our hearts there is naught con-demns us,
they shall share. If He shall come at the dawn or mid-night,

REFRAIN

With our lamps all trimmed and bright?
Will He an - swer thee, "Well done"?
We shall have a glo - rious rest.
Will He find us watch - ing there?

Oh, can we say we are

read - y, Broth-er, Read - y for the soul's bright home? Say, will He

find you and me still watch-ing, Wait-ing, wait-ing, when the Lord shall come?

188 Is It the Crowning Day?

George Walker Whitcomb, 20th Century

Charles H. Marsh, 1886-1956

1. Je - sus may come to - day, Glad day, glad day! And I would see my
2. I may go home to - day, Glad day, glad day! Seemeth I hear their
3. Why should I anx-ious be? Glad day, glad day! Lights appear on the
4. Faithful I'll be to - day, Glad day, glad day! And I will free - ly

Friend; Dan-gers and trou-bles would end If Je - sus should come to-
song; Hail to the ra - di - ant throng, If I should go home to-
shore; Storms will affright nev - er - more, For He is "at hand" to-
tell Why I should love Him so well, For He is my All to-

REFRAIN

day. Glad day, glad day! Is it the crown-ing day? I'll

live for to-day, nor anx - ious be; Je - sus, my Lord, I

rit.

soon shall see. Glad day, glad day! Is it the crown-ing day?

189 What if It Were Today?

Lelia N. Morris, 1862-1929   Lelia N. Morris, 1862-1929

1. Je - sus is com - ing to earth a - gain, What if it were to - day?
2. Sa-tan's do-min - ion will then be o'er; Oh, that it were to - day!
3. Faithful and true would He find us here If He should come to - day?

Com - ing in pow - er and love to reign, What if it were to - day?
Sor - row and sigh - ing shall be no more; Oh, that it were to - day!
Watch-ing in glad - ness and not in fear, If He should come to - day?

Com-ing to claim His cho - sen bride, All the redeemed and pu-ri - fied,
Then shall the dead in Christ a - rise, Caught up to meet Him in the skies.
Signs of His com - ing mul - ti - ply; Morning light breaks in east-ern sky;

rit.   *a tempo*

O - ver this whole earth scat - tered wide. What if it were to - day?
When shall these glo - ries meet our eyes? What if it were to - day?
Watch, for the time is draw - ing nigh. What if it were to - day?

REFRAIN

Glo - ry, glo - ry! Joy to my heart 'twill bring;____
Joy to my heart 'twill bring;

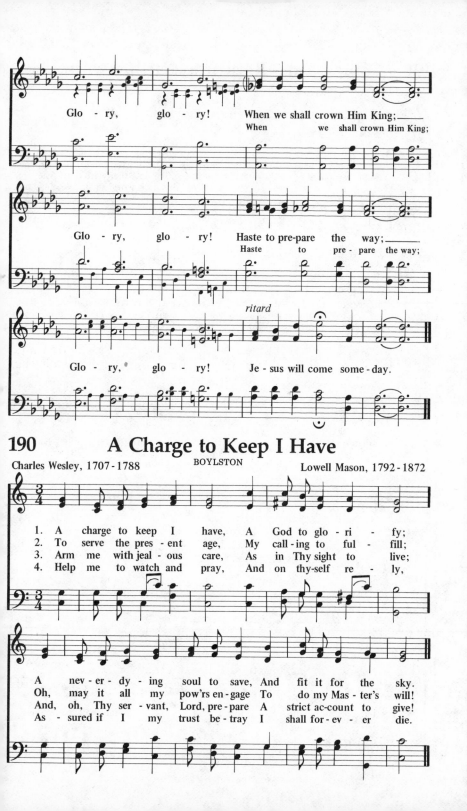

Glo - ry, glo - ry! When we shall crown Him King;___
When we shall crown Him King;

Glo - ry, glo - ry! Haste to pre - pare the way;___
Haste to pre - pare the way;

ritard

Glo - ry, glo - ry! Je - sus will come some - day.

190   A Charge to Keep I Have

Charles Wesley, 1707 - 1788   BOYLSTON   Lowell Mason, 1792 - 1872

1. A charge to keep I have, A God to glo - ri - fy;
2. To serve the pres - ent age, My call - ing to ful - fill;
3. Arm me with jeal - ous care, As in Thy sight to live;
4. Help me to watch and pray, And on thy - self re - ly,

A nev - er - dy - ing soul to save, And fit it for the sky.
Oh, may it all my pow'rs en - gage To do my Mas - ter's will!
And, oh, Thy ser - vant, Lord, pre - pare A strict ac - count to give!
As - sured if I my trust be - tray I shall for - ev - er die.

191 Our Lord's Return to Earth Again

James M. Kirk, 1854-1945

James M. Kirk, 1854-1945

1. I am watching for the com-ing of the glad mil-len-nial day, When our
2. Je-sus' com-ing back will be the an-swer to earth's sorr'wing cry, For the
3. Yes, the ransomed of the Lord shall come to Zi-on then with joy, And in
4. Then the sin and sor-row, pain and death of this dark world shall cease, In a

bless-ed Lord shall come and catch His wait-ing bride a-way. Oh! my heart is
knowledge of the Lord shall fill the earth and sea and sky. God shall take a-
all His ho-ly moun-tain noth-ing hurts or shall de-stroy. Per-fect peace shall
glo-rious reign with Je-sus of a thousand years of peace. All the earth is

filled with rapture as I la-bor, watch, and pray, For our Lord is coming back to
way all sickness and the suff'rer's tears will dry, When our Saviour shall come back to
reign in ev-'ry heart, and love with-out al-loy, Af-ter Je-sus shall come back to
groaning, cry-ing for that day of sweet re-lease, For our Je-sus shall come back to

REFRAIN

earth a-gain. Oh, our Lord is com-ing back to earth a-gain.
is com-ing back to earth a-gain.

Yes, our Lord is coming back to earth a-gain. Sa-tan will be bound a
is com-ing back to earth a-gain.

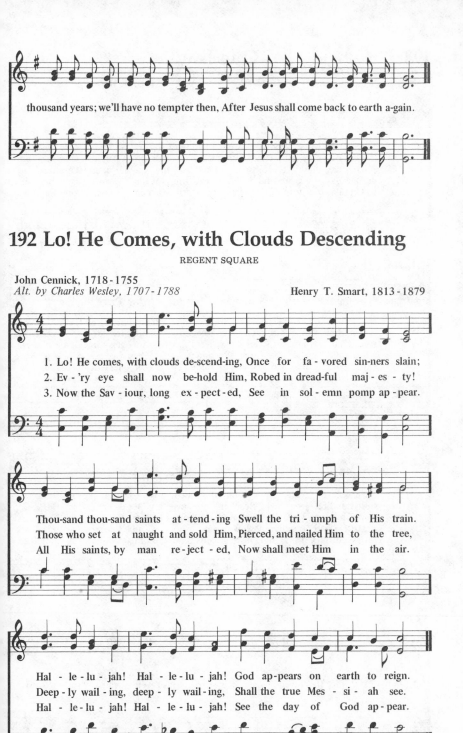

thousand years; we'll have no tempter then, After Jesus shall come back to earth a-gain.

192 Lo! He Comes, with Clouds Descending

REGENT SQUARE

John Cennick, 1718-1755
Alt. by Charles Wesley, 1707-1788   Henry T. Smart, 1813-1879

1. Lo! He comes, with clouds de-scend-ing, Once for fa - vored sin-ners slain;
2. Ev - 'ry eye shall now be-hold Him, Robed in dread-ful maj - es - ty!
3. Now the Sav - iour, long ex-pect-ed, See in sol - emn pomp ap-pear.

Thou-sand thou-sand saints at-tend-ing Swell the tri - umph of His train.
Those who set at naught and sold Him, Pierced, and nailed Him to the tree,
All His saints, by man re-ject - ed, Now shall meet Him in the air.

Hal - le - lu - jah! Hal - le - lu - jah! God ap-pears on earth to reign.
Deep - ly wail - ing, deep - ly wail - ing, Shall the true Mes - si - ah see.
Hal - le - lu - jah! Hal - le - lu - jah! See the day of God ap-pear.

193 One Day

J. Wilbur Chapman, 1859-1918   Charles H. Marsh, 1886-1956

1. One day when heav-en was filled with His prais - es,   One day when
2. One day they led Him up Cal - va - ry's moun - tain;   One day they
3. One day they left Him a - lone in the gar - den;   One day He
4. One day the grave could con - ceal Him no lon - ger;   One day the
5. One day the trum - pet will sound for His com - ing;   One day the

sin was as black as could be,   Je - sus came forth to be
nailed Him to die on the tree;   Suf - fer- ing an - guish, de-
rest - ed, from suf - fer - ing free;   An - gels came down o'er His
stone rolled a - way from the door.   Then He a - rose; o - ver
skies with His glo - ries will shine;   Won - der-ful day, my be-

born of a vir - gin—Dwelt among men, my Ex - am - ple is He!____
spised and re - ject - ed: Bear - ing our sins, my Re-deem- er is He!____
tomb to keep vig - il; Hope of the hope - less, my Sav-iour is He!____
death He had con-quered; Now is as - cend - ed, my Lord ev - er-more!____
lov - ed ones bring-ing. Glo - ri - ous Sav - iour, this Je - sus is mine!____

REFRAIN

Liv - ing, He loved me; dy - ing, He saved me; Bur - ied, He

car - ried my sins far a - way; Ris - ing, He jus - ti - fied

cresc. *rit.*

free- ly for - ev - er; One day He's com-ing— oh, glo - ri - ous day!

194   Am I a Soldier of the Cross?

ARLINGTON

Isaac Watts, 1674 - 1748

Thomas A. Arne, 1710 - 1778

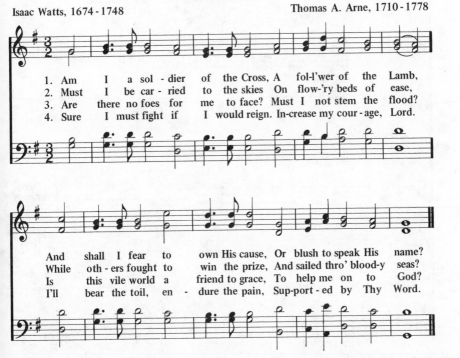

1. Am   I   a sol - dier   of the Cross, A   fol-l'wer of   the   Lamb,
2. Must   I   be car - ried   to   the skies On flow-'ry beds of   ease,
3. Are   there no foes for   me   to face? Must I   not stem the   flood?
4. Sure   I must fight if   I   would reign. In-crease my cour - age, Lord.

And   shall I fear   to   own His cause, Or   blush to speak His   name?
While   oth - ers fought to   win the prize, And sailed thro' blood-y   seas?
Is   this vile world a   friend to grace, To   help me on   to   God?
I'll   bear the toil, en - dure the pain, Sup-port - ed by Thy   Word.

195 Tell Me the Old, Old Story

EVANGEL

Katherine Hankey, 1834 - 1911

William H. Doane, 1832 - 1915

1. Tell me the old, old sto - ry Of un-seen things a - bove, Of Je - sus and His glo - ry, Of Je - sus and His love. Tell me the sto - ry sim - ply, As to a lit - tle child; For I am weak and wea - ry, And help - less and de - filed.

2. Tell me the sto - ry slow - ly, That I may take it in— That wonder-ful re - demp - tion, God's rem-e - dy for sin. Tell me the sto - ry of - ten, For I for - get so soon. The "ear - ly dew" of morn - ing Has passed a - way at noon.

3. Tell me the same old sto - ry When you have cause to fear That this world's emp - ty glo - ry Is cost-ing me too dear. Yes, and when that world's glo - ry Is dawn-ing on my soul, Tell me the old, old sto - ry: "Christ Je - sus makes thee whole."

REFRAIN

Tell me the old, old sto - ry. Tell me the old, old sto - ry. Tell me the old, old sto - ry, Of Je - sus and His love.

196   "Whosoever Will"

Philip P. Bliss, 1838-1876

Philip P. Bliss, 1838-1876

1. "Who-so-ev-er hear-eth," shout,   shout the sound! Spread the blessed tid-ings
2. Who-so-ev-er com-eth   need   not de-lay.   Now the door is o-pen;
3. "Who-so-ev-er will!" the prom-ise is se-cure; "Who-so-ev-er will" for-

all   the world a-round.   Tell the joy-ful news wher-ev-er man is found,
en-ter while you may.   Je-sus is the true, the   on-ly Liv-ing Way.
ev-er shall en-dure;   "Who-so-ev-er will!" 'tis life for-ev-er-more.

REFRAIN

"Who-so-ev-er will" may come.   "Who-so-ev-er will, who-so-ev-er will!"

Send the proc-la-ma-tion o-ver   vale and hill.   'Tis   a lov-ing

Fa-ther calls the wan-d'rer home;   "Who-so-ev-er will" may   come.

197 Christ Receiveth Sinful Men

NEUMEISTER

Erdmann Neumeister, 1671-1756
Tr. by Emma Frances Bevan, 1827-1909

James McGranahan, 1840-1907

1. Sin - ners Je - sus will re - ceive; Sound this word of grace to all
2. Come, and He will give you rest; Trust Him, for His Word is plain.
3. Now my heart con-demns me not; Pure be - fore the law I stand.
4. Christ re - ceiv - eth sin - ful men, E - ven me with all my sin.

Who the heaven - ly path - way leave, All who lin - ger, all who fall.
He will take the sin - ful - est; Christ re - ceiv - eth sin - ful men.
He who cleansed me from all spot Sat - is - fied its last de - mand.
Purged from ev - 'ry spot and stain, Heaven with Him I en - ter in.

REFRAIN

Sing it o'er_____ and o'er a - gain:_____ Christ re-
Sing it o'er a-gain, sing it o'er a - gain: Christ re-

ceiv - eth sin - ful men._____ Make the mes - sage
ceiv-eth sin-ful men; Christ re - ceiv - eth sin-ful men. Make the message plain;

clear and plain:_____ Christ re - ceiv - eth sin-ful men.
make the mes-sage plain: Christ re - ceiv - eth sin-ful men.

198

Jesus Saves

Priscilla J. Owens, 1829-1907

William J. Kirkpatrick, 1838-1921

1. We have heard the joy-ful sound:
2. Waft it on the roll-ing tide:
3. Sing a-bove the bat-tle strife:
4. Give the winds a might-y voice.

Je-sus saves! Je-sus saves!

Spread the tid-ings all a-round:
Tell to sin-ners far and wide:
By His death and end-less life,
Let the na-tions now re-joice.

Je-sus saves! Je-sus saves!

Bear the news to ev-'ry land; Climb the steeps and cross the waves.
Sing, ye is-lands of the sea; Ech-o back, ye o-cean caves.
Sing it soft-ly through the gloom, When the heart for mer-cy craves;
Shout sal-va-tion full and free, High-est hills and deep-est caves.

On-ward!—'tis our Lord's com-mand.
Earth shall keep her ju-bi-lee.
Sing in tri-umph o'er the tomb:
This our song of vic-to-ry:

Je-sus saves! Je-sus saves!

199   Look and Live

William A. Ogden, 1841 - 1897   William A. Ogden, 1841 - 1897

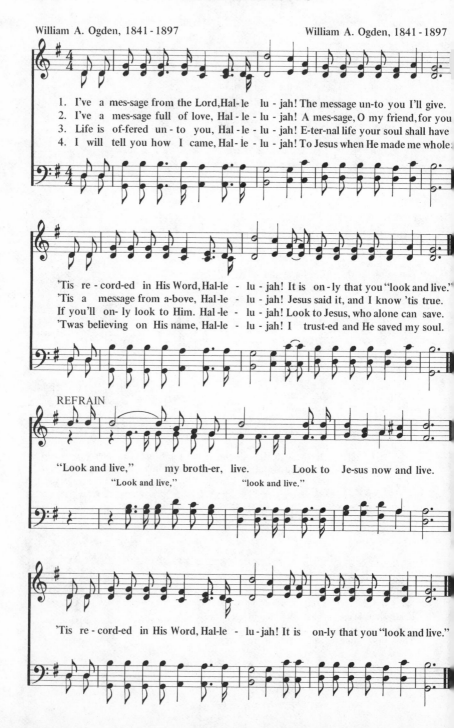

1. I've a mes-sage from the Lord, Hal- le lu - jah! The message un-to you I'll give.
2. I've a mes-sage full of love, Hal - le - lu - jah! A mes-sage, O my friend, for you
3. Life is of-fered un - to you, Hal - le - lu - jah! E-ter-nal life your soul shall have
4. I will tell you how I came, Hal - le - lu - jah! To Jesus when He made me whole.

'Tis re - cord-ed in His Word, Hal-le - lu - jah! It is on-ly that you "look and live."
'Tis a message from a-bove, Hal-le - lu - jah! Jesus said it, and I know 'tis true.
If you'll on- ly look to Him. Hal -le - lu - jah! Look to Jesus, who alone can save.
'Twas believing on His name, Hal-le - lu - jah! I trust-ed and He saved my soul.

REFRAIN

"Look and live," my broth-er, live. Look to Je-sus now and live.
"Look and live," "look and live."

'Tis re - cord-ed in His Word, Hal-le - lu-jah! It is on-ly that you "look and live."

Whosoever Meaneth Me

J. Edwin McConnell, 1892-1954   J. Edwin McConnell, 1892-1954

1. I am hap-py to-day and the sun shines bright; The clouds have been
2. All my hopes have been raised. Oh, His name be praised! His glo-ry has
3. Oh, what won-der-ful love! Oh, what grace di-vine, That Je-sus should

rolled a - way; For the Sav-iour said who-so-ev-er will May
filled my soul. I've been lift-ed up, and from sin set free. His
die for me! I was lost in sin; for the world I pined. But

REFRAIN

come with Him to stay (to stay). Who-so-ev-er sure-ly mean-eth me,
blood has made me whole (me whole).
now I am set free (set free).

Sure-ly mean-eth me! Oh, sure-ly mean-eth me! Who-so-ev-er

sure-ly mean-eth me. Who-so-ev-er mean-eth me.
mean-eth me.

201   'Tis Marvelous and Wonderful

Lelia N. Morris, 1862-1929   Lelia N. Morris, 1862-1929

1. The Sav - iour has come in His might - y pow'r, And spo - ken
2. 'Twas on - ly a fore-taste of joys di - vine In Ca - naan
3. From glo - ry to glo - ry He leads me on, From grace to
4. If fel - low-ship here with my Lord can be So in - ex -

peace to my soul; And all of my life from that ver - y hour I've
wait-ing for me; Where sweet-est of hon - ey and milk and wine Were
grace ev-'ry day; And bright - er and bright - er the glo - ry dawns, While
press-i - bly sweet, Oh, what will it be when His face we see, When

yield-ed to His con - trol, I've yield-ed to His con - trol.
drip-ping from ev - 'ry tree, Were drip-ping from ev - 'ry tree.
press-ing my home - ward way, While press-ing my home-ward way.
'round the white throne we meet, When 'round the white throne we meet?

REFRAIN

Won-der-ful, won-der-ful, Mar - vel - ous and won-der-ful, What
Oh, _____ it is won - der-ful! It is mar - vel - ous and won - der - ful, What
Male Voices Unison

He has done for my soul! The half has nev-er been told.
Je - sus has done for this soul of mine! The half has nev-er been told. _____

Copyright 1919. Renewed 1947 by Nazarene Publishing House.

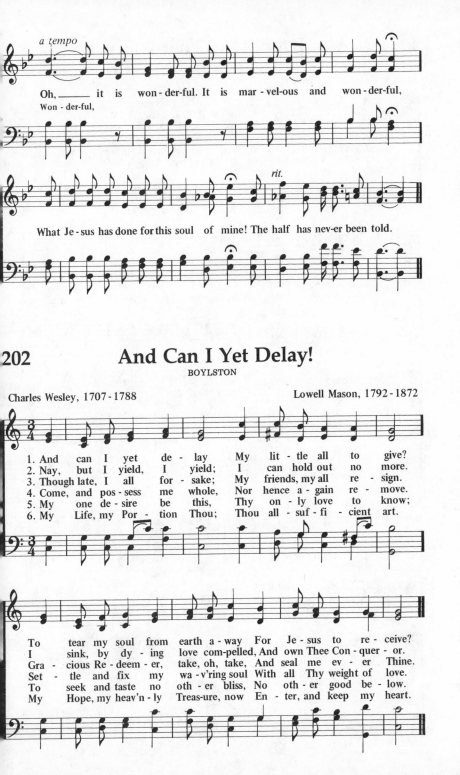

Oh, _____ it is won-der-ful. It is mar-vel-ous and won-der-ful,
Won-der-ful,

What Je-sus has done for this soul of mine! The half has nev-er been told.

202

And Can I Yet Delay!

BOYLSTON

Charles Wesley, 1707-1788

Lowell Mason, 1792-1872

1. And can I yet de - lay My lit - tle all to give?
2. Nay, but I yield, I yield; I can hold out no more.
3. Though late, I all for - sake; My friends, my all re - sign.
4. Come, and pos - sess me whole, Nor hence a - gain re - move.
5. My one de - sire be this, Thy on - ly love to know;
6. My Life, my Por - tion Thou; Thou all - suf - fi - cient art.

To tear my soul from earth a - way For Je - sus to re - ceive?
I sink, by dy - ing love com-pelled, And own Thee Con - quer - or.
Gra - cious Re - deem - er, take, oh, take, And seal me ev - er Thine.
Set - tle and fix my wa - v'ring soul With all Thy weight of love.
To seek and taste no oth - er bliss, No oth - er good be - low.
My Hope, my heav'n - ly Treas-ure, now En - ter, and keep my heart.

203   Ho! Every One That Is Thirsty

Lucy J. Rider, 20th Century

Lucy J. Rider, 20th Century
Arr. by Floyd W. Hawkins, 1904

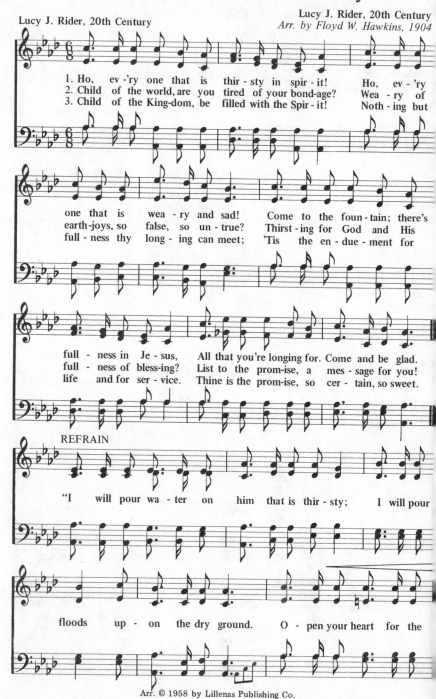

1. Ho, ev-'ry one that is thir-sty in spir-it! Ho, ev-'ry
2. Child of the world, are you tired of your bond-age? Wea-ry of
3. Child of the King-dom, be filled with the Spir-it! Noth-ing but

one that is wea-ry and sad! Come to the foun-tain; there's
earth-joys, so false, so un-true? Thirst-ing for God and His
full-ness thy long-ing can meet; 'Tis the en-due-ment for

full-ness in Je-sus, All that you're longing for. Come and be glad.
full-ness of bless-ing? List to the prom-ise, a mes-sage for you!
life and for ser-vice. Thine is the prom-ise, so cer-tain, so sweet.

REFRAIN

"I will pour wa-ter on him that is thir-sty; I will pour

floods up-on the dry ground. O-pen your heart for the

Arr. © 1958 by Lillenas Publishing Co.

gift   I am bring-ing.   While ye are seek-ing Me   I   will be found."

204   # Friendship with Jesus

Joe C. Ludgate, 19th Century   *Arr. from* Stephen Foster, 1826 - 1864

1. A   friend of Je - sus! Oh, what bliss   That   one   so   vile   as   I
2. A   Friend when other friendships cease, A   Friend when oth-ers   fail,
3. A   Friend when sickness lays me low,   A   Friend when death draws near,
4. A   Friend when life's short race is o'er, A   Friend when earth is   past,

Should   ev - er have   a Friend like   this   To   lead me to   the sky!
A   Friend   who gives me joy and   peace, A   Friend when foes as-sail!
A   Friend   as thro' the vale   I   go,   A   Friend to help and cheer!
A   Friend   to meet on heav - en's   shore, A   Friend when home at last!

REFRAIN

Friend - ship with   Je - sus!   Fel - low - ship di - vine!

Oh, what bless-ed, sweet com-mu - nion! Je - sus is a Friend of   mine.

205 The Healing Waters

H. H. Heimar, 19th Century

L. L. Pickett, 19th Century

1. Oh, the joy of sins for-giv'n! Oh, the bliss the Blood-washed know,
2. Now with Je-sus cru-ci-fied, At His feet I'm rest-ing low.
3. Oh, this pre-cious per-fect love! How it keeps the heart a-glow,
4. Oh, to lean on Je-sus' breast, While the tem-pests come and go!
5. Cleansed from ev-'ry sin and stain, Whit-er than the driv-en snow,

Oh, the peace a-kin to heav'n, Where the heal-ing wa-ters flow!
Let me ev-er-more a-bide Where the heal-ing wa-ters flow.
Stream-ing from the fount a-bove, Where the heal-ing wa-ters flow!
Here is bless-ed peace and rest, Where the heal-ing wa-ters flow.
Now I sing my sweet re-frain, Where the heal-ing wa-ters flow.

REFRAIN

Where the heal - ing wa - ters flow,
Where the heal-ing wa-ters flow, Where the heal-ing wa-ters flow,

Where the joys ce - les - tial glow,
Where the joys ce-les-tial glow, Where the joys ce-les-tial glow,

Oh, there's peace and rest and love,
Oh, there's peace and rest and love, Oh, there's peace and rest and love,

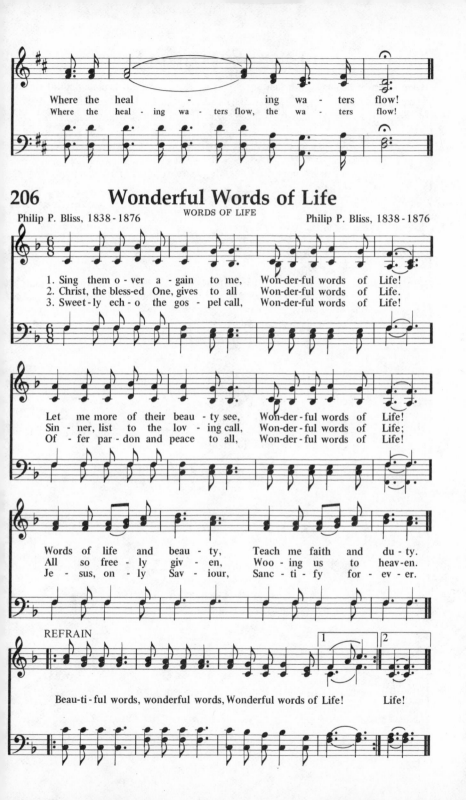

Where the heal - ing wa - ters flow!
Where the heal - ing wa - ters flow, the wa - ters flow!

206 Wonderful Words of Life

WORDS OF LIFE

Philip P. Bliss, 1838 - 1876   Philip P. Bliss, 1838 - 1876

1. Sing them o - ver a - gain to me, Won-der-ful words of Life!
2. Christ, the bless-ed One, gives to all Won-der-ful words of Life.
3. Sweet-ly ech - o the gos - pel call, Won-der-ful words of Life!

Let me more of their beau - ty see, Won-der-ful words of Life!
Sin - ner, list to the lov - ing call, Won-der-ful words of Life;
Of - fer par - don and peace to all, Won-der-ful words of Life!

Words of life and beau - ty, Teach me faith and du - ty.
All so free - ly giv - en, Woo - ing us to heav - en.
Je - sus, on - ly Sav - iour, Sanc - ti - fy for - ev - er.

REFRAIN

Beau-ti-ful words, wonderful words, Wonderful words of Life!   Life!

207

Turn Your Eyes upon Jesus

THE HEAVENLY VISION

Helen Howarth Lemmel, 20th Century   Helen Howarth Lemmel, 20th Century

1. O soul, are you wea-ry and troub - led? No light in the
2. Thro' death in - to life ev - er - last - ing He passed, and we
3. His word shall not fail you—He prom - ised; Be-lieve Him, and

dark - ness you see? There's light for a look at the Sav - iour,
fol - low Him there. O - ver us sin no more hath do - min - ion—
all will be well. Then go to a world that is dy - ing,

And life more a - bun - dant and free!
For more than con-qu'rors we are!
His per - fect sal - va - tion to tell!

REFRAIN

Turn your eyes up-on Je -

sus; Look full in His won-der-ful face; And the things of

p

earth will grow strange-ly dim In the light of His glo - ry and grace.

208 Ye Must Be Born Again

William T. Sleeper, 1819-1904

George C. Stebbins, 1846-1945

1. A rul-er once came to Je-sus by night To ask Him the
2. Ye chil-dren of men, at-tend to the word So sol-emn-ly
3. O ye who would en-ter that glo-ri-ous rest, And sing with the
4. A dear one in heav-en thy heart yearns to see, At the beau-ti-ful

way of sal-va-tion and light. The Mas-ter made an-swer in words true and plain,
ut-tered by Je-sus, the Lord; And let not this mes-sage to you be in vain,
ransomed the song of the blest, The life ev-er-last-ing if ye would ob-tain,
gate may be watching for thee; Then list to the note of this sol-emn re-frain,

REFRAIN

"Ye must be born a-gain." _____ "Ye must be born a-
a-gain."

gain; _____ Ye must be born a-gain. _____ I ver-i-ly,
a-gain; a-gain.

ver-i-ly say un-to thee, Ye must be born a-gain."
a-gain."

209 He Is Able to Deliver Thee

William A. Ogden, 1841 - 1897   William A. Ogden, 1841 - 1897

1. 'Tis the grand-est theme thro' the a - ges rung; 'Tis the grand-est
2. 'Tis the grand-est theme in the earth or main; 'Tis the grand-est
3. 'Tis the grand-est theme; let the tid-ings roll To the guil - ty

theme for a mor - tal tongue; 'Tis the grand-est theme that the world e'er sung,
theme for a mor - tal strain; 'Tis the grand-est theme, tell the world a - gain,
heart, to the sin - ful soul: Look to God in faith; He will make thee whole.

REFRAIN

"Our God is a-ble to de - liv-er thee." He is a - ble to de-
a - ble, He is a - ble

liv - er thee. He is a - ble to de - liv - er thee. Tho' by
a - ble, He is a - ble

sin op - prest, Go to Him for rest. "Our God is a - ble to de-liv-er thee."

Mighty to Save

Ralph Schurman, 1898-1970   Ralph Schurman, 1898-1970

1. Won - der - ful Sav - iour, born in a man - ger, Still He is
2. He was de - spised, re - ject - ed, and smit - ten; To us His
3. Won - der - ful, Coun - s'lor, E - ter - nal Fa - ther, He is the
4. Thine is the King - dom; Thine is the pow - er; Thine is the

might-y to save; Dy - ing on Cal - v'ry, ris - en in glo - ry,
par - don He gave. Once dead, He liv - eth, free - ly for-giv - eth,
Giv - er of peace. Our El - der Broth - er, we need no oth - er;
glo - ry al - way. While we are watch-ing, work - ing, and long-ing,

REFRAIN

Je - sus is might-y to save.
Vic - tor o'er sin and the grave.   Might-y   to save and strong to de - liv - er,
Our prayer,"Thy kingdom increase."
Come quickly—e - ven to - day.

Je - sus is might-y to save.   Might - y   to save and
                yes, might-y to save.

strong to de-liv - er, Je - sus is might - y to save.
                                yes, might - y to save.

211 The Song of the Soul Set Free

Oswald J. Smith, 1890 -　　　　　　　　　　　　Alfred H. Ackley, 1887 - 196(

1. Fair - est of ten thousand　Is　Je - sus Christ, my Sav-iour,　The Lil - y of the
2. Once my heart was burdened,　But now I　am for - giv - en,　And with a song o
3. When He came to save me,　He set the joy bells ring-ing,　And now I'm ev - er
4. An - gels can - not sing it,　This song of joy and free-dom,　For mor-tals on - ly

Val - ley,　The Bright and Morn-ing Star.　He is all my glo - ry,　And
glad - ness,　I'm on my way to heav'n.　Christ is my Re-deem-er;　My
sing - ing,　For Christ has ran-somed me.　Once I lived in dark-ness;　The
know it,　The ran - somed and the free.　Slaves were they in bond-age,　And

in this heart of mine　For - ev - er-more I'm sing-ing　A song of love di - vine
Song of Songs is He;　My Saviour, Lord, and Mas-ter. To Him my praise shall be.
light I could not see.　But now I sing His prais-es,　For He has set me free.
deep-est mis - er - y;　But now they sing tri-um-phant, Their song of lib - er - ty.

REFRAIN

'Tis　the　song of the soul set　free (set free); And its mel - o - dy is　ring-ing.

'Tis　the　song of the soul set　free (set free); Joy and peace to me it's bring-ing.

'Tis the song of the soul set free (set free); And my heart is ev - er sing-ing, Hal-le-

lu - jah! Hal-le-lu - jah! The song of the soul set free!
Hal-le-lu-jah! Hal-le-lu-jah!

212 Amazing Grace

John Newton, 1725 - 1807

Early American Melody

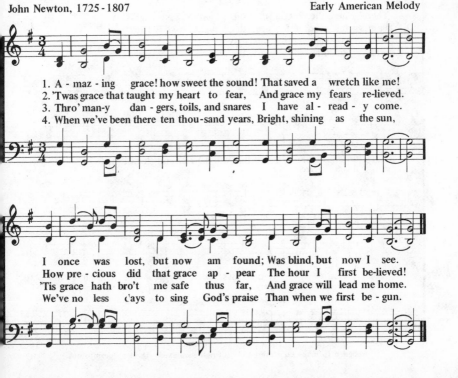

1. A - maz - ing grace! how sweet the sound! That saved a wretch like me!
2. 'Twas grace that taught my heart to fear, And grace my fears re-lieved.
3. Thro' man-y dan - gers, toils, and snares I have al - read - y come.
4. When we've been there ten thou-sand years, Bright, shining as the sun,

I once was lost, but now am found; Was blind, but now I see.
How pre - cious did that grace ap - pear The hour I first be-lieved!
'Tis grace hath bro't me safe thus far, And grace will lead me home.
We've no less days to sing God's praise Than when we first be - gun.

213 Grace Greater than Our Sin

MOODY

Julia H. Johnston, 1849-1919

Daniel B. Towner, 1850-1919

1. Mar - vel - ous grace of our lov - ing Lord, Grace that ex - ceeds our
2. Sin and de - spair, like the sea waves cold, Threat-en the soul with
3. Dark is the stain that we can - not hide. What can a - vail to
4. Mar - vel - ous, in - fi - nite, match-less grace, Free - ly be-stowed on

sin and our guilt, Yon - der on Cal - va - ry's mount out - poured,
in - fi - nite loss. Grace that is great - er, yes, grace un - told,
wash it a - way? Look! there is flow - ing a crim - son tide;
all who be - lieve! You that are long - ing to see His face,

REFRAIN

There where the blood of the Lamb was spilt! Grace, grace,
Points to the ref - uge, the might - y Cross. Grace, grace,
Whit - er than snow you may be to - day. Mar - ve - lous grace,
Will you this mo - ment His grace re - ceive? Mar - ve - lous grace,

God's grace, Grace that will par-don and cleanse with - in! Grace,
in - fi - nite grace, Mar - ve-lous

grace, God's grace, Grace that is great - er than all our sin!
grace, in - fi - nite grace,

214   Burdens Are Lifted at Calvary

John M. Moore, 1925-

John M. Moore, 1925-

1. Days are filled with sor - row and care; Hearts are lone - ly and drear.
2. Cast your care on Je - sus to - day; Leave your wor - ry and fear.
3. Trou-bled soul, the Sav-iour can see Ev - 'ry heart - ache and tear.

Bur-dens are lift - ed at Cal - va - ry; Je - sus is ver - y near.
Bur-dens are lift - ed at Cal - va - ry; Je - sus is ver - y near.
Bur-dens are lift - ed at Cal - va - ry; Je - sus is ver - y near.

REFRAIN

Bur-dens are lift - ed at Cal - va - ry, Cal - va - ry, Cal - va - ry.

Bur - dens are lift - ed at Cal - va - ry; Je - sus is ver - y near.

ver - y near.

215 Wonderful Grace of Jesus

Haldor Lillenas, 1885 - 1959   Haldor Lillenas, 1885 - 1959

1. Won - der - ful grace of Je - sus, Great-er than all my sin;
2. Won - der - ful grace of Je - sus, Reach-ing to all the lost—
3. Won - der - ful grace of Je - sus, Reach-ing the most de - filed,

How shall my tongue de - scribe it? Where shall His praise be-gin?
By it I have been par - doned, Saved to the ut - ter - most.
By its trans-form-ing pow - er Mak - ing him God's dear child,

Tak - ing a - way my bur - den, Set - ting my spir - it free;
Chains have been torn a - sun - der, Giv - ing me lib - er - ty;
Pur - chas-ing peace and heav - en, For all e - ter - ni - ty;

For the won - der - ful grace of Je - sus Reach - es me.
For the won - der - ful grace of Je - sus Reach - es me.
And the won - der - ful grace of Je - sus Reach - es me.

REFRAIN

Won - der - ful the match-less grace of Je - sus, the match - less grace of Je - sus,

Deep - er than the might - y, roll - ing sea! the roll - ing sea!

Won - der - ful grace, all - suf - fi -
High - er than the moun-tain, spar - kling like a foun - tain, All-suf - fi-cient

cient for me, for e - ven me!
grace for e - ven me! Broad-er than the scope of my trans-

gres - sions, Great - er far than all my sin and shame!
gres - sions, sing it! my sin and shame!

Oh, mag - ni - fy the pre - cious name of Je - sus! Praise His name!

216 His Grace Is Enough for Me

J. Bruce Evans, 20th Century   J. Bruce Evans, 20th Century

1. Just when I am dis-heart-ened, Just when with cares oppressed, Just when my
2. Just when my hopes have van-ished, Just when my friends forsake, Just when the
3. Just when my tears are flow-ing, Just when with an-guish bent, Just when temp-

way is dark-est, Just when I am dis-tressed, Then is my Sav-iour near me;
fight is thick-est, Just when with fear I shake, Then comes a still, small whis-per,
ta-tion's hard-est, Just when with sad-ness rent, Then comes a tho't of com-fort,

He knows my ev'ry care. Je-sus will nev-er leave me; He helps my burdens
"Fear not, My child, I'm near." Je-sus brings peace and com-fort; I love His voice to
I know my Fa-ther knows. Je-sus has grace suf-fi-cient To conquer all my

REFRAIN

bear.
hear. His grace is e-nough for me, for me; His grace is e-nough for me.
foes.

Thro' sor-row and pain, Thro' loss or gain, His grace is e-nough for me.

217 His Grace Aboundeth More

Kate Ulmer, 19th Century

William J. Kirkpatrick, 1838-1921

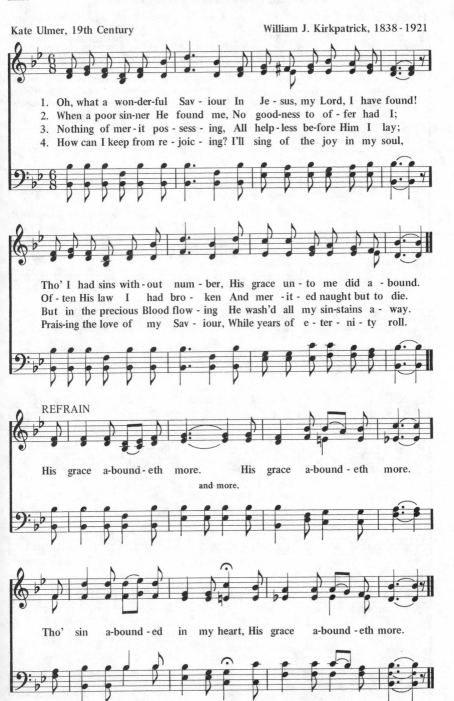

1. Oh, what a won-der-ful Sav - iour In Je - sus, my Lord, I have found!
2. When a poor sin-ner He found me, No good-ness to of - fer had I;
3. Nothing of mer-it pos - sess - ing, All help-less be-fore Him I lay;
4. How can I keep from re - joic - ing? I'll sing of the joy in my soul,

Tho' I had sins with-out num - ber, His grace un - to me did a - bound.
Of - ten His law I had bro - ken And mer - it - ed naught but to die.
But in the precious Blood flow - ing He wash'd all my sin-stains a - way.
Prais-ing the love of my Sav - iour, While years of e - ter - ni - ty roll.

REFRAIN

His grace a-bound-eth more. His grace a-bound - eth more.
and more.

Tho' sin a-bound-ed in my heart, His grace a-bound - eth more.

218   Wonderful Story of Love

J. M. Driver, 19th Century   J. M. Driver, 19th Century

1. Won-der-ful sto-ry of love! Tell it to me a - gain. Won-der-ful
2. Won-der-ful sto-ry of love! Tho' you are far a - way— Won-der-ful
3. Won-der-ful sto-ry of love! Je - sus pro-vides a rest— Won-der-ful

sto-ry of love! Wake the im-mor-tal strain! Angels with rapture announce it;
sto-ry of love! Still He doth call to - day: Calling from Calvary's mountain,
sto-ry of love! For all the pure and blest: Rest in those mansions a-bove us,

Shepherds with wonder re-ceive it; Sin - ner, oh, won't you be - lieve it?
Down from the crystal-bright fountain, E'en from the dawn of cre - a - tion,
With those who've gone on before us, Sing-ing the rap - tur - ous cho - rus,

REFRAIN

Wonderful sto-ry of love! Won - der - ful! Won - der -
Wonderful sto -ry of love! Wonderful sto -ry of

ful! Won - der - ful! Won-der-ful sto - ry of love!
love! Won-der-ful sto - ry of love!

219 My Saviour's Love

Charles H. Gabriel, 1856 - 1932   Charles H. Gabriel, 1856 - 1932

1. I stand a - mazed in the pres - ence Of Je - sus the Naz - a - rene,
2. For me it was in the gar - den He prayed: "Not My will, but Thine."
3. In pit - y an - gels be - held Him, And came from the world of light
4. He took my sins and my sor - rows; He made them His ver - y own;
5. When with the ran - somed in glo - ry His face I at last shall see,

And won - der how He could love me, A sin - ner, condemned, unclean.
He had no tears for His own griefs, But sweat-drops of blood for mine.
To com - fort Him in the sor - rows He bore for my soul that night.
He bore the bur - den to Cal - v'ry, And suf - fered, and died a - lone.
'Twill be my joy thro' the a - ges To sing of His love for me.

REFRAIN

How mar - vel-ous! How won-der-ful! And my song shall ev - er be:
Oh, how mar - vel - ous! Oh, how won - der - ful!

How mar - vel-ous, how won-der-ful Is my Sav-iour's love for me!
Oh, how mar - vel - ous! Oh, how won - der - ful

220 Such Love

C. Bishop, 20th Century

Robert Harkness, 1877-1961

1. That God should love a sin-ner such as I, Should yearn to change my
2. That Christ should join so free-ly in the scheme, Although it meant His
3. That for a will-ful out-cast such as I The Fa-ther planned, the
4. And now He takes me to His heart—a son; He asks me not to

sor-row in-to bliss, Nor rest till He had planned to bring me nigh,
death on Cal-va-ry— Did ev-er hu-man tongue find no-bler theme
Sav-iour bled and died, Re-demp-tion for a worth-less slave to buy,
fill a ser-vant's place. The "far-off coun-try" wan-d'rings all are done;

REFRAIN

How won-der-ful is love like this!
Than love di-vine that ran-somed me? Such love,____ such
Who long had law and grace de-fied! Such love,
Wide-o-pen are His arms of grace.

won-drous love! Such love, Such love, such won-drous love! That God should

love a sin-ner such as I, How won-der-ful is love like this!

Copyright 1929. Renewed 1957 by Lillenas Publishing Co.

221 And Can It Be?

SAGINA

Charles Wesley, 1707-1788

Thomas Campbell, 1777-1844

1. And can it be that I should gain An in-t'rest in the Sav-iour's blood! Died He for me, who caused His pain? For me, who Him to death pur-sued? A - maz-ing love! How can it be That Thou, my God, shouldst die for me? A-maz-ing love! How

2. He left His Fa-ther's throne a - bove, So free, so in-fi-nite His grace! Emp-tied him-self of all but love, And bled for Ad - am's help-less race. 'Tis mer-cy all, im-mense and free! For, O my God, it found out me!

3. Long my im-pris-oned spir - it lay, Fast bound in sin and na - ture's night. Thine eyes dif-fused a quick-'ning ray. I woke; the dun - geon flamed with light. My chains fell off; my heart was free. I rose, went forth, and fol - lowed Thee.

REFRAIN

A - maz-ing love!

can it be That Thou, my God, shouldst die for me?

How can it be That Thou, my God,

222 Revive Us Again

William P. McKay, 1839-1885

John J. Husband, 1760-1825

1. We praise Thee, O God, For the Son of Thy love; For Je - sus, who
2. We praise Thee, O God, For Thy Spir - it of Light, Who has shown us our
3. All glo - ry and praise To the Lamb that was slain, Who has borne all our
4. Re - vive us a - gain; Fill each heart with Thy love; May each soul be re -

REFRAIN

died And is now gone a - bove.
Sav - iour And scat-tered our night.
sins And has cleansed ev-'ry stain.   Hal - le - lu - jah! Thine the glo - ry! Hal-le-
kin - dled With fire from a - bove.

lu - jah! A - men! Hal - le - lu - jah! Thine the glo - ry! Re - vive us a - gain.

223 Spirit of the Living God

Daniel Iverson, 20th Century

Daniel Iverson, 20th Century

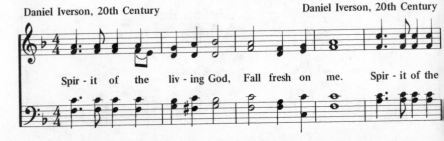

Spir - it of the liv - ing God, Fall fresh on me. Spir - it of the

living God, Fall fresh on me. Melt me, mold me, fill me,

use me. Spir-it of the liv-ing God, Fall fresh on me.

224 Send a Great Revival in My Soul

B. B. McKinney, 1886-1952   B. B. McKinney, 1886-1952

Send a great re-viv-al in my soul.   Send a great re-
in my soul.

viv-al in my soul.   Let the Ho-ly Spir-it come and
in my soul.

take con-trol, And send a great re-viv-al in my soul.
in my soul.

225 There Shall Be Showers of Blessing

SHOWERS OF BLESSING

Daniel W. Whittle, 1840-1901

James McGranahan, 1840-1907

1. "There shall be show-ers of bless-ing"— This is the prom-ise of love.
2. "There shall be show-ers of bless-ing"— Pre-cious re-viv-ing a-gain—
3. "There shall be show-ers of bless-ing." Send them up-on us, O Lord.
4. "There shall be show-ers of bless-ing." Oh, that to-day they might fall,

There shall be sea-sons re-fresh-ing, Sent from the Sav-iour a-bove.
O-ver the hills and the val-leys, Sound of a-bun-dance of rain.
Grant to us now a re-fresh-ing; Come, and now hon-or Thy Word.
Now as to God we're con-fess-ing, Now as on Je-sus we call!

REFRAIN

Show - ers of bless-ing, Show-ers of bless-ing we need.
Show - ers, show-ers of bless-ing,

Mer-cy-drops round us are fall-ing,— But for the show-ers we plead.

226 Sweeping This Way

Mrs. C. H. Good, 20th Century
Author of chorus unknown

Judson W. Van DeVenter, 1855-1939
Arr. by Haldor Lillenas, 1885-1959

1. O - ver the hill - tops, down from the skies, Com-ing from glo - ry— lift up your
2. As He has prom-ised, so shall it be: Bless-ings from glo - ry on you and
3. Prophets have told it: In the last days Hearts shall be filled with glo - ri - ous
4. Tar - ry for pow - er; this is our need. Pa - tient-ly la - bor, sow-ing the

eyes! While we are watch - ing and while we pray, A might - y re -
me; Wa - ters a - bun - dant, floods to o'er - flow. A might - y re -
praise; Our sons and daugh - ters both shall pro - claim The news of re -
seed. Soon comes the har - vest— glo - ri - ous day! A might - y re -

REFRAIN

viv - al is sweep-ing this way.
viv - al is com - ing, I know.
demp - tion thro' His great name.
viv - al is sweep-ing this way.

Sweep-ing this way, yes, sweep-ing this

way, A might-y re - viv - al is sweep-ing this way. Keep on be -

liev - ing; trust and o - bey. A might-y re - viv - al is sweeping this way.

227 Jesus, I Come

William T. Sleeper, 1819-1904

George C. Stebbins, 1846-1945

1. Out of my bond-age, sor-row, and night, Je-sus, I come; Je-sus, I come.
2. Out of my shame-ful fail-ure and loss, Je-sus, I come; Je-sus, I come.
3. Out of un-rest and ar-ro-gant pride, Je-sus, I come; Je-sus, I come.
4. Out of the fear and dread of the tomb, Je-sus, I come; Je-sus, I come.

In - to Thy free-dom, glad-ness, and light,
In - to the glo-rious gain of Thy cross,
In - to Thy bless-ed will to a-bide,
In - to the joy and light of Thy home,

Je-sus, I come to Thee.

Out of my sick-ness in-to Thy health, Out of my want and in-to Thy wealth,
Out of earth's sorrows in-to Thy balm, Out of life's storms and in-to Thy calm,
Out of my-self to dwell in Thy love, Out of de-spair in-to rap-tures a-bove,
Out of the depths of ru-in un-told, In - to the peace of Thy sheltering fold,

Out of my sin and in - to thy-self,
Out of dis-tress to ju-bi-lant psalm,
Up-ward for aye on wings like a dove,
Ev - er Thy glo-rious face to be-hold,

Je-sus, I come to Thee.

228 Softly and Tenderly

THOMPSON

Will L. Thompson, 1847 - 1909   Will L. Thompson, 1847 - 1909

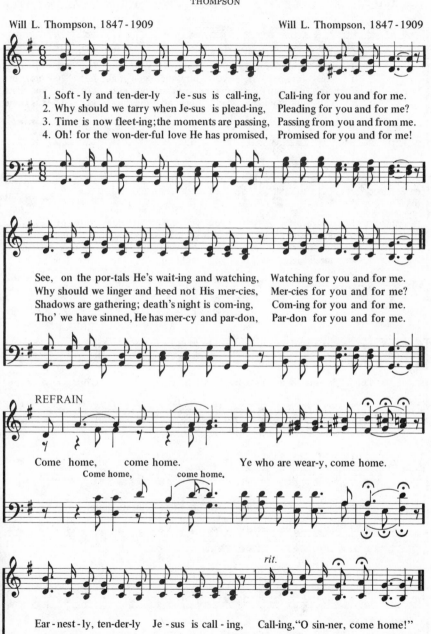

1. Soft - ly and ten-der-ly   Je - sus is call-ing,   Call-ing for you and for me.
2. Why should we tarry when Je-sus is plead-ing,   Pleading for you and for me?
3. Time is now fleet-ing; the moments are passing,   Passing from you and from me.
4. Oh! for the won-der-ful love He has promised,   Promised for you and for me!

See, on the por-tals He's wait-ing and watching,   Watching for you and for me.
Why should we linger and heed not His mer-cies,   Mer-cies for you and for me?
Shadows are gathering; death's night is com-ing,   Com-ing for you and for me.
Tho' we have sinned, He has mer-cy and par-don,   Par-don for you and for me.

REFRAIN

Come home,   come home.   Ye who are wear-y, come home.

Come home,   come home.

rit.

Ear - nest - ly, ten-der-ly   Je - sus is call - ing,   Call-ing, "O sin-ner, come home!"

229   Let Jesus Come into Your Heart

Lelia N. Morris, 1862 - 1929   Lelia N. Morris, 1862 - 1929

1. If you are tired of the load of your sin, Let Je - sus come in - to your heart.
2. If 'tis for pu - ri - ty now that you sigh, Let Je - sus come in - to your heart.
3. If there's a tem - pest your voice can - not still, Let Je - sus come in - to your heart.
4. If you would join the glad songs of the blest, Let Je - sus come in - to your heart.

If you de - sire a new life to be - gin,
Fountains for cleans - ing are flow-ing near-by,
If there's a void this world nev - er can fill,
If you would en - ter the man-sions of rest,

REFRAIN

Let Je - sus come in - to your heart.

Just now, your doubt-ings give o'er. Just now, re - ject Him no more. Just now, throw o - pen the door; Let Je - sus come in - to your heart.

230 Come Just as You Are

Haldor Lillenas, 1885-1959   Haldor Lillenas, 1885-1959

1. Ye who are troub-led and burdened by sin,
2. Deep in your heart sin has writ-ten its scar;
3. Sin-ful and guil-ty, heart-bro-ken and lost, Come just as you are.
4. Naught of your goodness for sin can a-tone;
5. Come with your heartache, your sorrow and pain;

Come to the Sav-iour, a new life be-gin. Oh, come just as you are!
Tho' from your Fa-ther you've wandered a-far, Oh, come just as you are!
Think what your ransom on Cal-va-ry cost! Oh, come just as you are!
Trust in the mer-it of Je-sus a-lone, And come just as you are.
No one has come to the Sav-iour in vain. Oh, come just as you are!

REFRAIN

Come just as you are. Oh, come just as you are!

Turn from your sin, let the Sav-iour come in, And come just as you are.

231

Pass Me Not

Fanny J. Crosby, 1820-1915

William H. Doane, 1832-1915

1. Pass me not, O gen-tle Sav-iour; Hear my hum-ble cry. While on
2. Let me at the throne of mer-cy Find a sweet re-lief; Kneel-ing
3. Trust-ing on-ly in Thy mer-it, Would I seek Thy face. Heal my
4. Thou, the Spring of all my com-fort, More than life to me, Whom have

REFRAIN

oth-ers Thou art call-ing, Do not pass me by.
there in deep con-tri-tion, Help my un-be-lief.
wounded, bro-ken spir-it. Save me by Thy grace. Sav-iour, Sav-iour,
I on earth be-side Thee? Whom in heav'n but Thee?

Hear my humble cry. While on oth-ers Thou art call-ing, Do not pass me by.

232

Just as I Am

WOODWORTH

Charlotte Elliott, 1789-1871

William B. Bradbury, 1816-1868

1. Just as I am, with-out one plea But that Thy blood was shed for me,
2. Just as I am, and wait-ing not To rid my soul of one dark blot,
3. Just as I am, tho' tossed a-bout With many a con-flict, many a doubt,
4. Just as I am— Thou wilt re-ceive, Wilt welcome, par-don, cleanse, relieve;
5. Just as I am! Thy love unknown Hath bro-ken ev-'ry bar-rier down;

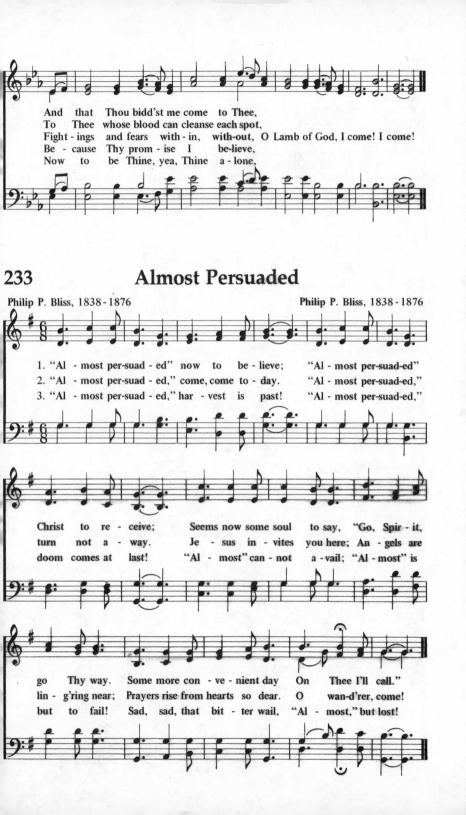

And that Thou bidd'st me come to Thee,
To Thee whose blood can cleanse each spot,
Fight - ings and fears with - in, with-out, O Lamb of God, I come! I come!
Be - cause Thy prom - ise I be-lieve,
Now to be Thine, yea, Thine a - lone,

233

Almost Persuaded

Philip P. Bliss, 1838 - 1876   Philip P. Bliss, 1838 - 1876

1. "Al - most per-suad - ed" now to be - lieve;   "Al - most per-suad-ed"
2. "Al - most per-suad - ed," come, come to - day.   "Al - most per-suad-ed,"
3. "Al - most per-suad - ed," har - vest is past!   "Al - most per-suad-ed,"

Christ to re - ceive;   Seems now some soul to say, "Go, Spir - it,
turn not a - way.   Je - sus in - vites you here; An - gels are
doom comes at last!   "Al - most" can - not a - vail; "Al - most" is

go Thy way.   Some more con - ve - nient day   On   Thee I'll call."
lin - g'ring near;   Prayers rise from hearts so dear.   O   wan-d'rer, come!
but to fail!   Sad, sad, that bit - ter wail,   "Al - most," but lost!

234 Give Me Thy Heart

BOURNE

Eliza E. Hewitt, 1851 - 1920

William J. Kirkpatrick, 1838 - 1921

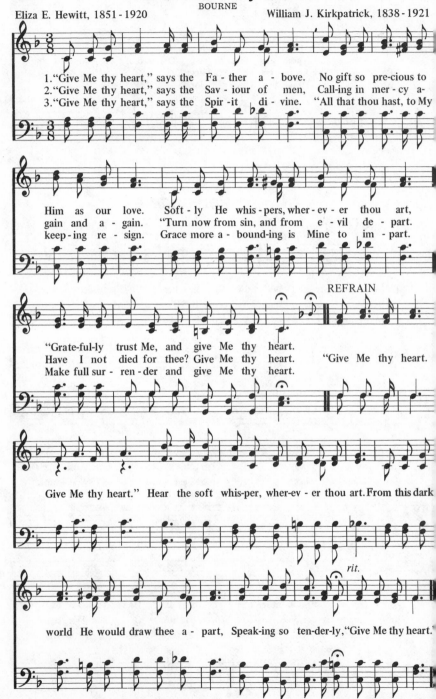

1. "Give Me thy heart," says the Fa - ther a - bove. No gift so pre-cious to
2. "Give Me thy heart," says the Sav - iour of men, Call-ing in mer - cy a-
3. "Give Me thy heart," says the Spir -it di - vine. "All that thou hast, to My

Him as our love. Soft - ly He whis-pers, wher - ev - er thou art,
gain and a - gain. "Turn now from sin, and from e - vil de - part.
keep-ing re - sign. Grace more a - bound-ing is Mine to im - part.

REFRAIN

"Grate-ful-ly trust Me, and give Me thy heart.
Have I not died for thee? Give Me thy heart. "Give Me thy heart.
Make full sur - ren - der and give Me thy heart.

Give Me thy heart." Hear the soft whis-per, wher-ev - er thou art. From this dark

rit.

world He would draw thee a - part, Speak-ing so ten-der-ly, "Give Me thy heart."

235

The Saviour Is Waiting

Ralph Carmichael, 20th Century

Ralph Carmichael, 20th Century

1. The Sav-iour is wait-ing to en-ter your heart. Why don't you let Him come in? There's noth-ing in this world to keep you a-part. What is your an-swer to Him?
2. If you'll take one step t'ward the Sav-iour, my friend, You'll find His arms o-pen wide. Re-ceive Him, and all of your dark-ness will end; With-in your heart He'll a-bide.

REFRAIN

Time af-ter time He has wait-ed be-fore, And now He is wait-ing a-gain,___ To see if you're will-ing to o-pen the door. Oh, how He wants to come in!

236 Jesus Is Calling

Fanny J. Crosby, 1820-1915

George C. Stebbins, 1846-1945

1. Je - sus is ten - der - ly call - ing thee home— Call - ing to - day,
2. Je - sus is call - ing the wea - ry to rest— Call - ing to - day,
3. Je - sus is wait - ing; oh, come to Him now— Wait - ing to - day,
4. Je - sus is plead - ing; oh, list to His voice— Hear Him to - day,

call - ing to - day. Why from the sun - shine of love wilt thou roam
call - ing to - day. Bring Him thy bur - den and thou shalt be blest;
wait - ing to - day. Come with thy sins; at His feet low - ly bow.
hear Him to - day. They who be - lieve on His name shall re - joice.

REFRAIN

Far - ther and far - ther a - way?
He will not turn thee a - way.
Come, and no lon - ger de - lay.
Quick - ly a - rise and a - way.

Call - ing to - day,
Call - ing, call - ing to - day, to - day;

Call - ing to - day,
Call - ing, call - ing to - day, to - day;

Je - sus is
Je - sus is ten - der - ly

call - ing, Is ten - der - ly call - ing to - day.
call - ing to - day,

Don't Turn Him Away

Haldor Lillenas, 1885 - 1959
Refrain Arranged

Haldor Lillenas, 1885 - 1959

1. Pa - tient-ly, ten-der-ly plead - ing, Je-sus is stand-ing to - day;
2. Gracious, compassionate mer - cy Bro't Him from mansions a-bove;
3. Can you not now hear Him call - ing? Do not ill-treat such a Friend.
4. Now is the time to re - ceive Him; Grant Him ad-mis-sion to - day.

At your heart's door He knocks as be-fore. Oh, turn Him no lon-ger a - way!
Caused Him to wait Just out-side your gate. Oh, yield to His won-der-ful love!
Give up your sin. Oh, let Him come in! Lo! He will be true to the end.
Grieve Him no more, But o - pen your door, And turn Him no lon-ger a - way.

REFRAIN

Don't turn Him away. Don't turn Him a-way. He has come back to your heart again,

Al - tho' you've gone a-stray. Oh, how you'll need Him to plead your cause On that e-

ter-nal day! Don't turn the Saviour away from your heart; Don't turn Him away.

Copyright 1925. Renewed 1953 by Lillenas Publishing Co.

238 For You I Am Praying

INTERCESSION

S. O'Maley Cluff, 1837-1910

Ira D. Sankey, 1840-1908

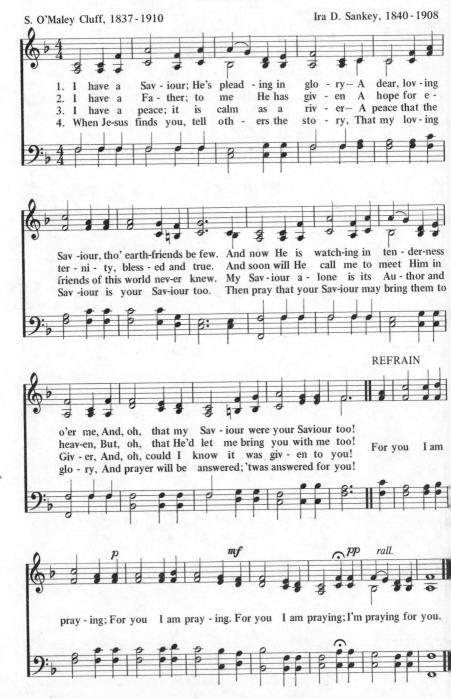

1. I have a Sav-iour; He's plead-ing in glo-ry— A dear, lov-ing
2. I have a Fa-ther; to me He has giv-en A hope for e-
3. I have a peace; it is calm as a riv-er— A peace that the
4. When Je-sus finds you, tell oth-ers the sto-ry, That my lov-ing

Sav-iour, tho' earth-friends be few. And now He is watch-ing in ten-der-ness
ter-ni-ty, bless-ed and true. And soon will He call me to meet Him in
friends of this world nev-er knew. My Sav-iour a-lone is its Au-thor and
Sav-iour is your Sav-iour too. Then pray that your Sav-iour may bring them to

REFRAIN

o'er me, And, oh, that my Sav-iour were your Saviour too!
heav-en, But, oh, that He'd let me bring you with me too!
Giv-er, And, oh, could I know it was giv-en to you!
glo-ry, And prayer will be answered; 'twas answered for you!

For you I am

_p_ _mf_ _pp_ _rall._

pray-ing; For you I am pray-ing. For you I am praying; I'm praying for you.

239 Room at the Cross for You

Ira F. Stanphill, 1914 -

Ira F. Stanphill, 1914 -

with feeling

1. The Cross up-on which Je - sus died Is a shel - ter in
2. Tho' mil - lions have found Him a Friend And have turned from the
3. The hand of my Sav - iour is strong, And the love of my

which we can hide, And its grace so free is suf - fi-cient for me,
sins they have sinned, The Sav-iour still waits to o - pen the gates
Sav - iour is long; Through sun-shine or rain, through loss or in gain,

REFRAIN

And deep is its foun - tain—as wide as the sea.
And wel-come a sin - ner be - fore it's too late. There's room at the
The Blood flows from Cal-v'ry to cleanse ev - 'ry stain.

Cross for you; There's room at the Cross for you. Tho' millions have

come, There's still room for one. Yes, there's room at the Cross for you.

240   You Must Open the Door

Ina Duley Ogdon, b. 1877   Homer A. Rodeheaver, 1880-1955

1. There's a Sav-iour who stands at the door of your heart. He is
2. He has come from the Fa-ther sal - va - tion to bring, And His
3. He is lov - ing and kind, full of in - fi - nite grace. In your
4. He will lead you at last to that bless - ed a - bode, To the

long - ing to en-ter—why let Him de-part? He has pa-tient-ly
name is called Je - sus, Re - deem-er and King. To save you and
heart, in your life, will you give Him a place? He is wait-ing to
cit - y of God, at the end of the road, Where the night nev - er

called you so of-ten be-fore, But you must o-pen the door.
keep you He pleads ev - er - more, But you must o-pen the door.
bless you, your soul to re-store, But you must o-pen the door.
falls, when life's jour-ney is o'er; But you must o-pen the door.

REFRAIN

You must o-pen the door; You must o-pen the door. When

Je - sus comes in, He will save you from sin, But you must o-pen the door.

241 His Way with Thee

NUSBAUM

Cyrus S. Nusbaum, 1861 - 1937   Cyrus S. Nusbaum, 1861 - 1937

1. Would you live for Je - sus, and be always pure and good? Would you walk with
2. Would you have Him make you free, and follow at His call? Would you know the
3. Would you in His king-dom find a place of constant rest? Would you prove Him

Him with - in the nar - row road? Would you have Him bear your burden, car - ry
peace that comes by giv - ing all? Would you have Him save you, so that you need
true in prov - i - den-tial test? Would you in His ser-vice la - bor al - ways

all your load?
nev - er fall?   Let Him have His way with thee. His pow'r can make you what you
at your best?

ought to be. His blood can cleanse your heart and make you free. His love can

fill your soul, and you will see 'Twas best for Him to have His way with thee.

242   Jesus Paid It All

Elvina M. Hall, 1820 - 1889

John T. Grape, 1835 - 1915

1. I hear the Sav-iour say: "Thy strength in-deed is small. Child of
2. Lord, now in - deed I find Thy pow'r, and Thine a-lone, Can
3. For noth - ing good have I Where - by Thy grace to claim—I'll
4. And when be - fore the throne I stand in Him complete, "Je - sus

weak-ness, watch and pray. Find in Me thine All in All."
change the lep-er's spots, And melt the heart of stone.
wash my gar-ments white In the blood of Cal-v'ry's Lamb.
died my soul to save," My lips shall still re - peat.

REFRAIN

Je-sus paid it all;

All to Him I owe. Sin had left a crimson stain; He washed it white as snow.

243   I'll Live for Him

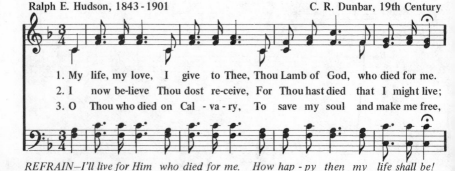

Ralph E. Hudson, 1843 - 1901

C. R. Dunbar, 19th Century

1. My life, my love, I give to Thee, Thou Lamb of God, who died for me.
2. I now be-lieve Thou dost re-ceive, For Thou hast died that I might live;
3. O Thou who died on Cal - va - ry, To save my soul and make me free,

REFRAIN—I'll live for Him who died for me. How hap - py then my life shall be!

Oh, may I ev - er faith-ful be,
And now henceforth I'll trust in Thee, My Sav-iour and my God!
I'll con - se-crate my life to Thee,

I'll live for Him who died for me, My Sav-iour and my God!

244   I Do Believe

Charles Wesley, 1707 - 1788   Unknown

1. Fa - ther, I stretch my hands to Thee; No oth - er help I know.
2. What did Thine on - ly Son en-dure Be - fore I drew my breath!
3. Au - thor of faith, to Thee I lift My wea - ry, long - ing eyes.
4. Sure - ly Thou canst not let me die; Oh, speak, and I shall live.
5. How would my faint - ing soul re-joice Could I but see Thy face!

Fine

If Thou withdraw thy - self from me, Ah, whith-er shall I go?
What pain, what la - bor, to se - cure My soul from end - less death!
Oh, let me now re - ceive that gift; My soul, without it, dies.
And here I will un - wea-ried lie Till Thou Thy Spir - it give.
Now let me hear Thy quick'ning voice, And taste Thy par-d'ning grace.

D.S: And thro' His blood, His precious blood, I shall from sin be free.

REFRAIN   D.S.

I do be - lieve, I now be - lieve That Je - sus died for me;

245 Is My Name Written There?

Mary A. Kidder, 1820-1905

Frank M. Davis, 1839-1896

1. Lord, I care not for rich - es, Nei - ther sil - ver nor gold. I would
2. Lord, my sins they are man - y Like the sands of the sea; But Thy
3. Oh, that beau - ti - ful cit - y, With its man-sions of light, With its

make sure of heav - en; I would en - ter the fold. In the book of Thy
blood, O my Sav - iour, Is suf - fi - cient for me. For Thy prom-ise is
glo - ri - fied be - ings In pure gar-ments of white, Where no e - vil thing

king-dom, With its pa - ges so fair, Tell me, Je - sus, my Sav-iour, Is my
writ - ten, In bright let - ters that glow, "Tho' your sins be as scar-let, I will
com-eth To de - spoil what is fair, Where the an-gels are watching—Yes, my

REFRAIN

name writ-ten there?
make them like snow."   Is my name writ- ten there, On the page white and
name's written there!   Yes, my name's, etc.

fair. In the book of Thy king-dom, Is my name writ - ten there?
                          Yes, my name's writ-ten there.

246   Is Thy Heart Right with God?

Elisha A. Hoffman, 1839-1929   Elisha A. Hoffman, 1839-1929

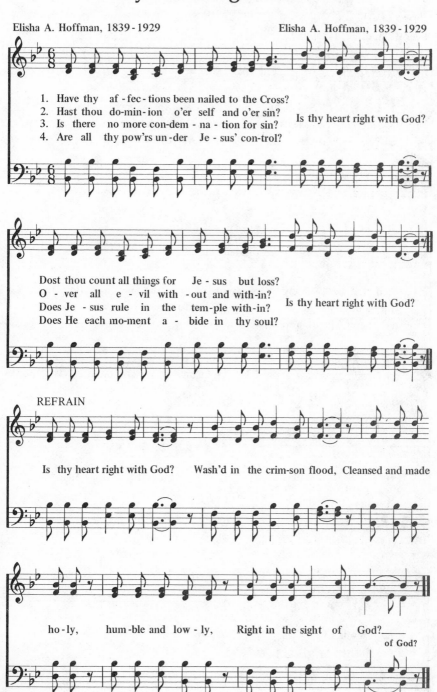

1. Have thy af-fec-tions been nailed to the Cross?
2. Hast thou do-min-ion o'er self and o'er sin?
3. Is there no more con-dem-na-tion for sin?
4. Are all thy pow'rs un-der Je-sus' con-trol?

Is thy heart right with God?

Dost thou count all things for Je-sus but loss?
O-ver all e-vil with-out and with-in?
Does Je-sus rule in the tem-ple with-in?
Does He each mo-ment a-bide in thy soul?

Is thy heart right with God?

REFRAIN

Is thy heart right with God? Wash'd in the crim-son flood, Cleansed and made ho-ly, hum-ble and low-ly, Right in the sight of God?___

of God?

247

Only Trust Him

STOCKTON

John H. Stockton, 1813 - 1877

John H. Stockton, 1813 - 1877

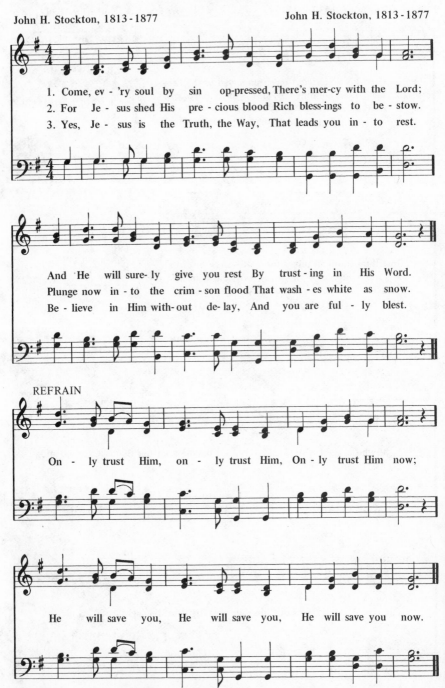

1. Come, ev - 'ry soul by sin op-pressed, There's mer-cy with the Lord;
2. For Je - sus shed His pre - cious blood Rich bless-ings to be - stow.
3. Yes, Je - sus is the Truth, the Way, That leads you in - to rest.

And He will sure-ly give you rest By trust-ing in His Word.
Plunge now in - to the crim - son flood That wash - es white as snow.
Be - lieve in Him with-out de - lay, And you are ful - ly blest.

REFRAIN

On - ly trust Him, on - ly trust Him, On - ly trust Him now;

He will save you, He will save you, He will save you now.

248 Wherever He Leads I'll Go

FALLS CREEK

B. B. McKinney, 1886 - 1952   B. B. McKinney, 1886 - 1952

1. "Take up thy cross and fol - low Me," I heard my Mas - ter say.
2. He drew me clos - er to His side. I sought His will to know,
3. It may be through the shad-ows dim, Or o'er the stor - my sea.
4. My heart, my life, my all I bring To Christ, who loves me so.

"I gave My life to ran-som thee; Sur - ren-der your all to - day."
And in that will I now a - bide; Wher-ev - er He leads I'll go.
I take my cross and fol - low Him, Wher-ev - er He lead - eth me.
He is my Mas - ter, Lord, and King; Wher-ev - er He leads I'll go.

REFRAIN

Wher - ev - er He leads I'll go; Wher - ev - er He leads I'll go.

I'll fol-low my Christ, who loves me so. Wher-ev - er He leads I'll go.

249 Lord, I'm Coming Home

COMING HOME

William J. Kirkpatrick, 1838-1921   William J. Kirkpatrick, 1838-1921

1. I've wan-dered far a - way from God;
2. I've wast - ed man - y pre - cious years;
3. I'm tired of sin and stray - ing, Lord;
4. My soul is sick, my heart is sore;

Now I'm com-ing home.

The paths of sin too long I've trod;
I now re - pent with bit - ter tears;
I'll trust Thy love, be - lieve Thy Word;
My strength re - new, my hope re - store;

Lord, I'm com-ing home.

REFRAIN

Com -ing home, com - ing home, Nev - er - more to roam!

O - pen wide Thine arms of love; Lord, I'm com-ing home.

250 Are You Washed in the Blood?

WASHED IN THE BLOOD

Elisha A. Hoffman, 1839 - 1929

Elisha A. Hoffman, 1839 - 1929

1. Have you been to Je - sus for the cleans-ing pow'r?
2. Are you walk - ing dai - ly by the Sav - iour's side?
3. When the Bridegroom cometh will your robes be white?
4. Lay a - side the gar-ments that are stained with sin.

Are you washed in the

blood of the Lamb?

Are you ful - ly trust-ing in His grace this hour? Are you
Do you rest each mo-ment in the Cru - ci - fied? Are you
Will your soul be read - y for the man-sions bright, And be
There's a foun - tain flow-ing for the soul un - clean. Oh, be

REFRAIN

1-3 washed in the blood of the Lamb? Are you washed in the blood,
4 washed in the blood of the Lamb!

Are you washed in the blood,

In the soul - cleans-ing blood of the Lamb? Are your gar-ments

of the Lamb?

spot - less? Are they white as snow? Are you washed in the blood of the Lamb?

251 I Am Coming, Lord
WELCOME VOICE

Lewis Hartsough, 1828 - 1919   Lewis Hartsough, 1828 - 1919

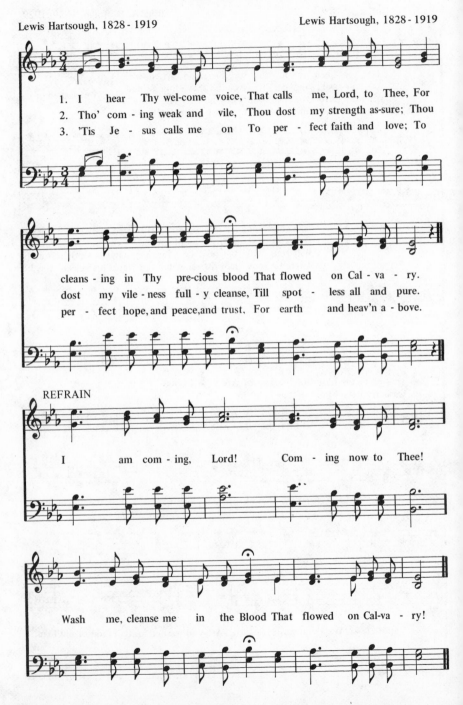

1. I hear Thy wel-come voice, That calls me, Lord, to Thee, For
2. Tho' com-ing weak and vile, Thou dost my strength as-sure; Thou
3. 'Tis Je-sus calls me on To per - fect faith and love; To

cleans-ing in Thy pre-cious blood That flowed on Cal - va - ry.
dost my vile-ness full - y cleanse, Till spot - less all and pure.
per - fect hope, and peace, and trust, For earth and heav'n a - bove.

REFRAIN

I am com - ing, Lord! Com - ing now to Thee!

Wash me, cleanse me in the Blood That flowed on Cal-va - ry!

252 When We All Get to Heaven

HEAVEN

Eliza E. Hewitt, 1851-1920

Emily D. Wilson, 1865-1942

1. Sing the won-drous love of Je - sus; Sing His mer - cy and His grace.
2. While we walk the pil - grim path-way, Clouds will o - ver - spread the sky;
3. Let us then be true and faith - ful, Trust-ing, serv - ing ev - 'ry day.
4. On - ward to the prize be - fore us! Soon His beau - ty we'll be - hold.

In the man-sions, bright and bless - ed, He'll pre - pare for us a place.
But when trav'-ling days are o - ver, Not a shad-ow, not a sigh!
Just one glimpse of Him in glo - ry Will the toils of life re - pay.
Soon the pearl - y gates will o - pen; We shall tread the streets of gold.

for us a place.

REFRAIN

When we all get to heav - en, What a day of re -
When we all   What a

joic - ing that will be! When we all see
day of re - joic - ing that will be!   When we all

Je - sus, We'll sing and shout the vic - to - ry.
and   shout the vic - to - ry.

253 My Saviour First of All

Fanny J. Crosby, 1820-1915

John R. Sweney, 1837-1899

1. When my life-work is end-ed, and I cross the swell-ing tide, When the
2. Oh, the soul-thrill-ing rap-ture when I view His bless-ed face, And the
3. Oh, the dear ones in glo-ry, how they beck-on me to come, And our
4. Thro' the gates to the cit-y in a robe of spot-less white, He will

bright and glorious morning I shall see, I shall know my Re-deem-er when I
lus-ter of His kind-ly beam-ing eye! How my full heart will praise Him for the
part-ing at the riv-er I re-call! To the sweet vales of E-den they will
lead me where no tears will ev-er fall. In the glad song of a-ges I shall

reach the oth-er side, And His smile will be the first to wel-come me.
mer-cy, love, and grace That pre-pare for me a man-sion in the sky!
sing my wel-come home; But I long to meet my Sav-iour first of all.
min-gle with de-light; But I long to meet my Sav-iour first of all.

REFRAIN

I shall know Him. I shall know Him, And redeem'd by His side I shall stand.
I shall know Him.

I shall know Him. I shall know Him By the print of the nails in his hand.
I shall know Him.

254
O That Will Be Glory

Charles H. Gabriel, 1856-1932   Charles H. Gabriel, 1856-1932

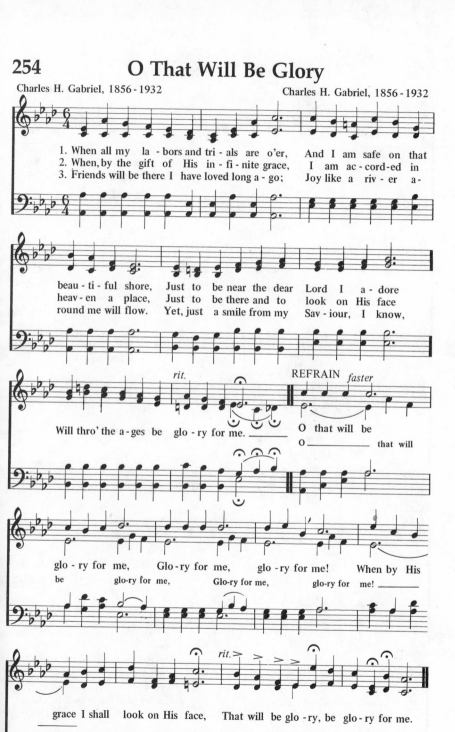

1. When all my la - bors and tri - als are o'er, And I am safe on that
2. When, by the gift of His in - fi - nite grace, I am ac - cord - ed in
3. Friends will be there I have loved long a - go; Joy like a riv - er a-

beau - ti - ful shore, Just to be near the dear Lord I a - dore
heav - en a place, Just to be there and to look on His face
round me will flow. Yet, just a smile from my Sav - iour, I know,

Will thro' the a - ges be glo - ry for me. _____ O that will be
O _____ that will

glo - ry for me, Glo - ry for me, glo - ry for me! When by His
be   glo-ry for me,   Glo-ry for me,   glo-ry for me! _____

grace I shall look on His face, That will be glo - ry, be glo - ry for me.

255 Sweet By-and-by

Sanford F. Bennett, 1836-1898

Joseph P. Webster, 1819-1875

1. There's a land that is fair - er than day, And by faith we can
2. We shall sing on that beau - ti - ful shore The me - lo - di - ous
3. To our boun - ti - ful Fa - ther a - bove We will of - fer our

see it a - far; For the Fa - ther waits o - ver the way, To pre-
songs of the blest, And our spir - its shall sor - row no more, Not a
trib - ute of praise, For the glo - ri - ous gift of His love And the

REFRAIN

pare us a dwell - ing place there. In the sweet by-and-
sigh for the bless - ing of rest. In the sweet
bless-ings that hal - low our days.

by, We shall meet on that beau - ti - ful shore. In the
by-and-by, by -and-by.

sweet by - and - by, We shall meet on that beau-ti-ful shore.
In the sweet by-and-by,

256 We Shall See the King Someday

Lewis E. Jones, 1865 - 1936

Lewis E. Jones, 1865 - 1936

1. Tho' the way we jour-ney may be of-ten drear, We shall see the
2. Af-ter pain and an-guish, af-ter toil and care, We shall see the
3. Af-ter foes are con-quered, af-ter bat-tles won, We shall see the
4. There with all the loved ones who have gone be-fore, We shall see the

King some-day (some-day). On that bless-ed morning clouds will dis-ap-pear.
King some-day (some-day); Thro' the end-less a-ges joy and blessings share.
King some-day (some-day). Af-ter strife is o-ver, af-ter set of sun,
King some-day (some-day). Sor-row past for-ev-er on that peaceful shore,

REFRAIN

We shall see the King some-day. We shall see the King some-day.
some-day.

We will shout and sing some-day.
some-day.
Gathered round the throne,

When He shall call His own, We shall see the King some-day.

257 When We See Christ

Esther Kerr Rusthoi, 1909 - 1962   Esther Kerr Rusthoi, 1909 - 1962

1. Oft-times the day seems long, Our tri - als hard to bear; We're tempted to com-
2. Sometimes the sky looks dark, With not a ray of light; We're tossed and driven
3. Life's day will soon be o'er, All storms for-ev-er past. We'll cross the great di-

plain, To mur-mur and de- spair. But Christ will soon ap -pear To catch His
on, No hu-man help in sight. But there is One in heav'n Who knows our
vide To glo -ry, safe at last. We'll share the joys of heav'n, A harp, a

bride a - way, All tears for - ev - er o -ver In God's e - ter - nal day.
deep - est care. Let Je - sus solve your prob-lem; Just go to Him in pray'r.
home, a crown. The tempt-er will be ban-ished; We'll lay our bur-dens down.

REFRAIN

It will be worth it all____ When we see Je - sus.____ Life's trials will

seem so small____ When we see Christ!___ One glimpse of His dear face___ All

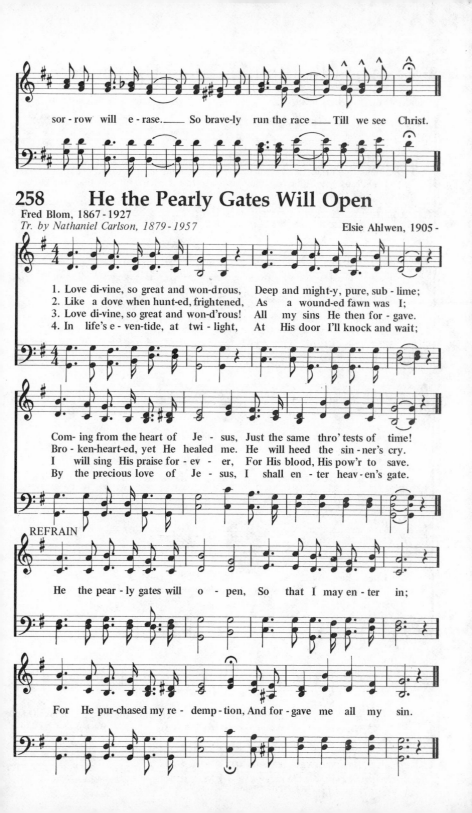

sor - row will e - rase.___ So brave-ly run the race___ Till we see Christ.

258   He the Pearly Gates Will Open

Fred Blom, 1867-1927
Tr. by Nathaniel Carlson, 1879-1957

Elsie Ahlwen, 1905-

1. Love di-vine, so great and won-drous,   Deep and might-y, pure, sub - lime;
2. Like a dove when hunt-ed, frightened,   As a wound-ed fawn was I;
3. Love di-vine, so great and won-d'rous!   All my sins He then for - gave.
4. In life's e - ven-tide, at twi - light,   At His door I'll knock and wait;

Com- ing from the heart of Je - sus, Just the same thro' tests of time!
Bro - ken-heart-ed, yet He healed me. He will heed the sin - ner's cry.
I will sing His praise for - ev - er, For His blood, His pow'r to save.
By the precious love of Je - sus, I shall en - ter heav-en's gate.

REFRAIN

He the pear - ly gates will o - pen, So that I may en - ter in;

For He pur-chased my re - demp - tion, And for-gave me all my sin.

259 When the Roll Is Called Up Yonder

James M. Black, 1856 - 1938   James M. Black, 1856 - 1938

1. When the trum-pet of the Lord shall sound, and time shall be no more, And the
2. On that bright and cloudless morning when the dead in Christ shall rise, And the
3. Let us la - bor for the Mas-ter from the dawn till set - ting sun; Let us

morning breaks, e - ter - nal, bright, and fair; When the saved of earth shall gath-er
glo - ry of His res - ur - rec - tion share; When His cho - sen ones shall gath-er
talk of all His wondrous love and care. Then when all of life is o - ver,

o - ver on the oth - er shore, And the roll is called up yon-der, I'll be there.
to their home be-yond the skies, And the roll is called up yon-der, I'll be there.
and our work on earth is done, And the roll is called up yon-der, I'll be there.

REFRAIN

When the roll_____ is called up yon - der, When the
When the roll is called up yon - der, I'll be there.

roll _____ is called up yon - der, When the roll _____ is called up
When the roll is called up yon-der, I'll be there.   When the roll is called up

yon - der, When the roll is called up yon - der, I'll be there.

260   **Saved by Grace**
CROSBY

Fanny J. Crosby, 1820 - 1915   George C. Stebbins, 1846 - 1945

1. Some-day the sil - ver cord will break, And I no more as now shall sing.
2. Some-day my earth - ly house will fall; I can -not tell how soon 'twill be.
3. Some-day, when fades the gold - en sun Be-neath the ro - sy - tint - ed west,
4. Some-day—till then I'll watch and wait, My lamp all trimmed and burn-ing bright,

But, oh, the joy when I shall wake With-in the pal - ace of the King!
But this I know— my All in All Has now a place in heav'n for me.
My bless - ed Lord will say, "Well done!" And I shall en - ter in - to rest.
That when my Sav - iour opes the gate, My soul to Him may take its flight.

REFRAIN

And I shall see Him face-to - face, And tell the sto-ry—Saved by grace;
shall see   -to-face,

rit.

And I shall see Him face-to - face And tell the sto-ry—Saved by grace.
shall see   -to-face,

261

In the New Jerusalem

C. B. Widmeyer, 1884 -   C. B. Widmeyer, 1884 -

1. When the toils of life are o - ver And we lay our ar - mor down, And we
2. Tho' the way is sometimes lone - ly, He will hold me with His hand. Thro' the
3. When the last good-by is spo-ken And the tear stains wiped a-way, And our
4. When we join the ran-somed ar - my In the sum-mer-land a - bove, And the

bid fare-well to earth with all its cares, We shall meet and greet our
test - ings and the tri - als I must go. But I'll trust and glad - ly
eyes shall catch a glimpse of glo - ry fair, Then with bound-ing hearts we'll
face of our dear Sav - iour we be - hold, We will sing and shout for-

loved ones, And our Christ we then shall crown In the new Je - ru - sa - lem.
fol - low, For some-time I'll un - der-stand, In the new Je - ru - sa - lem.
meet Him Who hath washed our sins a - way, In the new Je - ru - sa - lem.
ev - er And we'll grow in per - fect love, In the new Je - ru - sa - lem.

REFRAIN

There'll be sing - ing, there'll be shout-ing When the saints come march-ing home,

In Je - ru - sa - lem, In Je - ru - sa - lem;
In the new Je - ru - sa - lem, In the new Je - ru - sa - lem;

Copyright 1911. Renewed 1939 by Nazarene Publishing House.

Wav - ing palms with loud ho - san-nas As the King shall take His throne,

In the new Je - ru - sa - lem.
In the new
Je - ru - sa - lem.

262 From All That Dwell Below the Skies
DUKE STREET

Stanzas 1, 4, Isaac Watts, 1674 - 1748
Stanzas 2, 3, Anonymous

John Hatton, d. 1793

1. From all that dwell be - low the skies Let the Cre-
2. In ev - 'ry land be - gin the song; To ev - 'ry
3. Your lof - ty themes, ye mor - tals, bring; In songs of
4. E - ter - nal are Thy mer - cies, Lord; E - ter - nal

a - tor's praise a - rise. Let the Re - deem - er's name be
land the strains be - long. In cheer-ful sounds all voic - es
praise di - vine - ly sing. The great sal - va - tion loud pro-
truth at - tends Thy word. Thy praise shall sound from shore to

sung Thro' ev - 'ry land, by ev - 'ry tongue.
raise, And fill the world with loud - est praise.
claim, And shout for joy the Sav - iour's name.
shore, Till suns shall rise and set no more.

263

Where They Need No Sun

Haldor Lillenas, 1885-1959　　　　　　　　　　Haldor Lillenas, 1885-1959

1. When my earth-ly day is wan-ing and my mor-tal robes I fold,
2. O'er the fields of end-less glo-ry I shall wan-der with de-light,
3. With the count-less Blood-washed millions I shall sing be-yond the skies

With the dawn-ing of e-ter-ni-ty be-gun, I shall en-ter gates of
For with sad-ness and with pain I shall be done. No more sor-row, no more
Praise to God and to the Lamb for sin-ners slain. As the sound of man-y

pearl to walk on streets of shin-ing gold In that cit-y where they need no sun.
sick-ness in that home so pure and bright, In that cit-y where they need no sun!
wa-ters this tri-um-phant song shall rise And resound thro'-out God's vast do-main.

REFRAIN

In that cit-y where they need no sun,____ When at last my earth-ly
they need no sun,

race is run,____ I shall see my Sav-iour's face, Rev-el
my race is run,

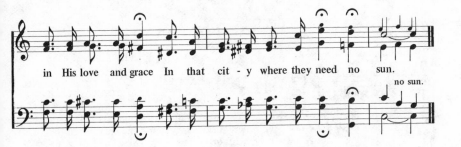

in His love and grace In that cit - y where they need no sun.

no sun.

264 Where Cross the Crowded Ways of Life

GERMANY

Frank Mason North, 1850-1935   *From* William Gardiner's "Sacred Melodies," 1815

1. Where cross the crowd - ed ways of life, Where sound the
2. In haunts of wretch - ed - ness and need, On shad-owed
3. From ten - der child - hood's help - less - ness, From wom-an's
4. The cup of wa - ter given for Thee Still holds the
5. O Mas - ter, from the moun - tain - side Make haste to
6. Till sons of men shall learn Thy love And fol - low

cries of race and clan, A - bove the noise of
thresh - olds dark with fears, From paths where hide the
grief, man's bur - dened toil, From fam - ished souls, from
fresh - ness of Thy grace; Yet long these mul - ti -
heal these hearts of pain; A - mong these rest - less
where Thy feet have trod; Till, glo - rious from Thy

self - ish strife, We hear Thy voice, O Son of Man!
lures of greed, We catch the vi - sion of Thy tears.
sor - row's stress, Thy heart has nev - er known re - coil.
tudes to see The sweet com - pas - sion of Thy face.
throngs a - bide. Oh, tread the cit - y's streets a - gain.
heaven a - bove, Shall come the cit - y of our God!

265 Living Forever

Haldor Lillenas, 1885-1959

Haldor Lillenas, 1885-1959

1. Liv-ing for-ev-er, oh, mar-vel-ous thought! Je-sus to
me im-mor-tal-i-ty brought. Liv-ing for-ev-er, though
stars may de-cay, Suns cease to shine, and the worlds pass a-way!

2. Liv-ing for-ev-er where death is un-known, Dwell-ing where
sin nev-er reigned on the throne; Liv-ing for-ev-er where
sor-row-less days, Days nev-er end-ing are fra-grant with praise!

3. Liv-ing for-ev-er where love nev-er dies, In that fair
land where are said no good-bys; Liv-ing for-ev-er where
hope is ful-filled And all the voic-es of sor-row are stilled!

4. Liv-ing for-ev-er— oh, des-ti-ny bright— In that bright
E-den where com-eth no night! Liv-ing for-ev-er with
Je-sus will be Heav-en and glo-ry suf-fi-cient for me.

rit.

REFRAIN

Liv-ing for-ev-er; Dy-ing, no, nev-er;
Liv-ing for-ev-er; yes, liv-ing for-ev-er; Dy-ing, no, nev-er; dy-ing, no, nev-er;

Life___ ev-er-last-ing My por-tion shall be.___
Life nev-er-end-ing, a life ev-er-last-ing My por-tion shall be, my por-tion shall be.

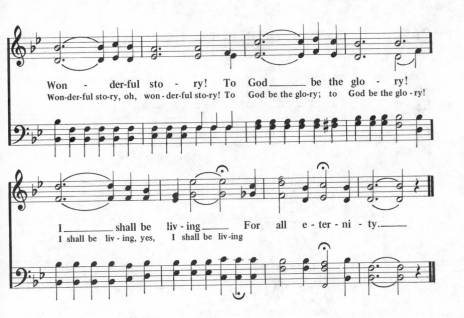

Won - der-ful sto - ry! To God____ be the glo - ry!
Won-der-ful sto-ry, oh, won-der-ful sto-ry! To God be the glo-ry; to God be the glo-ry!

I____ shall be liv - ing____ For all e - ter - ni - ty.____
I shall be liv - ing, yes, I shall be liv-ing

266 Holy Ghost, with Light Divine

MERCY

Andrew Reed, 1787 - 1862

Louis M. Gottschalk, 1829 - 1869

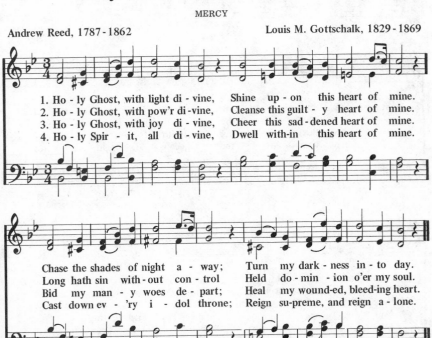

1. Ho - ly Ghost, with light di - vine, Shine up - on this heart of mine.
2. Ho - ly Ghost, with pow'r di - vine, Cleanse this guilt - y heart of mine.
3. Ho - ly Ghost, with joy di - vine, Cheer this sad - dened heart of mine.
4. Ho - ly Spir - it, all di - vine, Dwell with-in this heart of mine.

Chase the shades of night a - way; Turn my dark - ness in - to day.
Long hath sin with - out con - trol Held do - min - ion o'er my soul.
Bid my man - y woes de - part; Heal my wound-ed, bleed-ing heart.
Cast down ev - 'ry i - dol throne; Reign su-preme, and reign a - lone.

267 Spirit of God, Descend

MORECAMBE

George Croly, 1780-1860

Frederick C. Atkinson, 1841-1897

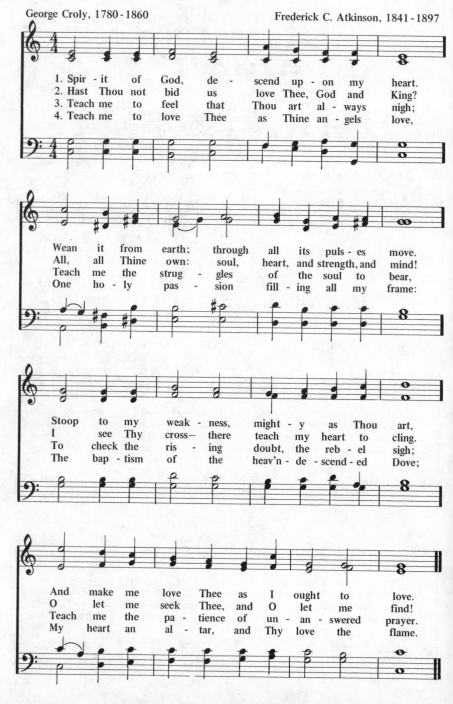

1. Spir-it of God, de - scend up - on my heart.
2. Hast Thou not bid us love Thee, God and King?
3. Teach me to feel that Thou art al - ways nigh;
4. Teach me to love Thee as Thine an - gels love,

Wean it from earth; through all its puls - es move.
All, all Thine own: soul, heart, and strength, and mind!
Teach me the strug - gles of the soul to bear,
One ho - ly pas - sion fill - ing all my frame:

Stoop to my weak - ness, might - y as Thou art,
I see Thy cross— there teach my heart to cling.
To check the ris - ing doubt, the reb - el sigh;
The bap - tism of the heav'n - de - scend - ed Dove;

And make me love Thee as I ought to love.
O let me seek Thee, and O let me find!
Teach me the pa - tience of un - an - swered prayer.
My heart an al - tar, and Thy love the flame.

268   Holy Spirit, Be My Guide

Mildred Cope, 1924 -   Mildred Cope, 1924 -

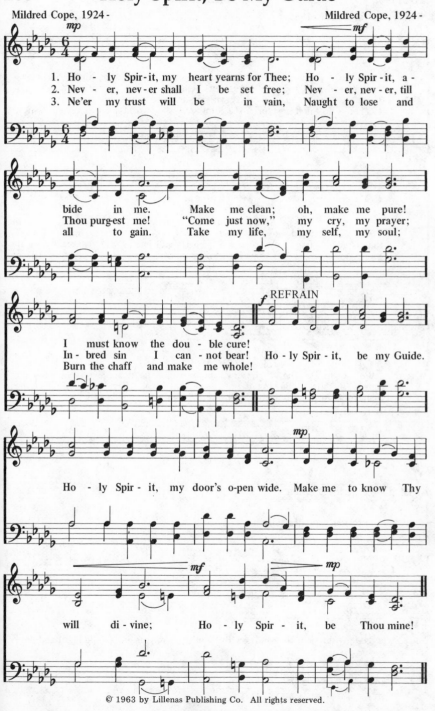

1. Ho - ly Spir-it, my heart yearns for Thee; Ho - ly Spir-it, a-
2. Nev - er, nev-er shall I be set free; Nev - er, nev-er, till
3. Ne'er my trust will be in vain, Naught to lose and

bide in me. Make me clean; oh, make me pure!
Thou purg-est me! "Come just now," my cry, my prayer;
all to gain. Take my life, my self, my soul;

REFRAIN

I must know the dou - ble cure!
In - bred sin I can - not bear! Ho - ly Spir - it, be my Guide.
Burn the chaff and make me whole!

Ho - ly Spir - it, my door's o-pen wide. Make me to know Thy

will di - vine; Ho - ly Spir - it, be Thou mine!

269 He Abides

Herbert Buffum, 1879-1939

D. M. Shanks, 20th Century

1. I'm re - joic - ing night and day, As I walk the pil - grim way,
2. Once my heart was full of sin, Once I had no peace with - in,
3. He is with me ev - 'ry-where, And He knows my ev - 'ry care.
4. There's no thirst-ing for the things Of the world—they've tak-en wings;

For the hand of God in all my life I see. And the
Till I heard how Je - sus died up - on the tree. Then I
I'm as hap - py as a bird and just as free; For the
Long a - go I gave them up, and in - stant - ly All my

rea - son of my bliss, Yes, the se - cret all is this: That the
fell down at His feet, And there came a peace so sweet. Now the
Spir - it has con - trol, Je - sus sat - is - fies my soul, Since the
night was turned to day, All my bur - dens rolled a - way. Now the

REFRAIN

Com-fort-er a-bides with me. He a - bides, He a - bides.
He a-bides, He a-bides.

Hal-le - lu - jah, He a-bides with me! I'm re - joic - ing night and day,

As I walk the nar-row way, For the Com-fort-er a-bides with me.

270   Fill Me Now

Elwood H. Stokes, 1815-1895

John R. Sweney, 1837-1899

1. Hov-er o'er me, Ho-ly Spir-it, Bathe my trem-bling heart and brow;
2. Thou canst fill me, gra-cious Spir-it, Though I can-not tell Thee how;
3. I am weak-ness, full of weak-ness; At Thy sa-cred feet I bow.
4. Cleanse and comfort, bless and save me; Bathe, O bathe my heart and brow.

Fill me with Thy hal-lowed pres-ence, Come, O come and fill me now.
But I need Thee, great-ly need Thee; Come, O come and fill me now.
Blest, di-vine, e-ter-nal Spir-it, Fill with love, and fill me now.
Thou art com-fort-ing and sav-ing; Thou art sweet-ly fill-ing now.

REFRAIN

Fill me now, fill me now; Je-sus, come and fill me now.

Fill me with Thy hal-lowed pres-ence; Come, O come and fill me now.

271 Bring Your Vessels, Not a Few

Lelia N. Morris, 1862-1929

Lelia N. Morris, 1862-1929

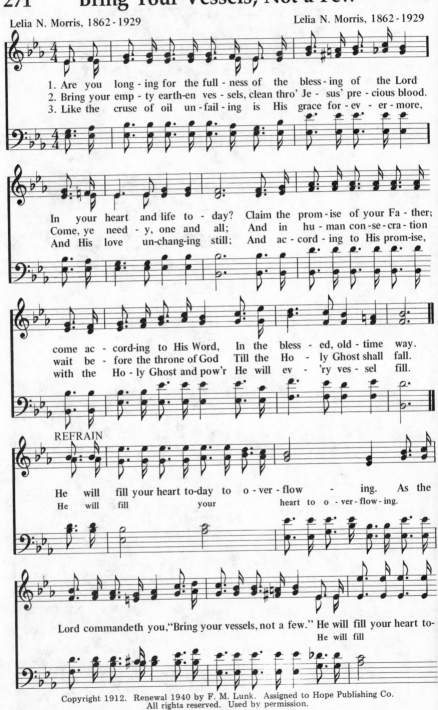

1. Are you long-ing for the full-ness of the bless-ing of the Lord
2. Bring your emp-ty earth-en ves-sels, clean thro' Je-sus' pre-cious blood.
3. Like the cruse of oil un-fail-ing is His grace for-ev-er-more,

In your heart and life to-day? Claim the prom-ise of your Fa-ther;
Come, ye need-y, one and all; And in hu-man con-se-cra-tion
And His love un-chang-ing still; And ac-cord-ing to His prom-ise,

come ac-cord-ing to His Word, In the bless-ed, old-time way.
wait be-fore the throne of God Till the Ho-ly Ghost shall fall.
with the Ho-ly Ghost and pow'r He will ev-'ry ves-sel fill.

REFRAIN

He will fill your heart to-day to o-ver-flow - ing. As the
He will fill your heart to o-ver-flow-ing.

Lord commandeth you, "Bring your vessels, not a few." He will fill your heart to-
He will fill

day to o - ver - flow - ing With the Ho - ly Ghost and pow'r.
your heart to o - ver-flow - ing

272 Breathe on Me
TRUETT

Edwin Hatch, 1835 - 1889
Alt. by B. B. McKinney, 1886 - 1952

B. B. McKinney, 1886 - 1952

1. Ho - ly Spir - it, breathe on me, Un - til my heart is clean.
2. Ho - ly Spir - it, breathe on me; My stub-born will sub - due.
3. Ho - ly Spir - it, breathe on me; Fill me with power di - vine.
4. Ho - ly Spir - it, breathe on me, Till I am all Thine own;

Let sun-shine fill its in-most part, With not a cloud be - tween.
Teach me in words of liv - ing flame What Christ would have me do.
Kin - dle a flame of love and zeal With - in this heart of mine.
Un - til my will is lost in Thine, To live for Thee a - lone.

REFRAIN

Breathe on me, breathe on me; Ho - ly Spir - it, breathe on me.

Take Thou my heart; cleanse ev - 'ry part. Ho - ly Spir - it, breathe on me.

273 Pentecostal Power

Charlotte G. Homer, 20th Century   Charles H. Gabriel, 1856-1932

1. Lord, as of old at Pen-te-cost Thou didst Thy pow'r dis-play,
2. For might-y works for Thee, pre-pare And strengthen ev-'ry heart.
3. All self con-sume, all sin de-stroy! With ear-nest zeal en-due
4. Speak, Lord. Be-fore Thy throne we wait; Thy prom-ise we be-lieve,

With cleans-ing, pu-ri-fy-ing flame De-scend on us to-day.
Come, take pos-ses-sion of Thine own, And nev-er-more de-part.
Each wait-ing heart to work for Thee. O Lord, our faith re-new!
And will not let Thee go un-til The bless-ing we re-ceive.

REFRAIN

Lord, send the old-time pow'r, the Pen-te-cos-tal pow'r! Thy floodgates of

bless-ing on us throw o-pen wide! Lord, send the old-time pow'r, the

Pen-te-cos-tal pow'r, That sin-ners be con-vert-ed and Thy name glo-ri-fied!

274 Since the Holy Ghost Abides

Rev. F. E. Hill, 20th Century   Mrs. F. E. Hill, 20th Century

1. Peace, blessed peace is   fill-ing now my soul, Since He pardon'd all my sin;
2. Rest, per-fect rest now   all my na-ture stills, Since His promis'd grace is mine;
3. Fire, ho - ly fire   is   burning in my heart, And   the glo-ry rolls in   tides;
4. Light, perfect light shines on this ho - ly way; Twice He touch'd my blinded eyes.

Love, per-fect love,   in bil-lows o'er me roll,   Since He cleans'd my heart with-in.
Joy,   per-fect joy   my hap - py spir-it thrills, Since the day   I said, "I'm Thine."
Pow'r, ho-ly pow'r   is   fill - ing ev - 'ry part, Since the Ho - ly Ghost a - bides.
Sight, per-fect sight   my vi - sion has to-day, Healed by Blood that sanc-ti-fies.

REFRAIN

Peace, per-fect peace! Love, perfect love! Sweeping o'er my soul in heav'n-ly tides!

Rest, per-fect rest!   Joy, per-fect joy!   is   mine since the Ho-ly Ghost a-bides.

275 The Comforter Has Come

Frank Bottome, 1823-1894

William J. Kirkpatrick, 1838-1921

1. Oh, spread the tid-ings 'round, wher-ev-er man is found, Wher-
2. The long, long night is past; the morn-ing breaks at last; And
3. Lo, the great King of Kings, with heal-ing in His wings, To
4. Oh, bound-less love di-vine! How shall this tongue of mine To

ev-er hu-man hearts and hu-man woes a-bound; Let ev-'ry Christian
hushed the dread-ful wail and fu-ry of the blast, As o'er the gold-en
ev-'ry cap-tive soul a full de-liv'rance brings; And thro' the va-cant
won-d'ring mor-tals tell the match-less grace di-vine— That I, a child of

tongue pro-claim the joy-ful sound:
hills the day ad-vanc-es fast! The Com-fort-er has come!
cells the song of tri-umph rings:
hell, should in His im-age shine!

REFRAIN

The Com-fort-er has come! The Com-fort-er has come! The Ho-ly Ghost from

heav'n, The Fa-ther's prom-ise giv'n! Oh, spread the tid-ings 'round,

wher - ev - er man is found: The Com - fort - er has come!

276 Have Thine Own Way, Lord

POLLARD

Adelaide A. Pollard, 1862 - 1934

George C. Stebbins, 1846 - 1945

1. Have Thine own way, Lord! Have Thine own way! Thou art the
2. Have Thine own way, Lord! Have Thine own way! Search me and
3. Have Thine own way, Lord! Have Thine own way! Wound - ed and
4. Have Thine own way, Lord! Have Thine own way! Hold o'er my

Pot - ter; I am the clay. Mold me and make me af - ter Thy
try me, Mas - ter, to - day! Whit - er than snow, Lord, wash me just
wea - ry, help me, I pray! Pow - er— all pow - er— sure - ly is
be - ing ab - so - lute sway! Fill with Thy Spir - it till all shall

will, While I am wait - ing, yield - ed and still.
now, As in Thy pres - ence hum - bly I bow.
Thine! Touch me and heal me, Sav - iour di - vine!
see Christ on - ly, al - ways liv - ing in me!

277 More like the Master

Charles H. Gabriel, 1856-1932

Charles H. Gabriel, 1856-1932

1. More like the Mas - ter I would ev - er be, More of His meekness
2. More like the Mas - ter is my dai - ly prayer; More strength to carry
3. More like the Mas - ter I would live and grow; More of His love to

more hu - mil - i - ty; More zeal to la - bor, more courage to be true,
cross-es I must bear; More earnest ef - fort to bring His kingdom in;
oth-ers I would show; More self-de - ni - al, like His in Gal - i - lee;

More con - se - cra - tion for work He bids me do.____ Take Thou my
More of His Spir - it, the wan - der-er to win.____
More like the Mas - ter I long to ev - er be.____ Take my heart, O

REFRAIN

heart;___ I would be Thine a - lone.___ Take Thou my heart___ and
take my heart; I would be Thine a - lone. Take my heart, O take my heart and

make it all Thine own.___ Purge me from sin,___ O Lord, I now im-
make it all Thine own. Purge Thou me from ev - 'ry sin, O Lord, I

plore.___ Wash me and keep___ me Thine for-ev-er - more.
now im - plore. Wash and keep, O wash and keep me Thine for-ev-er - more.

278 Higher Ground

Johnson Oatman, Jr., 1856-1922

Charles H. Gabriel, 1856-1932

1. I'm press-ing on the up-ward way, New heights I'm gain - ing ev - 'ry day;
2. My heart has no de - sire to stay Where doubts a - rise and fears dis-may;
3. I want to live a - bove the world, Tho' Sa - tan's darts at me are hurled;
4. I want to scale the ut-most height, And catch a gleam of glo - ry bright;

Still pray-ing as I on - ward bound, "Lord, plant my feet on high-er ground."
Tho' some may dwell where these a - bound, My prayer, my aim, is high-er ground.
For faith has caught the joy - ful sound, The song of saints on high-er ground.
But still I'll pray till heav'n I've found, "Lord, lead me on to high-er ground."

REFRAIN

Lord, lift me up and let me stand, By faith, on heav - en's ta - ble - land,

A high-er plane than I have found. Lord, plant my feet on high-er ground.

279 Deeper, Deeper

Charles P. Jones, 20th Century

Charles P. Jones, 20th Century

1. Deep-er, deep-er in the love of Je-sus Dai-ly let me go;
2. Deep-er, deep-er! Bless-ed Ho-ly Spir-it, Take me deep-er still,
3. Deep-er, deep-er! tho' it cost hard tri-als, Deep-er let me go!
4. Deep-er, high-er, ev-'ry day in Je-sus, Till all con-flicts past

High-er, high-er in the school of wis-dom, More of grace to know.
Till my life is whol-ly lost in Je-sus And His per-fect will.
Root-ed in the ho-ly love of Je-sus, Let me fruit-ful grow.
Finds me con-qu'ror, and in His own im-age Per-fect-ed at last.

REFRAIN

Oh, deep - er yet, I pray, And
Oh, deep-er yet, I pray, deep-er yet, I pray, And

high - er ev-'ry day, And wis -
high-er ev-'ry day, high-er ev-'ry day, And wis-er, bless-ed

- er, bless-ed Lord, In Thy pre-cious, ho-ly Word.
Lord, wis-er, bless-ed Lord,

280 Is Your All on the Altar?

Elisha A. Hoffman, 1839 - 1929   Elisha A. Hoffman, 1839 - 1929

1. You have longed for sweet peace, and for faith to in-crease, And have earnestly,
2. Would you walk with the Lord, in the light of His Word, And have peace and con-
3. Oh, we nev-er can know what the Lord will be-stow Of the bless-ings for
4. Who can tell all the love He will send from a-bove, And how happy our

fer-vent-ly prayed;   But you can-not have rest or be per-fect-ly blest
tent-ment al-way?   You must do His sweet will; to be free from all ill,
which we have prayed   Till our bod-y and soul He doth ful-ly control,
hearts will be made;   Of the fel-low-ship sweet we shall share at His feet,

REFRAIN

Un-til all on the al-tar is laid.
On the al-tar your all you must lay.
And our all on the al-tar is laid.
When our all on the al-tar is laid!

Is your all on the al-tar of

sac-ri-fice laid? Your heart does the Spir-it con-trol?_____ You can on-ly be

blest and have peace and sweet rest As you yield Him your body and soul.

281 Take My Life, and Let It Be

HENDON

Frances R. Havergal, 1836 - 1879

Henri A. Cesar Malan, 1787 - 1864

282 When Morning Gilds the Skies

LAUDES DOMINI

From the German, 19th Century
Trans. by Edward Caswall, 1814 - 1878

Joseph Barnby, 1838 - 1896

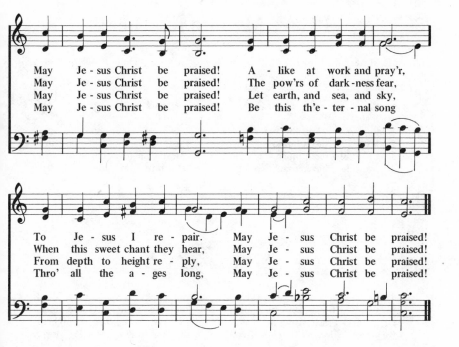

May Jesus Christ be praised! Alike at work and pray'r,
May Jesus Christ be praised! The pow'rs of dark-ness fear,
May Jesus Christ be praised! Let earth, and sea, and sky,
May Jesus Christ be praised! Be this th'e-ter-nal song

To Jesus I re-pair. May Jesus Christ be praised!
When this sweet chant they hear, May Jesus Christ be praised!
From depth to height re-ply, May Jesus Christ be praised!
Thro' all the a-ges long, May Jesus Christ be praised!

283 Dear Lord and Father of Mankind

REST

John Greenleaf Whittier, 1807-1892   Frederick C. Maker, 1844-1927

1. Dear Lord and Fa-ther of man-kind, For-give our fool-ish ways! Reclothe us
2. In sim-ple trust like theirs who heard, Be-side the Syr-ian sea, The gracious
3. Drop Thy still dews of qui-et-ness Till all our striv-ings cease. Take from our
4. Breathe thro' the heats of our de-sire Thy cool-ness and Thy balm. Let sense be

in our right-ful mind; In pur-er lives Thy ser-vice find; In deep-er rev'rence, praise.
call-ing of the Lord, Let us, like them, without a word, Rise up and fol-low Thee.
souls the strain and stress, And let our ordered lives confess The beau-ty of Thy peace.
dumb, let flesh retire; Speak thro' the earth quake, wind, and fire, O still small voice of calm!

284 I Gave My Life for Thee

KENOSIS

Frances R. Havergal, 1836 - 1879

Philip P. Bliss, 1838 - 1876

1. I gave My life for thee; My pre - cious blood I shed,
2. My Fa - ther's house of light, My glo - ry - cir - cled throne,
3. I suf - fered much for thee, More than thy tongue can tell,
4. And I have brought to thee, Down from My home a - bove,

That thou might'st ransomed be, And quick-ened from the dead.
I left for earth - ly night, For wan - d'rings sad and lone.
Of bit - t'rest ag - o - ny, To res - cue thee from hell.
Sal - va - tion full and free, My par - don and My love.

I gave, I gave My life for thee. What hast thou giv'n for Me?
I left, I left it all for thee. Hast thou left aught for Me?
I've borne, I've borne it all for thee. What hast thou borne for Me?
I bring, I bring rich gifts to thee. What hast thou brought to Me?

I gave, I gave My life for thee. What hast thou giv'n for Me?
I left, I left it all for thee. Hast thou left aught for Me?
I've borne, I've borne it all for thee. What hast thou borne for Me?
I bring, I bring rich gifts to thee. What hast thou brought to Me?

285 Have Thy Way, Lord

George Bennard, 1873-1958   George Bennard, 1873-1958

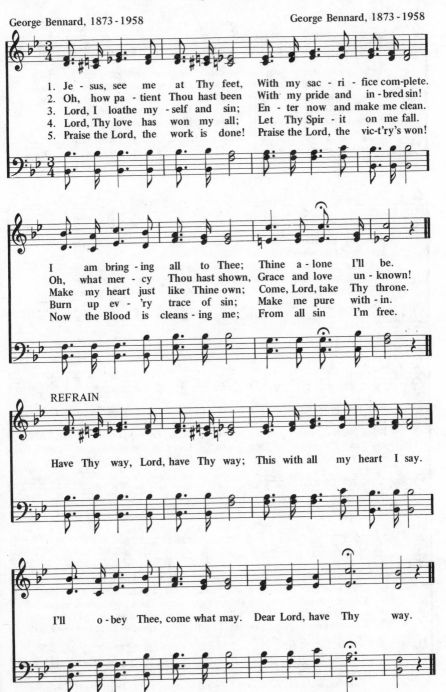

1. Je - sus, see me at Thy feet, With my sac - ri - fice com - plete.
2. Oh, how pa - tient Thou hast been With my pride and in - bred sin!
3. Lord, I loathe my - self and sin; En - ter now and make me clean.
4. Lord, Thy love has won my all; Let Thy Spir - it on me fall.
5. Praise the Lord, the work is done! Praise the Lord, the vic-t'ry's won!

I am bring - ing all to Thee; Thine a - lone I'll be.
Oh, what mer - cy Thou hast shown, Grace and love un - known!
Make my heart just like Thine own; Come, Lord, take Thy throne.
Burn up ev - 'ry trace of sin; Make me pure with - in.
Now the Blood is cleans - ing me; From all sin I'm free.

REFRAIN

Have Thy way, Lord, have Thy way; This with all my heart I say.

I'll o - bey Thee, come what may. Dear Lord, have Thy way.

286 Deeper and Deeper

Oswald J. Smith, 1890-

Oswald J. Smith, 1890-

1. In - to the heart of Je - sus Deep-er and deep-er I go,
2. In - to the will of Je - sus Deep-er and deep-er I go,
3. In - to the cross of Je - sus Deep-er and deep-er I go,
4. In - to the joy of Je - sus Deep-er and deep-er I go,
5. In - to the love of Je - sus Deep-er and deep-er I go,

Seek-ing to know the rea - son Why He should love me so,
Pray-ing for grace to fol - low, Seek-ing His way to know;
Fol - low-ing thru the gar - den, Fac - ing the dread - ed foe;
Ris - ing, with soul en-rap - tured, Far from the world be - low.
Prais-ing the One who brought me Out of my sin and woe;

Why He should stoop to lift me Up from the mir - y clay,
Bow-ing in full sur-ren - der Low at His bless - ed feet,
Drink-ing the cup of sor - row, Sob-bing with bro - ken heart,
Joy in the place of sor - row, Peace in the midst of pain,
And thru e - ter - nal a - ges Grate-ful-ly I shall sing,

Sav - ing my soul, mak-ing me whole, Tho' I had wan-dered a - way.
Bid - ding Him take, break me, and make, Till I am mold-ed and meet.
"O Sav-iour, help! dear Sav-iour, help! Grace for my weak-ness im-part."
Je - sus will give, Je - sus will give; He will up-hold and sus-tain.
"Oh, how He loved! Oh, how He loved! Je - sus, my Lord and my King!"

287 I Surrender All

SURRENDER

Judson W. Van Deventer, 1855-1939

Winfield S. Weeden, 1847-1908

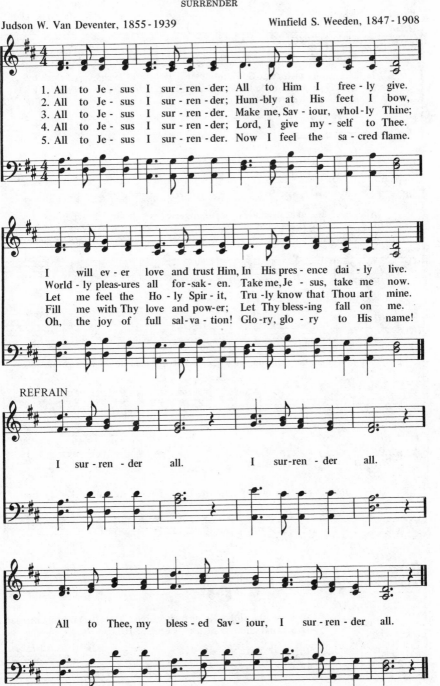

1. All to Je-sus I sur-ren-der; All to Him I free-ly give.
2. All to Je-sus I sur-ren-der; Hum-bly at His feet I bow,
3. All to Je-sus I sur-ren-der. Make me, Sav-iour, whol-ly Thine;
4. All to Je-sus I sur-ren-der; Lord, I give my-self to Thee.
5. All to Je-sus I sur-ren-der. Now I feel the sa-cred flame.

I will ev-er love and trust Him, In His pres-ence dai-ly live.
World-ly pleas-ures all for-sak-en. Take me, Je-sus, take me now.
Let me feel the Ho-ly Spir-it, Tru-ly know that Thou art mine.
Fill me with Thy love and pow-er; Let Thy bless-ing fall on me.
Oh, the joy of full sal-va-tion! Glo-ry, glo-ry to His name!

REFRAIN

I sur-ren-der all. I sur-ren-der all.

All to Thee, my bless-ed Sav-iour, I sur-ren-der all.

288   Let Thy Mantle Fall on Me

Floyd W. Hawkins, 1904 -

Floyd W. Hawkins, 1904 -

1. E - li - jah was God's proph-et; E - li - sha stood close by,
2. Then E - li - jah made the prom-ise That, if faith - ful he would be,
3. As E - li - jah rose to heav-en In a char - i - ot of fire,

And ere the proph-et left him, He heard his ser - vant cry:
His pe - ti - tion would be grant-ed, And God's glo - ry he would see.
He did not for - get his ser - vant, Who ex - pressed one strong de-sire:

REFRAIN

"Let thy man-tle fall on me; Let thy man-tle fall on me.
on me.

A dou-ble por-tion of Thy Spir - it, Lord—Let thy man-tle fall on me!"

Piano
me!"

4. In the Upper Room they waited—'Twas the faithful Christian
5. That prayer of ear - ly Christians, Long a - go and far a-

band—And their pray'r was heard and an-swered O-ver in the glo-ry land.
way, Is the cry of all God's chil-dren; And He's just the same to-day!

REFRAIN
f
Let Thy Spir-it fall on me; Let Thy Spir-it fall on me.
on me.

rit.
D.S.
The prom-ised bless-ing—may it be out-poured. Let Thy Spir-it fall on me!

289 Jesus, Thine All-victorious Love

AZMON

Carl G. Glaser, 1784 - 1829
Arr. by Lowell Mason, 1792 - 1872

Charles Wesley, 1707 - 1788

1. Je - sus, Thine all - vic - to - rious love Shed in my heart a - broad;
2. Oh, that in me the sa - cred fire Might now be - gin to glow,
3. Oh, that it now from heav'n might fall, And all my sins con - sume!
4. Re - fin - ing Fire, go thro' my heart; Il - lu - mi - nate my soul;
5. My stead-fast soul, from fall - ing free, Shall then no lon - ger move,

Then shall my feet no lon - ger rove, Root - ed and fixed in God.
Burn up the dross of base de - sire, And make the moun-tains flow!
Come, Ho - ly Ghost, for Thee I call; Spir - it of Burn-ing, come!
Scat - ter Thy life thro' ev - 'ry part, And sanc - ti - fy the whole.
While Christ is all the world to me, And all my heart is love.

290 Holiness unto the Lord

Lelia N. Morris, 1862-1929

Lelia N. Morris, 1862-1929

1. "Called un - to ho - li - ness," Church of our God, Pur - chase of
2. "Called un - to ho - li - ness," chil - dren of light, Walk - ing with
3. "Called un - to ho - li - ness," praise His dear name! This bless - ed
4. "Called un - to ho - li - ness," bride of the Lamb, Wait - ing the

Je - sus, re - deemed by His blood; Called from the world and its
Je - sus in gar - ments of white; Rai - ment un - sul - lied, nor
se - cret to faith now made plain: Not our own righ - teous-ness,
Bride-groom's re-turn - ing a - gain! Lift up your heads, for the

i - dols to flee, Called from the bond - age of sin to be free.
tarnished with sin; God's Ho - ly Spir - it a - bid - ing with-in.
but Christ with-in, Liv - ing, and reign - ing, and sav - ing from sin.
day draw-eth near When in His beau - ty the King shall ap - pear.

REFRAIN

"Ho-li-ness un - to the Lord" is our watch-word and song, "Ho-li-ness un - to the

Lord" as we're march-ing a-long. Sing it, shout it,
"Ho - li-ness un - to the Lord"; sing,

loud   and long,   "Ho-li-ness un-to the Lord," now and for-ev - er.
"Ho - li-ness un - to the Lord,"

291

All for Jesus

Mary D. James, 19th Century

Asa Hull, b. 1828

1. All   for Je - sus! all for Je - sus!   All   my be-ing's ransomed pow'rs:
2. Let   my hands perform His bid - ding;   Let   my feet run in His ways;
3. Since my eyes were fixed on Je - sus,   I've lost sight of all   be - side,
4. Oh, what won-der! how a - maz - ing!   Je - sus, glo-rious King of Kings,

All   my tho'ts and words and do - ings, All   my days and all my hours.
Let   my eyes see Je - sus on - ly;   Let   my lips speak forth His praise.
So   en-chained my spir-it's vi - sion, Look - ing at the Cru - ci - fied.
Deigns to call me His be - lov - ed,   Lets me rest be-neath His wings.

All for Je-sus! all for Je - sus! All   my days and all my hours; hours.
All for Je-sus! all for Je - sus! Let my lips speak forth His praise; praise.
All for Je-sus! all for Je - sus! Look-ing at the Cru - ci - fied; fied.
All for Je-sus! all for Je - sus! Rest-ing now be - neath His wings; wings.

292   # Blessed Quietness

Manie Payne Ferguson, b. 1850   *Arr. from* W. S. Marshall, 19th Century

1. Joys are flow-ing like a riv - er Since the Com - fort - er has come.
2. Springing in - to life and glad - ness All a - round this glorious Guest,
3. Like the rain that falls from heav - en, Like the sun-light from the sky,
4. What a won-der - ful sal - va - tion, Where we al - ways see His face!

He a - bides with us for - ev - er, Makes the trust - ing heart His home.
Ban-ished un - be - lief and sad - ness, And we just o - bey and rest.
So the Ho - ly Ghost is giv - en, Com - ing on us from on high.
What a peace-ful hab - i - ta - tion! What a qui - et rest - ing place!

REFRAIN

Blessed qui - et - ness! Ho - ly qui-et-ness! What as - sur - ance in my soul!

rit.

On the storm-y sea Je - sus speaks to me, And the bil-lows cease to roll.

293 The Glorious Hope

ARIEL

Samuel Medley, 1738-1799

Arr. by Lowell Mason, 1792-1872

1. Oh, glo - rious hope of per - fect love! It lifts me up to things a - bove; It bears on ea - gles' wings. It gives my rav - ished soul a taste, And makes me for some mo -ments feast With Je - sus' priests and kings, With Je - sus' priests and kings.

2. Re - joic - ing now in ear - nest hope, I stand, and from the moun - tain - top See all the land be - low. Riv - ers of milk and hon - ey rise, And all the fruits of par - a - dise In end - less plen - ty grow, In end-less plen - ty grow.

3. A land of corn, and wine, and oil; Fa - vored with God's pe - cul - iar smile, With ev - 'ry bless - ing blest; There dwells the Lord, our Righ-teous-ness, And keeps His own in per - fect peace, And ev - er - last - ing rest, And ev - er - last - ing rest.

4. Oh, that I might at once go up; No more on this side Jor - dan stop, But now the land pos - sess; This mo - ment end my le - gal years, Sor - rows and sins, and doubts and fears, A howl - ing wil - der - ness, A howl-ing wil - der - ness!

How the Fire Fell

Johnson Oatman, Jr. 1856-1922

Miriam E. Oatman, 20th Century

1. Oh, I love to tell the bless - ed sto - ry
2. All my doubts and fears are gone for - ev - er
3. To the world no more my heart is turn - ing
4. There's a crown a - wait - ing me in heav - en

Since the Lord

For my soul re - ceived a flood of glo - ry
For His peace flowed o'er me like a riv - er
For on me His Spir - it fell with burn - ing
For a heart made clean to me was giv - en

sanc - ti - fied me;

When the Lord sanc - ti - fied me.

REFRAIN

Oh, I nev - er shall for - get how the fire fell, How the fire fell, how the fire fell. Oh, I nev - er shall for - get how the fire fell When the Lord sanc - ti - fied me.

295 Holiness Forevermore

Haldor Lillenas, 1885-1959   Haldor Lillenas, 1885-1959

1. There's a bless-ed and tri-um-phant song: Ho-li-ness for-ev-er-more!
2. We will praise the Lord for vic-to-ry, Ho-li-ness for-ev-er-more!
3. From this stan-dard we will not de-part, Ho-li-ness for-ev-er-more!
4. We will shout our glo-rious lib-er-ty, Ho-li-ness for-ev-er-more!

It is sung by the might-y, Blood-washed throng:
From the car-nal mind we now are free.
'Tis the song of the pu-ri-fied in heart,
We shall sing it by the crys-tal sea,
Ho-li-ness for-ev-er-more!

REFRAIN

mf

Ho-li-ness for-ev-er-more! Ho-li-ness for-
Sing the hap-py song!

ev-er-more! We will sing it, shout it,
As we march a-long,   and   and

ff

Preach it, and live it, Ho-li-ness for-ev-er-more!

296 Sanctifying Power

Lelia N. Morris, 1862-1929

Lelia N. Morris, 1862-1929

1. There is sanc-ti-fy-ing pow'r, Like a sweet, re-fresh-ing show'r, Wait-ing
2. I'm so glad it reach-es me, All un-wor-thy tho' I be, O-ver-
3. This God's will for you and me, That we sanc-ti-fied should be, Dwell-ing
4. Songs of prais-es let us sing To our bless-ed Lord and King For this

for each con-se-crat-ed heart: Pow'r to cleanse us from all sin, Pow'r to
com-ing grace made free-ly mine. Since the Com-fort-er a-bides, And with-
in this land of plen-teous-ness. Fling your doubts and fears a-side, Bold-ly
great sal-va-tion rich and free; Ev-'ry need-ed grace sup-plied, Ev-'ry

keep us pure with-in, Pow'r for ser-vice which He will im-part.
in my heart re-sides, I am walk-ing in the light di-vine.
cross the Jor-dan's tide, And your her-i-tage in Christ pos-sess.
long-ing sat-is-fied, Saved for time and for e-ter-ni-ty.

REFRAIN

I'm so glad, I'm so glad For this
I'm so glad, hal-le-lu-jah, I'm so glad

sav-ing, sanc-ti-fy-ing pow'r! Waves of glo-ry o'er me roll; Peace a-

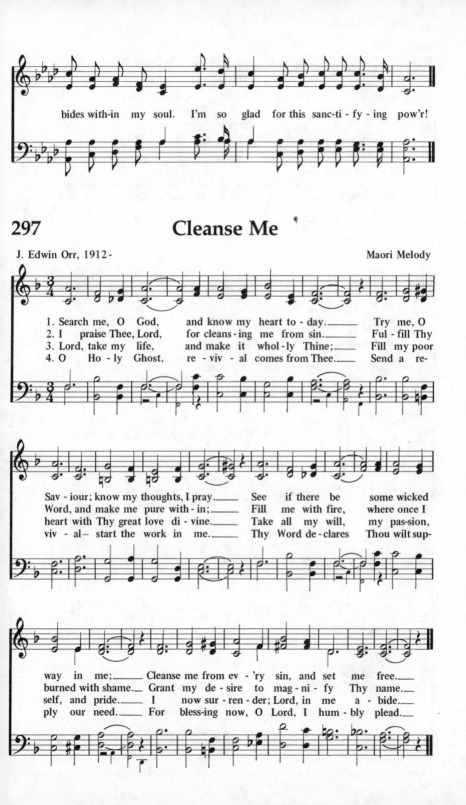

bides with-in my soul. I'm so glad for this sanc-ti-fy-ing pow'r!

297 Cleanse Me

J. Edwin Orr, 1912-

Maori Melody

1. Search me, O God, and know my heart to-day. Try me, O
2. I praise Thee, Lord, for cleans-ing me from sin. Ful-fill Thy
3. Lord, take my life, and make it whol-ly Thine; Fill my poor
4. O Ho-ly Ghost, re-viv-al comes from Thee. Send a re-

Sav-iour; know my thoughts, I pray. See if there be some wicked
Word, and make me pure with-in; Fill me with fire, where once I
heart with Thy great love di-vine. Take all my will, my pas-sion,
viv-al— start the work in me. Thy Word de-clares Thou wilt sup-

way in me; Cleanse me from ev-'ry sin, and set me free.
burned with shame. Grant my de-sire to mag-ni-fy Thy name.
self, and pride. I now sur-ren-der; Lord, in me a-bide.
ply our need. For bless-ing now, O Lord, I hum-bly plead.

298   A Heart like Thine

Judson W. Van Deventer, 1855 - 1939   Judson W. Van Deventer, 1855 - 1939

1. Give me a love that knows no ill; Give me the grace to
2. On - ly a joy, a few brief years; On - ly a dream, a
3. O - pen mine eyes that I may see; Show me the cross of
4. Pil - low my head up - on Thy breast; Shel - ter my soul and

do Thy will. Par - don and cleanse this soul of mine;
vale of tears; Vain is this world I now re - sign.
Cal - va - ry; There may I go and not re - pine.
give me rest; Fill me with love as I re - cline.

REFRAIN

Give me a heart like Thine. Come to my soul, bless-ed

Je - sus. Hear me, O Sav - iour di - vine! O - pen the

foun - tain and cleanse me; Give me a heart like Thine.
a heart like Thine.

Walking in the King's Highway

Florence Horton, 20th Century

Florence Horton, 20th Century

1. We shall see the des-ert as the rose,
2. We shall see the glo-ry of the Lord,
3. There the rain shall come up-on the ground, Walk-ing in the
4. There no rav-'nous beast shall make a - fraid,
5. No un - clean thing shall pass o'er here,

There'll be sing - ing where sal - va - tion goes,
And be - hold the beau - ty of His Word,
King's high - way; And the springs of wa - ter will be found,
For the pu - ri - fied the way was made,
But the ran - somed ones with - out a fear,

REFRAIN

Walk-ing in the King's high - way. There's a high-way there and a

way, (and a way,) Where sor-row shall flee a - way; (flee a-way;) And the

light shines bright as the day, (as the day,) Walk-ing in the King's high - way.

300 The Cleansing Wave

KNAPP

Phoebe Palmer Knapp, 1839-1908   Phoebe Palmer Knapp, 1839-1908

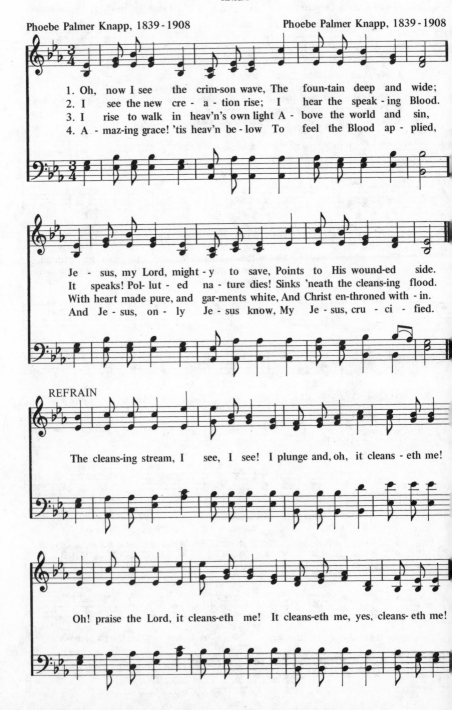

1. Oh, now I see the crim-son wave, The foun-tain deep and wide;
2. I see the new cre - a - tion rise; I hear the speak - ing Blood.
3. I rise to walk in heav'n's own light A - bove the world and sin,
4. A - maz-ing grace! 'tis heav'n be - low To feel the Blood ap - plied,

Je - sus, my Lord, might - y to save, Points to His wound-ed side.
It speaks! Pol- lut - ed na - ture dies! Sinks 'neath the cleans-ing flood.
With heart made pure, and gar-ments white, And Christ en-throned with - in.
And Je - sus, on - ly Je - sus know, My Je - sus, cru - ci - fied.

REFRAIN

The cleans-ing stream, I see, I see! I plunge and, oh, it cleans - eth me!

Oh! praise the Lord, it cleans-eth me! It cleans-eth me, yes, cleans- eth me!

301 Whiter than Snow

FISCHER

James Nicholson, 1828-1876

William G. Fischer, 1835-1912

1. Lord Je - sus, I long to be per - fect - ly whole; I want Thee for-
2. Lord Je - sus, look down from Thy throne in the skies, And help me to
3. Lord Je - sus, for this I most hum - bly en - treat. I wait, bless - ed
4. Lord Je - sus, Thou se - est I pa - tient - ly wait. Come now, and with-
5. The bless - ing by faith I re - ceive from a - bove. Oh, glo - ry! My

ev - er to live in my soul. Break down ev - 'ry i - dol, cast out ev - 'ry
make a complete sac - ri - fice. I give up my - self, and what - ev - er I
Lord, at Thy cru - ci - fied feet. By faith, for my cleans - ing I see Thy blood
in me a new heart cre - ate. To those who have sought Thee Thou never saidst
soul is made perfect in love. My prayer has pre - vailed, and this mo - ment I

REFRAIN

foe. Now wash me and I shall be whit - er than snow. Whit - er than
know. Now wash me and I shall be whit - er than snow. Whit - er than
flow. Now wash me and I shall be whit - er than snow. Whit - er than
no. Now wash me and I shall be whit - er than snow. Whit - er than
know The Blood is ap - plied, I am whit - er than snow. Whit - er than

snow, yes, whit - er than snow; Now wash me and I shall be whit - er than snow.
5. snow, yes, whit - er than snow; The Blood is ap - plied; I am whit - er than snow.

302 Since the Fullness of His Love Came In

Eliza E. Hewitt, 1851-1920

Bentley D. Ackley, 1872-1958

1. Once my way was dark and drear - y, For my heart was full of sin;
2. There is grace for all the low - ly, Grace to keep the trust-ing soul;
3. Let me spread a - broad the sto - ry, Oth - er souls to Je - sus win;

But the sky is bright and cheer-y, Since the full - ness of His love came in.
Pow'r to cleanse and make me ho - ly. Je - sus shall my yield-ed life con-trol.
For the Cross is now my glo - ry, Since the full - ness of His love came in.

REFRAIN

I can nev - er tell how much I love Him; I can nev - er tell His

love for me. For it pass - eth hu - man meas - ure, Like a

deep, un-fath-omed sea.
deep, un- fath - omed sea.

'Tis re - deem - ing love in

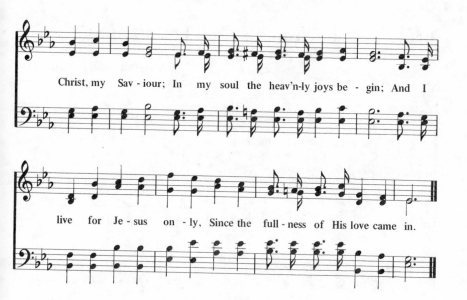

Christ, my Sav-iour; In my soul the heav'n-ly joys be-gin; And I
live for Je-sus on-ly, Since the full-ness of His love came in.

303   Breathe on Me, Breath of God

TRENTHAM

Edwin Hatch, 1835 - 1889

Robert Jackson, 1842 - 1914

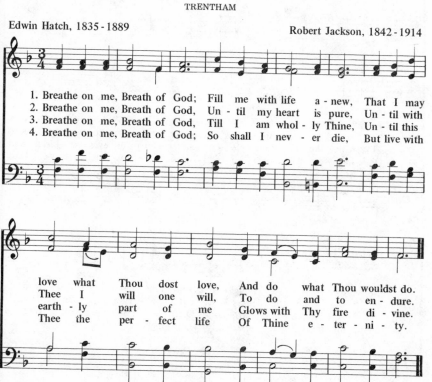

1. Breathe on me, Breath of God; Fill me with life a - new, That I may
2. Breathe on me, Breath of God, Un - til my heart is pure, Un - til with
3. Breathe on me, Breath of God, Till I am whol - ly Thine, Un - til this
4. Breathe on me, Breath of God; So shall I nev - er die, But live with

love what Thou dost love, And do what Thou wouldst do.
Thee I will one will, To do and to en - dure.
earth - ly part of me Glows with Thy fire di - vine.
Thee the per - fect life Of Thine e - ter - ni - ty.

304 The Church's One Foundation

AURELIA

Samuel J. Stone, 1839-1900

Samuel S. Wesley, 1810-1876

1. The Church -'s one Foun - da - tion Is Je - sus Christ, her Lord.
2. E - lect from ev - 'ry na - tion, Yet one o'er all the earth;
3. 'Mid toil and trib - u - la - tion, And tu - mult of her war,
4. Yet she on earth hath u - nion With God, the Three in One,

She is His new cre - a - tion By wa - ter and the word.
Her char - ter of sal - va - tion, One Lord, one faith, one birth;
She waits the con - sum - ma - tion Of peace for - ev - er - more;
And mys - tic, sweet com - mu - nion With those whose rest is won.

From heav'n He came and sought her To be His ho - ly bride; With
One ho - ly name she bless - es; Par - takes one ho - ly food; And
Till, with the vi - sion glo - rious, Her long - ing eyes are blest, And
Oh, hap - py ones and ho - ly! Lord, give us grace that we, Like

His own blood He bought her, And for her life He died.
to one hope she press - es, With ev - 'ry grace en - dued.
the great Church vic - to - rious Shall be the Church at rest.
them, the meek and low - ly, On high may dwell with Thee.

305 A Glorious Church

Ralph E. Hudson, 1843 - 1901   Ralph E. Hudson, 1843 - 1901

1. Do you hear them com - ing, Broth - er, Throng - ing up the
2. Do you hear the stir - ring an - thems Fill - ing all the
3. Nev - er fear the clouds of sor - row; Nev - er fear the
4. Wave the ban - ner, shout His prais - es, For our vic - to-

steeps of light, Clad in glo - rious, shin - ing gar - ments—
earth and sky? 'Tis a grand, vic - to - rious ar - my.
storms of sin. We shall tri - umph on the mor - row;
ry is nigh! We shall join our con - qu'ring Sav - iour;

REFRAIN

Blood-washed garments pure and white?
Lift its ban-ner up on high!   'Tis a glo - rious Church with-
E - ven now our joys be - gin.
We shall reign with Him on high!

out spot or wrin-kle, Washed in the blood of the Lamb. 'Tis a

glo - rious Church, with- out spot or wrin-kle, Washed in the blood of the Lamb.

306 In Christ There Is No East or West

ST. PETER

John Oxenham, 1852-1941

Alexander R. Reinagle, 1799-1877

1. In Christ there is no East or West, In Him no South or North;
2. In Him shall true hearts ev-'ry-where Their high com-mu-nion find;
3. Join hands then, brothers of the faith, What-e'er your race may be;
4. In Christ now meet both East and West; In Him meet South and North.

But one great fel-low-ship of love Thro'-out the whole wide earth.
His ser-vice is the gold-en cord Close bind-ing all man-kind.
Who serves my Fa-ther as a son Is sure-ly kin to me.
All Christ-ly souls are one in Him Thro'-out the whole wide earth.

307 Blest Be the Tie That Binds

DENNIS

John Fawcett, 1740-1817

Hans G. Nageli, 1773-1836

1. Blest be the tie that binds Our hearts in Chris-tian love;
2. Be-fore our Fa-ther's throne We pour our ar-dent prayers;
3. We share our mu-tual woes, Our mu-tual bur-dens bear;
4. When we a-sun-der part It gives us in-ward pain;

The fel-low-ship of kin-dred minds Is like to that a-bove.
Our fears, our hopes, our aims are one, Our com-forts and our cares.
And of-ten for each oth-er flows The sym-pa-thiz-ing tear.
But we shall still be joined in heart, And hope to meet a-gain.

308 Glorious Things of Thee Are Spoken

AUSTRIAN HYMN

John Newton, 1725-1807

Franz J. Haydn, 1732-1809

1. Glo - rious things of thee are spo - ken, Zi - on, cit - y of our God;
2. See, the streams of liv - ing wa - ters, Spring-ing from e - ter - nal Love,
3. Round each hab - i - ta - tion hov-ering, See the cloud and fire ap - pear

He whose word can - not be bro - ken Formed thee for His own a - bode.
Well sup - ply thy sons and daugh-ters, And all fear of want re - move.
For a glo - ry and a cov - ering, Show - ing that the Lord is near!

On the Rock of A - ges found - ed, What can shake thy sure re-pose?
Who can faint while such a riv - er Ev - er flows their thirst t'assuage?
Glo-rious things of thee are spo - ken, Zi - on, cit - y of our God;

With sal - va - tion's walls sur-round - ed, Thou may'st smile at all thy foes.
Grace which, like the Lord, the Giv - er, Nev - er fails from age to age!
He whose word can - not be bro - ken Formed thee for His own a - bode.

309 O Thou Whose Hand Hath Brought Us

AURELIA

Frederick W. Goadby, 1845 - 1880

Samuel S. Wesley, 1810 - 1876

1. O Thou whose hand hath brought us Un - to this joy - ful day,
2. For this new house we praise Thee, Reared at Thine own com - mand;
3. And oft as here we gath - er, And hearts in wor-ship blend,
4. And as the years roll on - ward, And strong af - fec - tions twine,
5. Lord God, our fa - thers' Help - er, Our Joy, and Hope, and Stay,

Ac - cept our glad thanks-giv - ing, And lis - ten as we pray;
For ev - 'ry gen - 'rous spir - it, And ev - 'ry will -ing hand.
May truth re - veal its pow - er, And fer - vent prayer as - cend.
And ten - der mem-'ries gath - er A - bout this sa - cred shrine,
Grant now a gra - cious ear - nest Of man - y a com - ing day.

And may our prep - a - ra - tion For this day's ser - vice be
And now with - in Thy tem - ple Thy glo - ry let us see,
Here may the bus - y toil - er Rise to the things a - bove;
May this its chief - est hon - or, Its glo - ry ev - er be,
Our yearn - ing hearts Thou know - est; We wait be - fore Thy throne.

With one ac - cord to of - fer Our - selves, O Lord, to Thee.
For all its strength and beau - ty Are noth-ing with - out Thee.
The young, the old, be strength-ened, And all men learn Thy love.
That mul - ti - tudes with - in it Have found their way to Thee.
Oh, come, and by Thy pres - ence Make this new house Thine own.

For All the Saints

SINE NOMINE

William W. How, 1823 - 1897   Ralph Vaughan Williams 1872 - 1958

310

1. For all the saints who from their la - bors rest, Who Thee by faith be - fore the world con - fessed, Thy name, O Je - sus, be for - ev - er blest. Al - le - lu - ia! Al - le - lu - ia!

2. Thou wast their Rock, their For-tress, and their Might; Thou, Lord, their Cap - tain in the well-fought fight; Thou, in the dark - ness drear, their one true Light. Al - le - lu - ia! Al - le - lu - ia!

3. Oh, blest com - mu - nion, fel - low-ship di - vine! We fee - bly strug - gle; they in glo - ry shine. Yet all are one in Thee, for all are Thine. Al - le - lu - ia! Al - le - lu - ia!

4. Oh, may Thy sol - diers, faith-ful, true, and bold, Fight as the saints who no - bly fought of old, And win with them the vic - tor's crown of gold. Al - le - lu - ia! Al - le - lu - ia!

5. And when the strife is fierce, the war-fare long, Steals on the ear the dis - tant tri - umph song, And hearts are brave a - gain, and arms are strong. Al - le - lu - ia! Al - le - lu - ia!

6. From earth's wide bounds, from o-cean's far-thest coast, Thru gates of pearl streams in the count-less host, Sing - ing to Fa - ther, Son, and Ho - ly Ghost. Al - le - lu - ia! Al - le - lu - ia!

Tune from *The English Hymnal.* Used by permission of Oxford University Press, London.

311 I Love Thy Kingdom, Lord

ST. THOMAS

Timothy Dwight, 1752-1817

Aaron Williams, 1731-1776

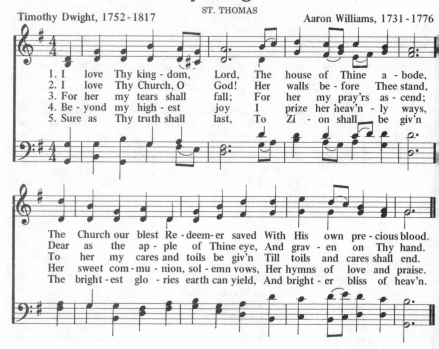

1. I love Thy king-dom, Lord, The house of Thine a-bode,
2. I love Thy Church, O God! Her walls be-fore Thee stand,
3. For her my tears shall fall; For her my pray'rs as-cend;
4. Be-yond my high-est joy I prize her heav'n-ly ways,
5. Sure as Thy truth shall last, To Zi-on shall be giv'n

The Church our blest Re-deem-er saved With His own pre-cious blood.
Dear as the ap-ple of Thine eye, And grav-en on Thy hand.
To her my cares and toils be giv'n Till toils and cares shall end.
Her sweet com-mu-nion, sol-emn vows, Her hymns of love and praise.
The bright-est glo-ries earth can yield, And bright-er bliss of heav'n.

312 Come, Holy Spirit, Heavenly Dove

ST. AGNES

Isaac Watts, 1674-1748

John B. Dykes, 1823-1876

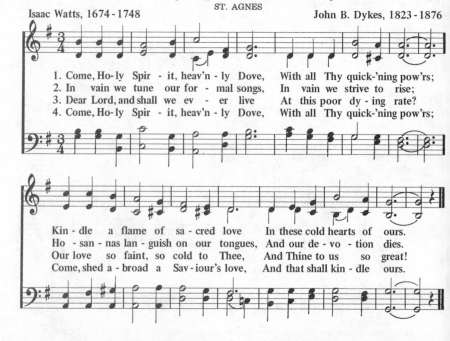

1. Come, Ho-ly Spir-it, heav'n-ly Dove, With all Thy quick-'ning pow'rs;
2. In vain we tune our for-mal songs, In vain we strive to rise;
3. Dear Lord, and shall we ev-er live At this poor dy-ing rate?
4. Come, Ho-ly Spir-it, heav'n-ly Dove, With all Thy quick-'ning pow'rs;

Kin-dle a flame of sa-cred love In these cold hearts of ours.
Ho-san-nas lan-guish on our tongues, And our de-vo-tion dies.
Our love so faint, so cold to Thee, And Thine to us so great!
Come, shed a-broad a Sav-iour's love, And that shall kin-dle ours.

313 **According to Thy Gracious Word**

MANOAH

James Montgomery, 1771-1854

From Greatorex's "Collection"

1. Ac - cord - ing to Thy gra - cious word, In meek hu - mil - i - ty,
2. Thy bod - y, bro - ken for my sake, My bread from heav'n shall be;
3. Re - mem - ber Thee, and all Thy pains, And all Thy love to me;
4. And when these fail - ing lips grow dumb, And mind and mem - 'ry flee,

This will I do, my dy - ing Lord; I will re - mem - ber Thee.
Thy tes - ta - men - tal cup I take, And thus re - mem - ber Thee.
Yea, while a breath, a pulse re - mains, Will I re - mem - ber Thee!
When Thou shalt in Thy king - dom come, Then, Lord, re - mem - ber me!

314 **Bread of the World in Mercy Broken**

EUCHARISTIC HYMN

Reginald Heber, 1783-1826

John S. B. Hodges, 1830-1915

1. Bread of the world in mer - cy bro - ken, Wine of the soul in mer - cy shed,
2. Look on the heart by sor - row bro - ken, Look on the tears by sin - ners shed,

By whom the words of life were spo - ken, And in whose death our sins are dead!
And be Thy feast to us the to - ken That by Thy grace our souls are fed.

315

Here at Thy Table, Lord

BREAD OF LIFE

May P. Hoyt, 19th Century

William F. Sherwin, 1826-1888

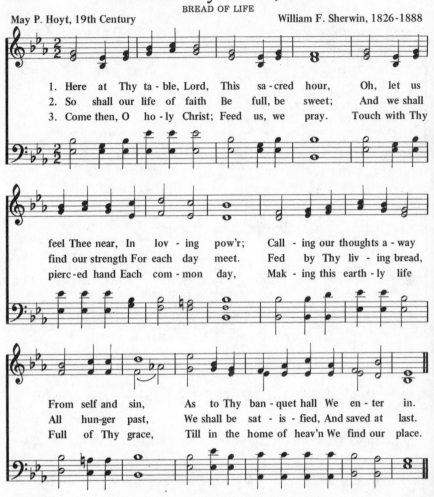

1. Here at Thy ta - ble, Lord, This sa - cred hour, Oh, let us
2. So shall our life of faith Be full, be sweet; And we shall
3. Come then, O ho - ly Christ; Feed us, we pray. Touch with Thy

feel Thee near, In lov - ing pow'r; Call - ing our thoughts a - way
find our strength For each day meet. Fed by Thy liv - ing bread,
pierc-ed hand Each com - mon day, Mak - ing this earth - ly life

From self and sin, As to Thy ban - quet hall We en - ter in.
All hun-ger past, We shall be sat - is - fied, And saved at last.
Full of Thy grace, Till in the home of heav'n We find our place.

316

Blest Feast of Love Divine

DENNIS

From Hans G. Nageli, 1773 - 1836
Arr. by Lowell Mason, 1792 - 1872

Edward Denney, 19th Century

1. Blest feast of love di - vine! 'Tis grace that makes us free
2. That Blood which flowed for sin, In sym - bol here we see,
3. Oh, if this glimpse of love Be so di - vine - ly sweet,

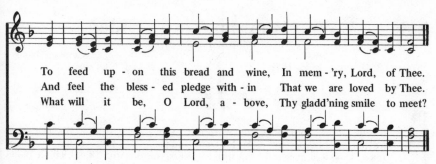

To feed up - on this bread and wine, In mem - 'ry, Lord, of Thee.
And feel the bless - ed pledge with - in That we are loved by Thee.
What will it be, O Lord, a - bove, Thy gladd'ning smile to meet?

317   Let Us Break Bread Together

Traditional
Arr. by Floyd W. Hawkins, 1904 -

Spiritual

1. Let us break bread to - geth - er on our knees;   Let us
2. Let us praise God to - geth - er on our knees;   Let us

on our knees;

break bread to-geth-er on our knees.   When I fall on my knees
praise God to-geth-er on our knees.   When I fall on my knees

on our knees.

with my face to the ris - ing sun, O Lord, have mer-cy on me.
with my face to the ris - ing sun, O Lord, have mer-cy on me.

318 Who Is on the Lord's Side?

ARMAGEDDON

Frances R. Havergal, 1836 - 1879

German Melody
Arr. by John Goss, 1800 - 1880

1. Who is on the Lord's side? Who will serve the King? Who will be His help-ers
2. Not for weight of glo-ry, Not for crown and palm, En-ter we the ar-my,
3. Je-sus, Thou hast bought us, Not with gold or gem, But with Thine own life-blood,
4. Fierce may be the conflict, Strong may be the foe, But the King's own ar-my

Oth-er lives to bring? Who will leave the world's side? Who will face the foe?
Raise the warrior psalm; But for love that claim-eth Lives for whom He died.
For Thy di-a-dem. With Thy blessing fill-ing Each who comes to Thee,
None can o-ver-throw. Round His standard rang-ing, Vic-t'ry to se-cure,

Who is on the Lord's side? Who for Him will go? By Thy call of mer-cy,
He whom Je-sus nam-eth Must be on His side. By Thy love con-strain-ing,
Thou hast made us willing, Thou hast made us free. By Thy grand re-demp-tion,
For His truth un-changing Makes the tri-umph sure. Joy-ful-ly en-list-ing,

By Thy grace di-vine, We are on the Lord's side. Sav-iour, we are Thine.

319 Onward, Christian Soldiers

ST. GERTRUDE

Sabine Baring-Gould, 1834-1924

Arthur Sullivan, 1842-1900

1. On - ward, Christian sol - diers! March-ing as to war, With the
2. Like a might - y ar - my Moves the Church of God. Broth - ers,
3. Crowns and thrones may per - ish, King - doms rise and wane; But the
4. On - ward, then, ye peo - ple! Join our hap - py throng; Blend with

cross of Je - sus Go - ing on be - fore. Christ, the roy - al Mas - ter,
we are tread-ing Where the saints have trod. We are not di - vid - ed;
Church of Je - sus Con-stant will re - main. Gates of hell can nev - er
ours your voic - es In the tri-umph song. Glo - ry, laud, and hon - or

Leads a-gainst the foe; For - ward in - to bat - tle, See, His ban-ners go!
All one bod - y we: One in hope and doc - trine, One in char-i - ty.
'Gainst that Church prevail; We have Christ's own promise, Which can nev-er fail.
Un - to Christ, the King; This thro' count-less a - ges Men and an-gels sing.

REFRAIN

On - ward, Chris-tian sol - diers! March-ing as to war,

With the cross of Je - sus Go - ing on be - fore.

320 Stand Up for Jesus

WEBB

George Duffield, Jr., 1818-1888

George J. Webb, 1803-1887

1. Stand up, stand up for Je - sus, Ye sol - diers of the Cross. Lift
2. Stand up, stand up for Je - sus. The trum - pet call o - bey; Forth
3. Stand up, stand up for Je - sus— Stand in His strength a - lone. The

high His roy - al ban - ner; It must not suf - fer loss. From
to the might - y con - flict, In this His glo - rious day. "Ye
arm of flesh will fail you— Ye dare not trust your own. Put

vic - t'ry un - to vic - t'ry, His ar - my shall He lead, Till
that are men now serve Him,"A - gainst un - num-bered foes; Let
on the gos - pel ar - mor And, watch - ing un - to prayer, Where

ev - 'ry foe is van - quished And Christ is Lord in - deed.
cour - age rise with dan - ger, And strength to strength op - pose.
du - ty calls or dan - ger, Be nev - er want - ing there.

321 He Rolled the Sea Away

Henry J. Zelley, 1859-1942

Henry L. Gilmour, 1837-1920

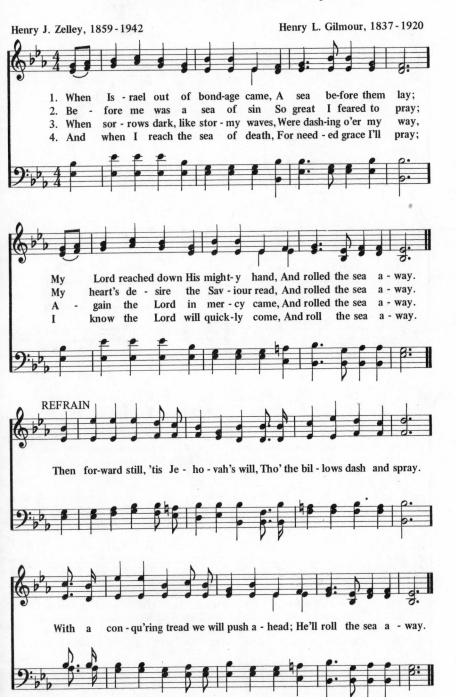

1. When Is-rael out of bond-age came, A sea be-fore them lay;
2. Be - fore me was a sea of sin So great I feared to pray;
3. When sor - rows dark, like stor - my waves, Were dash-ing o'er my way,
4. And when I reach the sea of death, For need - ed grace I'll pray;

My Lord reached down His might-y hand, And rolled the sea a - way.
My heart's de - sire the Sav - iour read, And rolled the sea a - way.
A - gain the Lord in mer - cy came, And rolled the sea a - way.
I know the Lord will quick-ly come, And roll the sea a - way.

REFRAIN

Then for-ward still, 'tis Je - ho - vah's will, Tho' the bil - lows dash and spray.

With a con - qu'ring tread we will push a - head; He'll roll the sea a - way.

322   Stand Up, Stand Up for Jesus

GEIBEL

George Duffield, Jr., 1818 - 1888

Adam Geibel, 1855 - 1933

1. Stand up, stand up for Je - sus, Ye sol - diers of the Cross.
2. Stand up, stand up for Je - sus. The trum-pet call o - bey;
3. Stand up, stand up for Je - sus; Stand in His strength a - lone.
4. Stand up, stand up for Je - sus; The strife will not be long.

Lift high His roy - al ban - ner; It must not suf - fer loss.
Forth to the might-y con - flict, In this His glo - rious day.
The arm of flesh will fail you; Ye dare not trust your own.
This day the noise of bat - tle; The next, the vic - tor's song.

From vic - t'ry un - to vic - t'ry His ar - my shall He lead,
Ye that are men now serve Him A - gainst un - num-bered foes;
Put on the gos - pel ar - mor; Each piece put on with prayer.
To him that o - ver - com - eth, A crown of life shall be;

Till ev - 'ry foe is van - quished, And Christ is Lord in - deed.
Let cour - age rise with dan - ger, And strength to strength op-pose.
Where du - ty calls or dan - ger, Be nev - er want-ing there.
He with the King of Glo - ry Shall reign e - ter - nal - ly.

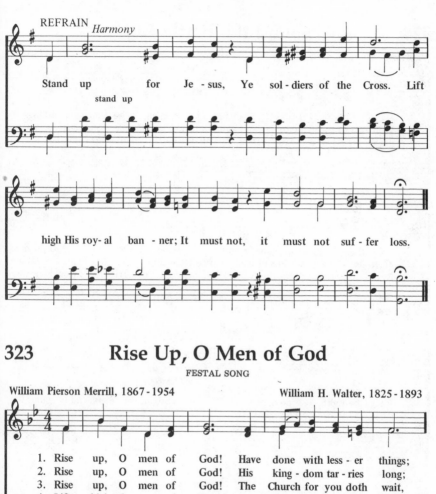

REFRAIN *Harmony*

Stand up   for   Je - sus,   Ye   sol - diers of the   Cross.   Lift
stand up

high His roy-al   ban - ner; It   must not,   it   must not   suf - fer   loss.

323   # Rise Up, O Men of God

FESTAL SONG

William Pierson Merrill, 1867 - 1954   William H. Walter, 1825 - 1893

1. Rise   up,   O   men of   God!   Have   done with less - er   things;
2. Rise   up,   O   men of   God!   His   king - dom tar - ries   long;
3. Rise   up,   O   men of   God!   The   Church for you doth   wait,
4. Lift   high the cross of   Christ!   Tread where His feet have   trod.

Give   heart and mind and   soul and strength To serve the King of Kings.
Bring   in   the   day   of   broth-er - hood And end the night of wrong.
Her   strength un - e - qual to her task; Rise up, and make her great!
As   broth - ers of   the   Son of Man, Rise up, O men of God!

324   Sound the Battle Cry

William F. Sherwin, 1826-1888   William F. Sherwin, 1826-1888

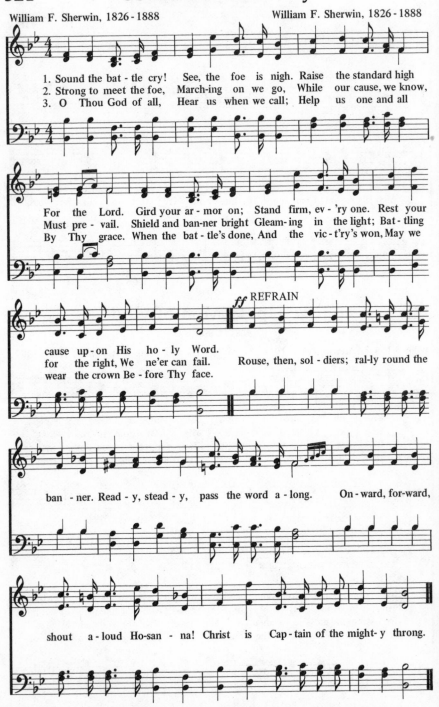

1. Sound the bat - tle cry! See, the foe is nigh. Raise the standard high
2. Strong to meet the foe, March-ing on we go, While our cause, we know,
3. O Thou God of all, Hear us when we call; Help us one and all

For the Lord. Gird your ar - mor on; Stand firm, ev - 'ry one. Rest your
Must pre - vail. Shield and ban-ner bright Gleam-ing in the light; Bat - tling
By Thy grace. When the bat - tle's done, And the vic - t'ry's won, May we

ff REFRAIN

cause up - on His ho - ly Word.
for the right, We ne'er can fail.   Rouse, then, sol - diers; ral-ly round the
wear the crown Be - fore Thy face.

ban - ner. Read - y, stead - y, pass the word a - long.   On - ward, for - ward,

shout a - loud Ho-san - na! Christ is Cap - tain of the might- y throng.

325 We're Marching to Zion

Isaac Watts, 1674-1748   Robert Lowry, 1826-1899

1. Come, we that love the Lord, And let our joys be known. Join
2. Let those re - fuse to sing Who nev - er knew our God; But
3. The hill of Zi - on yields A thou - sand sa - cred sweets Be -
4. Then let our songs a - bound, And ev - 'ry tear be dry. We're

in a song with sweet ac - cord, Join in a song with sweet ac-cord,
chil - dren of the heav'n - ly King, But chil-dren of the heav'n - ly King,
fore we reach the heav'n - ly fields, Be - fore we reach the heav'n - ly fields,
march - ing thro' Im - man - uel's ground, We're marching thro' Immanuel's ground,

And thus sur - round the throne, And thus sur-round the throne.
May speak their joys a - broad, May speak their joys a - broad.
Or walk the gold - en streets, Or walk the gold - en streets.
To fair - er worlds on high, To fair - er worlds on high.

(1) And thus sur-round the throne, And thus sur - round the throne.

REFRAIN

We're march - ing to Zi - on, Beau - ti - ful, beau - ti - ful Zi - on. We're
We're march - ing on to Zi - on,

march-ing up - ward to Zi - on, The beau-ti-ful cit-y of God.
Zi - on, Zi - on,

326 Jesus Calls Us

GALILEE

Cecil F. Alexander, 1818-1895

William H. Jude, 1851-1922

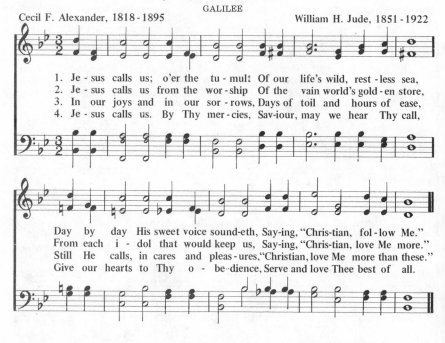

1. Je - sus calls us; o'er the tu - mult Of our life's wild, rest - less sea,
2. Je - sus calls us from the wor - ship Of the vain world's gold - en store,
3. In our joys and in our sor - rows, Days of toil and hours of ease,
4. Je - sus calls us. By Thy mer - cies, Sav-iour, may we hear Thy call,

Day by day His sweet voice sound-eth, Say-ing, "Chris-tian, fol - low Me."
From each i - dol that would keep us, Say-ing, "Chris-tian, love Me more."
Still He calls, in cares and pleas-ures, "Christian, love Me more than these."
Give our hearts to Thy o - be - dience, Serve and love Thee best of all.

327 Saviour, While My Heart Is Tender

EVENING PRAYER

John Burton, 1803-1877

George C. Stebbins, 1846-1945

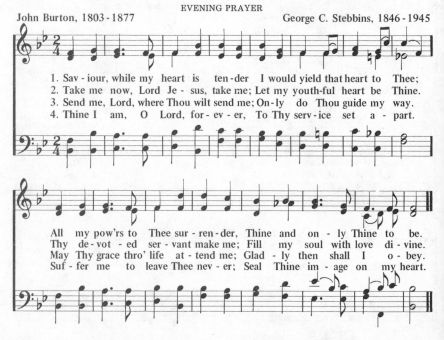

1. Sav - iour, while my heart is ten - der I would yield that heart to Thee;
2. Take me now, Lord Je - sus, take me; Let my youth-ful heart be Thine.
3. Send me, Lord, where Thou wilt send me; On-ly do Thou guide my way.
4. Thine I am, O Lord, for - ev - er, To Thy serv - ice set a - part.

All my pow'rs to Thee sur - ren - der, Thine and on - ly Thine to be.
Thy de - vot - ed ser - vant make me; Fill my soul with love di - vine.
May Thy grace thro' life at - tend me; Glad - ly then shall I o - bey.
Suf - fer me to leave Thee nev - er; Seal Thine im - age on my heart.

328

Follow On

CUSHING

William O. Cushing, 1823 - 1902

Robert Lowry, 1826 - 1899

1. Down in the val - ley with my Sav - iour I would go, Where the flow'rs are
2. Down in the val - ley with my Sav - iour I would go, Where the storms are
3. Down in the val - ley, or up - on the mountain steep, Close be - side my

bloom-ing and the sweet wa - ters flow. Ev - 'ry-where He leads me I would
sweep-ing and the dark wa - ters flow. With His hand to lead me I will
Sav - iour would my soul ev - er keep. He will lead me safe - ly in the

fol - low, fol - low on, Walk-ing in His foot-steps till the crown be won.
nev - er, nev - er fear; Dan - ger can-not fright me if my Lord is near.
path that He has trod, Up to where they gath-er on the hills of God.

REFRAIN

Fol - low! fol - low! I will fol-low Je-sus! Anywhere, ev'rywhere, I will follow on!

Fol - low! fol - low! I will fol-low Je-sus! Ev'rywhere He leads me I will follow on!

329 Where He Leads I'll Follow

OGDEN

William A. Ogden, 1841 - 1897

William A. Ogden, 1841 - 1897

1. Sweet are the prom-is - es; kind is the Word, Dear-er far than
2. Sweet is the ten - der love Je - sus hath shown, Sweet-er far than
3. List to His lov - ing words, "Come un - to me." Wea - ry, heav-y-

an - y mes - sage man ev - er heard. Pure was the mind of Christ,
an - y love that mor - tals have known. Kind to the err - ing one,
lad - en, there is sweet rest for thee. Trust in His prom-is - es,

sin - less, I see. He the great Ex - am-ple is, and Pat - tern for me.
faith-ful is He. He the great Ex -am-ple is, and Pat - tern for me.
faith-ful and sure; Lean up - on the Sav-iour, and thy soul is se-cure.

REFRAIN

Where He leads I'll fol - low,

Where He leads I'll fol - low, Where He leads I'll fol - low,

1

Fol - low all the way.

Fol-low all the way, yes, fol-low all the way.

2

Fol-low Jesus ev - 'ry day.

330 Anywhere with Jesus

TOWNER

Jessie B. Pounds, 1861-1921

Daniel B. Towner, 1850-1919

1. An-y-where with Je-sus I can safe-ly go, An-y-where He
2. An-y-where with Je-sus I am not a-lone. Oth-er friends may
3. An-y-where with Je-sus o-ver land and sea, Tell-ing souls in
4. An-y-where with Je-sus I can go to sleep When the dark-'ning

leads me in this world be-low. An-y-where without Him dear-est
fail me; He is still my own. Tho' His hand may lead me o-ver
dark-ness of sal-va-tion free; Read-y as He sum-mons me to
shad-ows round a-bout me creep, Know-ing I shall wak-en nev-er-

joys would fade. An-y-where with Je-sus I am not a-fraid.
drear-y ways, An-y-where with Je-sus is a house of praise.
go or stay, An-y-where with Je-sus when He points the way.
more to roam. An-y-where with Je-sus will be home, sweet home.

REFRAIN

An-y-where! An-y-where! Fear I can-not know.

An-y-where with Je-sus I can safe-ly go.

331 Stepping in the Light

Eliza E. Hewitt, 1851-1920

William J. Kirkpatrick, 1838-1921

1. Try-ing to walk in the steps of the Sav-iour, Try-ing to fol-low our
2. Pressing more closely to Him who is lead-ing, When we are tempt-ed to
3. Walking in foot-steps of gen-tle for-bear-ance, Footsteps of faith-ful-ness,
4. Try-ing to walk in the steps of the Sav-iour, Up-ward, still up-ward we'll

Sav-iour and King, Shap-ing our lives by His bless-ed ex-am-ple,
turn from the way; Trust-ing the arm that is strong to de-fend us,
mer-cy, and love; Look-ing to Him for the grace free-ly prom-ised,
fol-low our Guide. When we shall see Him, "the king in his beau-ty,"

Hap-py, how hap-py, the songs that we bring!
Hap-py, how hap-py, our prais-es each day!
Hap-py, how hap-py, our jour-ney a-bove!
Hap-py, how hap-py, our place at His side!

REFRAIN

How beau-ti-ful to walk in the

steps of the Sav-iour, Step-ping in the light, Step-ping in the light! How

beau-ti-ful to walk in the steps of the Sav-iour, Led in paths of light!

332 Follow, I Will Follow Thee

Howard L. Brown, 1889-1965
Margaret W. Brown, 1892-

Howard L. Brown, 1889-1965
Arr. by Herbert G. Tovey, 1888-

1. Je - sus calls me; I must fol - low, Fol - low Him to - day (to - day).
2. Je - sus calls me; I must fol - low, Fol - low ev - 'ry hour (ev-'ry hour);
3. Je - sus calls me; I must fol - low, Fol - low Him al - way (al - way).

When His ten - der voice is plead - ing, How can I de - lay?
Know the bless - ing of His pres - ence, Full - ness of His power.
When my Sav - iour goes be - fore me, I can nev - er stray.

REFRAIN

Fol - low, I will fol-low Thee, my Lord, Fol - low
Fol - low, fol - low, I will fol - low, Fol - low Thee, my Lord, my Lord, Fol - low, fol - low

ev - 'ry pass - ing day. My to - mor-rows are all
ev - 'ry pass - ing, Fol-low ev - 'ry day.
day, pass-ing day.

known to Thee; Thou wilt lead me all the way.
are known to Thee; Thou wilt lead, wilt

333 Living for Jesus

Thomas O. Chisholm, 1866-1960

C. Harold Lowden, 1883-

1. Liv-ing for Je-sus a life that is true, Striv-ing to please Him in
2. Liv-ing for Je-sus, who died in my place, Bear-ing on Cal-v'ry my
3. Liv-ing for Je-sus wher-ev-er I am, Do-ing each du-ty in
4. Liv-ing for Je-sus thro' earth's lit-tle while, My dear-est treas-ure, the

all that I do, Yield-ing al-le-giance, glad-heart-ed and free,
sin and dis-grace— Such love con-strains me to an-swer His call,
His ho-ly name, Will-ing to suf-fer af-flic-tion or loss,
light of His smile, Seek-ing the lost ones He died to re-deem,

REFRAIN

This is the path-way of bless-ing for me.
Fol-low His lead-ing, and give Him my all. O Je-sus, Lord and
Deem-ing each tri-al a part of my cross!
Bring-ing the wea-ry to find rest in Him!

Sav-iour, I give my-self to Thee; For Thou, in Thy a-tone-ment, Didst

give thy-self for me. I own no oth-er Mas-ter; My heart shall be Thy throne. My life I give, henceforth to live, O Christ, for Thee a - lone.

rit.

334 I Feel like Traveling On

William Hunter, 1811-1877

Arr. by James D. Vaughan, 1865-1941

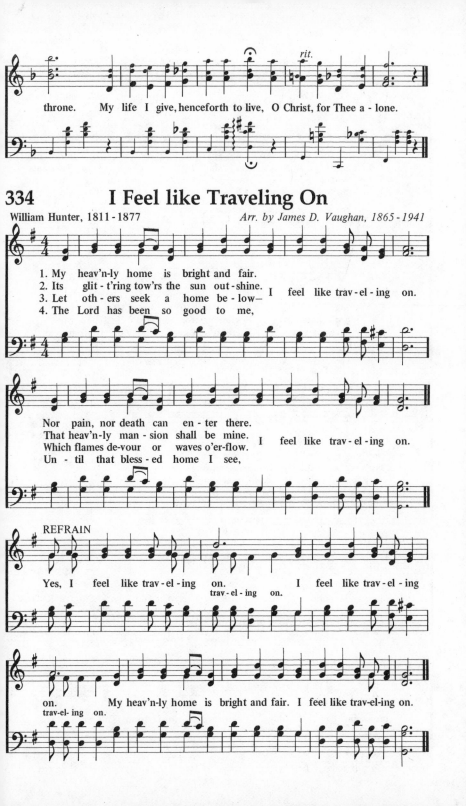

1. My heav'n-ly home is bright and fair.
2. Its glit-t'ring tow'rs the sun out-shine.
3. Let oth-ers seek a home be-low—
4. The Lord has been so good to me,

I I feel like trav-el-ing on.

Nor pain, nor death can en-ter there.
That heav'n-ly man-sion shall be mine.
Which flames de-vour or waves o'er-flow.
Un - til that bless-ed home I see,

I feel like trav-el-ing on.

REFRAIN

Yes, I feel like trav-el-ing on.
trav-el-ing on.
I feel like trav-el-ing

on.
trav-el-ing on.
My heav'n-ly home is bright and fair. I feel like trav-el-ing on.

335 Living for Jesus

Charles F. Weigle, 20th Century   Charles F. Weigle, 20th Century

1. Liv-ing for Je - sus, oh, what peace! Riv-ers of pleas - ure
2. Liv-ing for Je - sus, oh, what rest! Pleas-ing my Sav - iour,
3. Liv-ing for Je - sus, ev - 'ry - where, All of my bur - dens
4. Liv-ing for Je - sus, till at last In - to His glo - ry

nev - er cease. Tri - als may come, yet I'll not fear.
I am blest. On - ly to live for Him a - lone,
He doth bear. Friends may for-sake me; He'll be true.
I have passed; There to be-hold Him on His throne,

REFRAIN

Liv - ing for Je - sus, He is near.
Do - ing His will till life is done!
Trust-ing in Him, He'll guide me through.
Hear from His lips, "My child, well done!"

Help me to serve Thee more and more. Help me to praise Thee o'er and o'er; Live in Thy pres - ence day by day, Nev-er to turn from Thee a - way.

336 To the Work

Fanny J. Crosby, 1820-1915

William H. Doane, 1832-1915

1. To the work! to the work! We are ser-vants of God. Let us fol-low the path that our Mas-ter has trod. With the balm of His coun-sel our strength to re-new, Let us do with our might what our hands find to do.

2. To the work! to the work! Let the hun-gry be fed; To the foun-tain of life let the wea-ry be led. In the Cross and its ban-ner our glo-ry shall be, While we her-ald the tid-ings, "Sal-va-tion is free!"

3. To the work! to the work! There is la-bor for all; For the king-dom of dark-ness and er-ror shall fall; And the name of Je-ho-vah ex-alt-ed shall be, In the loud-swell-ing cho-rus, "Sal-va-tion is free!"

4. To the work! to the work! in the strength of the Lord; And a robe and a crown shall our la-bor re-ward, When the home of the faith-ful our dwell-ing shall be, And we shout with the ran-somed, "Sal-va-tion is free!"

REFRAIN

Toil-ing on, toil-ing on, Toil-ing on, toil-ing on;
(Toil-ing on, toil-ing on, Toil-ing on, toil-ing on;)
Let us hope, let us watch, And la-bor till the Mas-ter comes.
(and trust, and pray.)

337

Bring Them In

Alexcenah Thomas, 19th Century

William A. Ogden, 1841-1897

1. Hark, 'tis the Shepherd's voice I hear, Out in the des-ert dark and drear,
2. Who'll go and help this Shepherd kind, Help Him the wand'ring ones to find?
3. Out in the des-ert hear their cry, Out on the mountains wild and high.

Call - ing the sheep who've gone a-stray, Far from the Shepherd's fold a - way.
Who'll bring the lost ones to the fold, Where they'll be sheltered from the cold?
Hark! 'tis the Mas-ter speaks to thee, "Go, find My sheep wher-e'er they be."

REFRAIN

Bring them in, Bring them in, Bring them in from the fields of sin.
Bring them in, Bring them in, Bring the wand'ring ones to Je - sus.

338 Lord, Speak to Me, That I May Speak

CANONBURY

Frances R. Havergal, 1836-1879

Robert Schumann, 1810-1856

1. Lord, speak to me, that I may speak In liv - ing ech-oes of Thy tone;
2. Oh! teach me, Lord, that I may teach The precious things Thou dost impart;
3. Oh! give Thine own sweet rest to me, That I may speak with soothing pow'r
4. Oh! fill me with Thy full - ness, Lord, Un-til my ver - y heart o'er-flow
5. Oh! use me, Lord, use e - ven me, Just as Thou wilt, and when, and where;

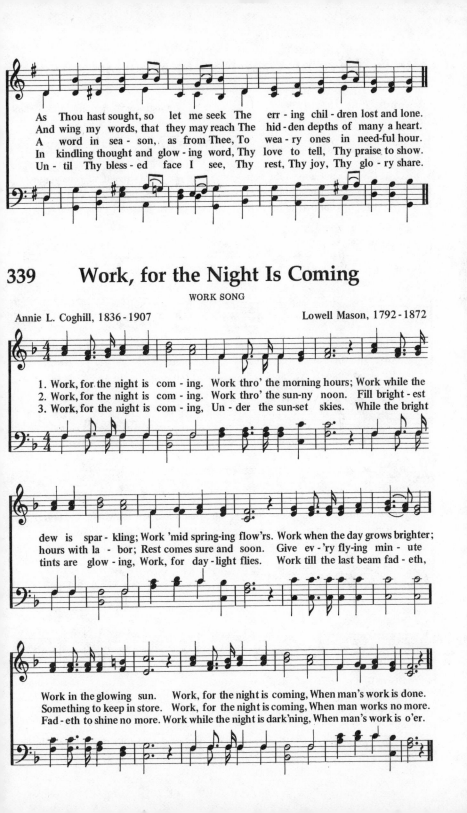

As Thou hast sought, so let me seek The err - ing chil - dren lost and lone.
And wing my words, that they may reach The hid - den depths of many a heart.
A word in sea - son, as from Thee, To wea - ry ones in need-ful hour.
In kindling thought and glow - ing word, Thy love to tell, Thy praise to show.
Un - til Thy bless - ed face I see, Thy rest, Thy joy, Thy glo - ry share.

339 Work, for the Night Is Coming

WORK SONG

Annie L. Coghill, 1836 - 1907

Lowell Mason, 1792 - 1872

1. Work, for the night is com - ing. Work thro' the morning hours; Work while the
2. Work, for the night is com - ing. Work thro' the sun-ny noon. Fill bright - est
3. Work, for the night is com - ing, Un - der the sun-set skies. While the bright

dew is spar - kling; Work 'mid spring-ing flow'rs. Work when the day grows brighter;
hours with la - bor; Rest comes sure and soon. Give ev - 'ry fly-ing min - ute
tints are glow - ing, Work, for day - light flies. Work till the last beam fad - eth,

Work in the glowing sun. Work, for the night is coming, When man's work is done.
Something to keep in store. Work, for the night is coming, When man works no more.
Fad - eth to shine no more. Work while the night is dark'ning, When man's work is o'er.

340 Give of Your Best to the Master

BARNARD

Howard B. Grose, 1851-1939

Charlotte A. Barnard, 1830-1869

1. Give of your best to the Mas - ter; Give of the strength of your youth;
2. Give of your best to the Mas - ter; Give Him first place in your heart;
3. Give of your best to the Mas - ter; Naught else is wor - thy His love.

Refrain: *Give of your best to the Mas - ter; Give of the strength of your youth;*

Fine

Throw your soul's fresh, glowing ar - dor In - to the bat - tle for truth.
Give Him first place in your ser - vice; Con-se-crate ev - 'ry part.
He gave him-self for your ran - som, Gave up His glo - ry a - bove;

Clad in sal - va - tion's full ar - mor, Join in the bat - tle for truth.

Je - sus has set the ex - am - ple; Daunt-less was He, young and brave.
Give, and to you shall be giv - en. God His be - lov - ed Son gave.
Laid down His life with-out mur - mur, You from sin's ru - in to save.

rall.   *D.C.*

Give Him your loy - al de - vo - tion;
Grate-ful-ly seek - ing to serve Him, Give Him the best that you have.
Give Him your heart's ad-o - ra - tion;

341   I Do Not Ask to Choose My Path

Henry J. Zelley, 1859-1942   Henry L. Gilmour, 1837-1920

1. I do not ask to choose my path. Lord, lead me in Thy way;
2. A - round me, Lord, are sin - ful men, Who scorn and dis - o - bey;
3. To those who once Thy love have known, But now are far a - stray,
4. Some saints of Thine are in dis - tress, And for de-liv - 'rance pray.
5. What-ev - er er - rand Thou hast, Lord, Send me, and I'll o - bey.

In - spire each tho't and prompt each word, And make me a blessing to - day.
Use me to win them from their sins, And make me a blessing to - day.
Help me to win them back to Thee, And make me a blessing to - day.
Oh, let me go and help them, Lord, And make me a blessing to - day.
Use me in an - y way Thou wilt, And make me a blessing to - day.

REFRAIN

Bless me, Lord, and make me a bless-ing; I'll glad-ly Thy message con-vey.

Use me to help some poor, need- y soul, And make me a bless-ing to - day.

342
Make Me a Blessing

SCHULER

Ira B. Wilson, 1880 - 1950

George S. Schuler, 1882 -

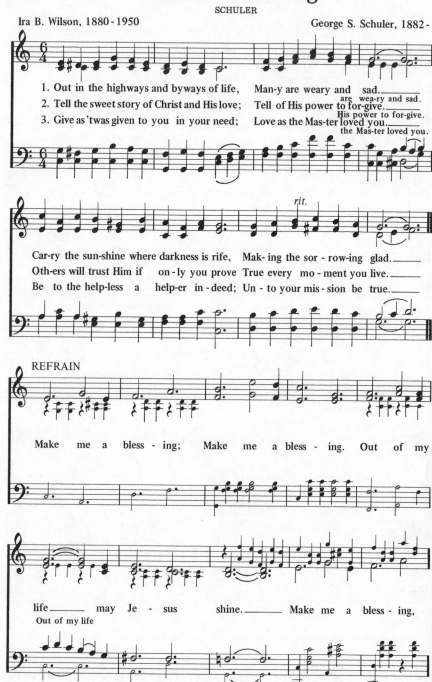

1. Out in the highways and byways of life, Man-y are weary and sad.
2. Tell the sweet story of Christ and His love; Tell of His power to for-give.
3. Give as 'twas given to you in your need; Love as the Mas-ter loved you.

Car-ry the sun-shine where darkness is rife, Mak- ing the sor - row-ing glad.
Oth-ers will trust Him if on - ly you prove True every mo - ment you live.
Be to the help-less a help-er in-deed; Un - to your mis - sion be true.

rit.

REFRAIN

Make me a bless - ing; Make me a bless - ing. Out of my

life_____ may Je - sus shine._____ Make me a bless - ing,
Out of my life

O Sav-iour, I pray._____ Make me a bless-ing to some-one to-day.

Tenors

I pray Thee, my Sav-iour.

343

Ready

TILLMAN

Unknown

Charlie D. Tillman, 1861 - 1943

1. Read-y to suf-fer grief or pain, Read-y to stand the test,
2. Read-y to go, read-y to bear, Read-y to watch and pray,
3. Read-y to speak, read-y to think, Read-y with heart and brain,
4. Read-y to speak, read-y to warn, Read-y o'er souls to yearn;

Read-y to stay at home and send Oth-ers if He sees best.
Read-y to stand a - side and give Till He shall clear the way.
Read-y to stand where He sees fit, Read-y to bear the strain.
Read-y in life, read-y in death, Read-y for His re - turn.

REFRAIN

Read-y to go, read-y to stay; Read-y my place to fill;

Read-y for ser-vice, low-ly or great; Read-y to do His will.

344　In the Service of the King

Alfred H. Ackley, 1887-1960

Bentley D. Ackley, 1872-1958

1. I am hap-py in the ser-vice of the King. I am hap-py,
2. I am hap-py in the ser-vice of the King. I am hap-py,
3. I am hap-py in the ser-vice of the King. I am hap-py,
4. I am hap-py in the ser-vice of the King. I am hap-py,

oh, so hap-py! I have peace and joy that noth-ing else can bring,
oh, so hap-py! Thro' the sun-shine and the shad-ow I can sing,
oh, so hap-py! To His guid-ing hand for-ev-er I will cling,
oh, so hap-py! All that I pos-sess to Him I glad-ly bring,

REFRAIN

In the ser - vice of the King. In the ser - vice

of the King Ev - 'ry tal - ent I will bring. I have

peace and joy and bless - ing In the ser-vice of the King.

345 We'll Work till Jesus Comes

LAND OF REST

Elizabeth Mills, 1805 - 1829

William Miller, 19th Century

1. O   land of rest, for thee I sigh! When will the mo-ment come
2. To   Je - sus Christ I   fled for rest; He bade me cease to   roam,
3. I   sought at once my   Sav-iour's side; No more my steps shall roam.

When   I shall lay my   ar - mor by, And dwell   in peace at   home?
And   lean for suc - cor   on His breast Till He   con-duct me   home.
With   Him I'll brave death's chill-ing tide, And reach   my heav'n-ly   home.

REFRAIN

We'll   work   till   Je - sus comes. We'll work   till   Je - sus comes.
We'll work   We'll work

We'll   work   till   Je - sus comes, And   we'll be gath - ered home!
We'll work

346 I Love to Tell the Story

HANKEY

Katherine Hankey, 1834-1911

William G. Fischer, 1835-1912

1. I love to tell the sto-ry Of un-seen things a-bove, Of Je-sus
2. I love to tell the sto-ry;More won-der-ful it seems Than all the
3. I love to tell the sto-ry;'Tis pleas-ant to re-peat What seems each
4. I love to tell the sto-ry, For those who know it best Seem hunger-

and His glo-ry, Of Je-sus and His love. I love to tell the sto-ry
gold-en fan-cies Of all our gol-den dreams. I love to tell the sto-ry;
time I tell it More won-der-ful-ly sweet. I love to tell the sto-ry,
ing and thirsting To hear it like the rest. And when in scenes of glo-ry

Be-cause I know 'tis true. It sat-is-fies my long-ings As nothing else can do.
It did so much for me, And that is just the rea-son I tell it now to thee.
For some have never heard The mes-sage of salvation From God's own holy Word.
I sing the new, new song, 'Twill be the old, old sto-ry That I have loved so long.

REFRAIN

I love to tell the sto-ry! 'Twill be my theme in glo-ry

To tell the old, old sto-ry Of Je-sus and His love.

347 We've a Story to Tell to the Nations

MESSAGE

H. Ernest Nichol, 1862-1928   H. Ernest Nichol, 1862-1928

1. We've a sto - ry to tell to the na - tions That shall turn their hearts
2. We've a song to be sung to the na - tions That shall lift their hearts
3. We've a mes - sage to give to the na - tions That the Lord who reign -
4. We've a Sav - iour to show to the na - tions Who the path of sor -

to the right, A sto - ry of truth and mer - cy, A
to the Lord, A song that shall con - quer e - vil And
eth a - bove Hath sent us His Son to save us, And
row hath trod, That all of the world's great peo - ples Might

sto - ry of peace and light, A sto - ry of peace and light.
shat - ter the spear and sword, And shat - ter the spear and sword.
show us that God is love, And show us that God is love.
come to the truth of God, Might come to the truth of God.

REFRAIN

For the dark-ness shall turn to dawn-ing And the dawn-ing to noon-day bright,

rall.

And Christ's great king-dom shall come to earth, The King-dom of love and light.

348 The Call for Reapers

HARVESTTIME

John O. Thompson, 1782-1818

J. B. O. Clemm, 19th Century

1. Far and near the fields are teem - ing With the waves of
2. Send them forth with morn's first beam - ing; Send them in the
3. O thou whom thy Lord is send - ing, Gath - er now the

ri - pened grain; Far and near their gold is gleam - ing
noon - tide's glare; When the sun's last rays are gleam - ing,
sheaves of gold. Heav'n - ward then at eve - ning wend - ing,

REFRAIN

O'er the sun - ny slope and plain.
Bid them gath - er ev - 'ry - where. Lord of har - vest,
Thou shalt come with joy un - told.

send forth reap - ers! Hear us, Lord; to Thee we cry. Send them

now the sheaves to gath - er, Ere the har - vest - time pass by.

349   # Rescue the Perishing

Fanny J. Crosby, 1820-1915   William H. Doane, 1832-1915

1. Res - cue the per-ish - ing; Care for the dy - ing; Snatch them in pit - y from
2. Tho' they are slighting Him, Still He is wait-ing, Wait - ing the pen - i- tent
3. Down in the hu-man heart, Crushed by the tempter, Feelings lie bur-ied that
4. Res - cue the per-ish - ing; Du - ty de-mands it. Strength for thy la - bor the

sin and the grave. Weep o'er the err -ing one; Lift up the fall - en;
child to re - ceive. Plead with them ear-nest-ly, Plead with them gent-ly;
grace can re - store. Touched by a lov - ing heart, Wak-ened by kind-ness,
Lord will pro-vide. Back to the nar-row way Pa - tient-ly win them;

REFRAIN

Tell them of Je - sus, the Might - y to Save.
He will for - give if they on - ly be-lieve.
Chords that are bro - ken will vi - brate once more.   Res- cue the per-ish-ing;
Tell the poor wand'rer a Sav - iour has died.

Care for the dy - ing. Je - sus is mer - ci - ful; Je - sus will save.

350 Tell the Blessed Story

Haldor Lillenas, 1885-1959   Haldor Lillenas, 1885-1959

1. Church of God, a - wak - en; heed the Lord's com - mand.
2. Has He not com - mis-sioned you the news to bear?
3. Stand no lon - ger i - dle while the mo - ments fly.
4. Pub - lish un - to all the world re - deem - ing grace.

Tell the bless-ed story of the Cross.

Fields are white for har-vest -ing on ev - 'ry hand.
"Go ye in - to all the world," and ev - 'ry-where
Mul - ti - tudes in hea-then dark-ness live and die.
Un - til in the home of rest you find your place,

REFRAIN

Tell the bless-ed sto - ry of the Cross. Tell the bless-ed sto - ry of the cross of Je - sus. Tell the bless-ed sto-ry of the hal-lowed Cross. Un-til ev-'ry na-tion learns of full sal - va - tion, Tell the bless-ed sto - ry of the Cross.

351 Send the Light

McCABE

Charles H. Gabriel, 1856 - 1932   Charles H. Gabriel, 1856 - 1932

1. There's a call comes ring-ing o'er the rest - less wave, "Send the light!
2. We have heard the Mac - e - do - nian call to - day,
3. Let us pray that grace may ev-'ry - where a - bound,
4. Let us not grow wea - ry in the work of love.   "Send the light!

Send the light!"   There are souls to res - cue, there are souls to save.
And a gold - en of - f'ring at the Cross we lay.
And a Christ-like spir - it ev - 'ry-where be found.
Send the light!" Let us gath - er jew - els for a crown a - bove.

Send the light! _____ Send the light!
Send the light!   Send the light!

REFRAIN

Send the light, _____ the bless-ed gos - pel light. Let it
Send the light, _____ and let its ra - diant beams Light the
Send the light, the   bless - ed gos - pel light.

shine _____ from shore to shore!
world _____ for - ev - er -
Let it shine   from shore to shore!   more.   for-ev - er-more.

352 If Jesus Goes with Me

C. Austin Miles, 1868-1946   C. Austin Miles, 1868-1946

1. It may be in the val-ley, where countless dan-gers hide; It may be in the
2. It may be I must car-ry the bless-ed word of life A-cross the burning
3. But if it be my por-tion to bear my cross at home, While oth-ers bear their
4. It is not mine to ques-tion the judg-ments of my Lord; It is but mine to

sun-shine that I, in peace, a-bide. But this one thing I know— if
des-erts to those in sin-ful strife; And tho' it be my lot to
bur-dens be-yond the bil-lows' foam, I'll prove my faith in Him, con-
fol-low the lead-ings of His Word. But if to go or stay, or

it be dark or fair, If Je-sus is with me, I'll go an-y-where!
bear my col-ors there, If Je-sus goes with me, I'll go an-y-where!
fess His judg-ments fair; And if He stays with me, I'll stay an-y-where!
wheth-er here or there, I'll be, with my Sav-iour, Con-tent an-y-where!

REFRAIN

If Je-sus goes with me, I'll go____ An-y-where! 'Tis heav-en to me, Wher-
                          I'll go

e'er I may be, If He is there! I count it a priv-i-lege here____ His
                                                              His cross, His

cross to bear.___ If Je - sus goes with me, I'll go___ An - y - where!
cross, His cross to bear.

353 The Morning Light Is Breaking
WEBB

Samuel F. Smith, 1808 - 1895   George J. Webb, 1803 - 1887

1. The morn - ing light is break - ing; The dark - ness dis - ap - pears.
2. See hea - then na - tions bend - ing Be - fore the God of love,
3. Blest riv - er of sal - va - tion, Pur - sue thine on - ward way;

The sons of earth are wak - ing To pen - i - ten - tial tears.
And thou - sand hearts as - cend - ing In grat - i - tude a - bove;
Flow thou to ev - 'ry na - tion, Nor in thy rich - ness stay.

Each breeze that sweeps the o - cean Brings tid - ings from a - far Of
While sin - ners, now con - fess - ing, The gos - pel call o - bey, And
Stay not till all the low - ly, Tri - um - phant, reach their home. Stay

na - tions in com - mo - tion, Pre - pared for Zi - on's war.
seek the Sav - iour's bless - ing, A na - tion in a day.
not till all the ho - ly Pro - claim, "The Lord is come!"

354 I'll Go Where You Want Me to Go

MANCHESTER

Mary Brown, 19th Century

Carrie E. Rounsefell, 1861 - 1930

1. It may not be on the mountain's height, Or o - ver the stor - my sea,
2. Per-haps to - day there are lov - ing words Which Je-sus would have me speak;
3. There's surely somewhere a low - ly place In earth's harvest fields so wide

It may not be at the bat - tle's front My Lord will have need of me;
There may be now, in the paths of sin, Some wand'rer whom I should seek.
Where I may la - bor thro' life's short day For Je - sus, the Cru - ci - fied.

But if by a still, small voice He calls To paths that I do not know,
O Sav-iour, if Thou wilt be my Guide, Tho' dark and rug-ged the way,
So, trust-ing my all to Thy ten - der care, and know-ing Thou lov - est me,

I'll an-swer, dear Lord, with my hand in Thine, "I'll go where You want me to go."
My voice shall ech - o the mes-sage sweet. I'll say what You want me to say.
I'll do Thy will with a heart sin-cere. I'll be what You want me to be.

REFRAIN

I'll go where You want me to go, dear Lord, Over mountain, or plain, or sea.

I'll   say what You want me to say,   dear Lord. I'll be what You want me to be.

355   Let the Lower Lights Be Burning

LOWER LIGHTS

Philip P. Bliss, 1838 - 1876

Philip P. Bliss, 1838 - 1876

1. Bright-ly beams our Fa-ther's mer-cy   From His light - house ev -er - more;
2. Dark the   night of sin has   set-tled, Loud the an - gry bil - lows roar;
3. Trim your fee - ble lamp, my broth-er! Some poor sail - or, tem-pest-tossed,

But   to   us He gives the keep-ing   Of the lights a - long the shore.
Ea - ger   eyes are watch-ing, long-ing For the lights a - long the shore.
Try - ing now to make the har - bor, In the dark - ness may be lost.

REFRAIN

Let   the low - er lights be burn-ing! Send a gleam   a - cross the wave!

Some poor   faint - ing, strug-gling sea-man You may res - cue, you may save.

356 O Zion, Haste

TIDINGS

Mary Ann Thomson, 1834-1923

James Walch, 1837-1901

1. O Zi - on, haste, thy mis - sion high ful - fill - ing,
2. Be - hold how man - y thou - sand still are ly - ing,
3. Pro - claim to ev - 'ry peo - ple, tongue, and na - tion
4. Give of thy sons to bear the mes - sage glo - rious;

To tell to all the world that God is Light; That He who
Bound in the dark - some pris - on house of sin, With none to
That God, in whom they live and move, is love. Tell how He
Give of thy wealth to speed them on their way; Pour out thy

made all na - tions is not will - ing One soul should per - ish,
tell them of the Sav - iour's dy - ing, Or of the life He
stooped to save His lost cre - a - tion, And died on earth that
soul for them in pray'r vic - to - rious; And all Thou spend - est

REFRAIN

lost in shades of night.
died for them to win. Pub - lish glad tid - ings, Tid - ings of
man might live a - bove.
Je - sus will re - pay.

peace; Tid - ings of Je - sus, Re - demp - tion, and re - lease.

357 Redeemed

Fanny J. Crosby, 1820-1915

William J. Kirkpatrick, 1838-1921

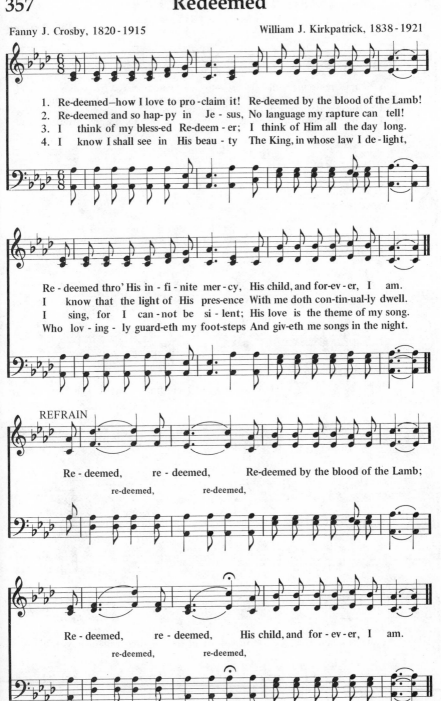

1. Re-deemed—how I love to pro-claim it! Re-deemed by the blood of the Lamb!
2. Re-deemed and so hap-py in Je-sus, No language my rapture can tell!
3. I think of my bless-ed Re-deem-er; I think of Him all the day long.
4. I know I shall see in His beau-ty The King, in whose law I de-light,

Re-deemed thro' His in-fi-nite mer-cy, His child, and for-ev-er, I am.
I know that the light of His pres-ence With me doth con-tin-ual-ly dwell.
I sing, for I can-not be si-lent; His love is the theme of my song.
Who lov-ing-ly guard-eth my foot-steps And giv-eth me songs in the night.

REFRAIN

Re-deemed, re-deemed, Re-deemed by the blood of the Lamb;
re-deemed, re-deemed,

Re-deemed, re-deemed, His child, and for-ev-er, I am.
re-deemed, re-deemed,

358 Hallelujah, I Am Free!

A. A. Jameson, 20th Century   A. A. Jameson, 20th Century

1. I am re-deemed, all glo-ry to the Lamb! Saved from all sin and pu-ri-fied I am; Bought by the Blood that flowed from Cal-va-ry, For the Lord has made me free.
2. I am re-deemed; my ran-som has been paid. All of my guilt on Je-sus has been laid; From all my sins I now have lib-er-ty. Hal-le-lu-jah, I am free!
3. I am re-deemed; my bond-age now is past. I was a slave, but I am free at last. Once I was blind, but now the light I see. Hal-le-lu-jah, I am free!
4. "I am re-deemed," my song shall ev-er be, Both while on earth and for e-ter-ni-ty. Praise be to God for all He is to me! Hal-le-lu-jah, I am free!

REFRAIN

Hal-le-lu-jah! I am free! Oh, what glo-rious lib-er-ty, Since the bless-ed Lord has cleansed and made me whole!___ made me whole! I am re-deemed, all glo-ry to His name! He a-bides with-in my soul.

359

I Love Him Better Every Day

Thoro Harris, 1874 - 1955

Thoro Harris, 1874 - 1955
Refrain by Adjt. Sidney Cox, 20th Century

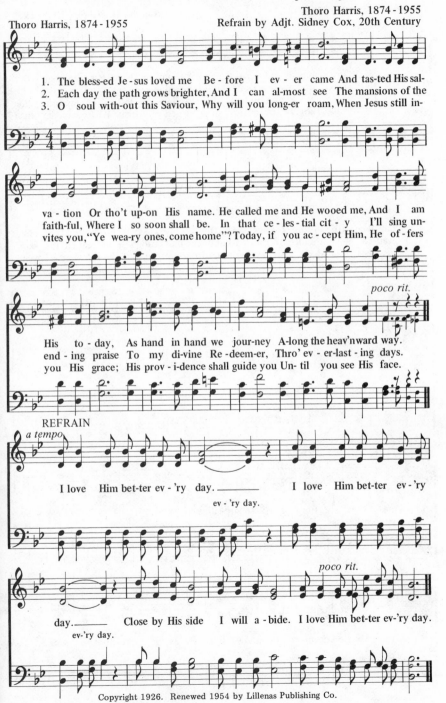

1. The bless-ed Je-sus loved me Be-fore I ev-er came And tas-ted His sal-
2. Each day the path grows brighter, And I can al-most see The mansions of the
3. O soul with-out this Saviour, Why will you long-er roam, When Jesus still in-

va-tion Or tho't up-on His name. He called me and He wooed me, And I am
faith-ful, Where I so soon shall be. In that ce-les-tial cit-y I'll sing un-
vites you, "Ye wea-ry ones, come home"? Today, if you ac-cept Him, He of-fers

poco rit.

His to-day, As hand in hand we jour-ney A-long the heav'n-ward way.
end-ing praise To my di-vine Re-deem-er, Thro' ev-er-last-ing days.
you His grace; His prov-i-dence shall guide you Un-til you see His face.

REFRAIN
a tempo

I love Him bet-ter ev-'ry day. ____ I love Him bet-ter ev-'ry
ev-'ry day.

poco rit.

day. ____ Close by His side I will a-bide. I love Him bet-ter ev-'ry day.
ev-'ry day.

360 He Is So Precious to Me

PRECIOUS TO ME

Charles H. Gabriel, 1856 - 1932

Charles H. Gabriel, 1856 - 1932

1. So pre - cious is Je - sus, my Sav - iour, my King, His praise all the
2. He stood at my heart's door 'mid sun-shine and rain, And pa - tient - ly
3. I stand on the moun-tain of bless - ing at last, No cloud in the
4. I praise Him be - cause He ap - point - ed a place Where someday, thro'

day long with rap-ture I sing. To Him in my weakness for strength I can cling,
wait-ed an en-trance to gain. What shame that so long He en-treat-ed in vain.
heav-ens a shad-ow to cast. His smile is up - on me, the val - ley is past,
faith in His won-der- ful grace, I know I shall see Him—shall look on His face,

REFRAIN
faster

For He is so pre-cious to me. For He is so pre-cious to
so

me, For He is so pre-cious to me; 'Tis heav-en be-
precious to me, so precious to me;

rit.

low My Re-deem-er to know, For He is so pre-cious to me.

361 Since I Have Been Redeemed

OTHELLO

Edwin O. Excell, 1851 - 1921

Edwin O. Excell, 1851 - 1921

1. I have a song I love to sing, Since I have been re-deemed,
2. I have a Christ that sat - is - fies, Since I have been re-deemed.
3. I have a wit - ness bright and clear, Since I have been re-deemed,
4. I have a home pre - pared for me, Since I have been re-deemed,

Of my Re-deem - er, Sav - iour, King,
To do His will my high - est prize, Since I have been re - deemed.
Dis - pel - ling ev - 'ry doubt and fear,
Where I shall dwell e - ter - nal - ly,

REFRAIN

Since I _____ have been re-deemed, _____ Since I have been re-
Since I have been re-deemed, Since I have been re-deemed,

deemed, I will glo - ry in His name. Since I _____ have been re-
Since I have been re - deemed, Since

deemed, _____ I will glo - ry in my Sav - iour's name.
I have been re - deemed,

362   My Soul Is Filled with Glory

J. M. Harris, 20th Century   J. M. Harris, 20th Century

1. Je - sus found me when a - far I wandered; Bro't me par - don from the
throne a - bove; Gave me peace that pass - eth un - der-stand-ing, Joy un -
speak - a - ble and full of love.

2. Thro' His Word He taught me full sal - va-tion, How His blood could cleanse and
sanc - ti - fy; Then by faith I plunged in - to the foun - tain. Now I'm
look - ing for that home on high.

3. Tri - als man - y will be - set my path-way, And temp - ta - tions I shall
sure - ly meet; But my Sav-iour prom - ised grace to help me Till I
lay my tro - phies at His feet.

REFRAIN

Praise the Lord! my soul is filled with glo-ry! Praise the Lord! I love to tell the sto-ry Of His grace that jus - ti - fies me free - ly, sanc - ti - fies me whol - ly, And I'm shout-ing, "Glo-ry!" till I get home.
keeps and gives me vic - t'ry,

363 It Is Truly Wonderful

Barney E. Warren, 1867-1951   Barney E. Warren, 1867-1951

1. He par - doned my trans - gres-sions; He sanc - ti - fied my soul;
2. He keeps me ev -'ry mo-ment By trust - ing in His grace.
3. He brings me thro' af - flic-tion; He leaves me not a - lone;
4. He pros - pers and pro - tects me; His bless - ings ev - er flow;
5. There's not a sin - gle bless-ing Which we re - ceive on earth

He hon - ors my con - fes - sions Since by His blood I'm whole.
'Tis thro' His blest a - tone-ment That I may see His face.
He's with me in temp - ta - tion; He keeps me for His own.
He fills me with His glo - ry; He makes me white as snow.
That does not come from heav - en, The source of our new birth.

REFRAIN

It is tru - ly won-der-ful What the Lord has done! It is
tru - ly won - der - ful! It is tru - ly won - der - ful! It is
tru - ly won-der-ful What the Lord has done! Glo - ry to His name!

364   I Belong to the King

Ida L. Reed, 1865 - 1951

Maurice A. Clifton, 19th Century

1. I be - long to the King, I'm a child of His love. I shall dwell in His
2. I be - long to the King, and He loves me I know, For His mer - cy and
3. I be - long to the King, and His prom-ise is sure, That we all shall be

pal - ace so fair; For He tells of its bliss in yon heav-en a - bove, And His
kind - ness so free Are un - ceas-ing - ly mine where-so-ev - er I go, And my
gath - ered at last In His king-dom a - bove, by life's wa-ters so pure, When this

chil - dren in splen - dor shall share.
Ref - uge un - fail - ing is He.
life with its tri - als is past.

REFRAIN

I be - long to the King, I'm a

child of His love, And He nev - er for - sak - eth His own. He will call me some-

day to His pal - ace a - bove. I shall dwell by His glo - ri - fied throne.

365　Jesus Has Lifted Me

Avis B. Christiansen, 1895—　　　　　　　　　Haldor Lillenas, 1885 - 1959

1. Out of the depths to the glo - ry a - bove, I have been
2. Out of the world in - to heav - en - ly rest, In - to the
3. Out of my - self in - to Him I a - dore, There to a -

lift - ed in won - der - ful love. From ev - 'ry fet - ter my
land of the ran - somed and blest, There in the glo - ry with
bide in His love ev - er - more, Thro' end - less a - ges His

spir - it is free— For Je - sus has lift - ed me!
Him I shall be— For Je - sus has lift - ed me!
glo - ry to see— My Je - sus has lift - ed me!
　　　　　　　　　　　　　　　　　　　　lift - ed me!

REFRAIN

Je - sus has lift - ed me! Je - sus has lift - ed me!
　　　　lift - ed me!　　　　　　　　　　lift - ed me!

Out of the night in - to glo - ri - ous light, Yes, Je - sus has lift - ed me!
　　　　　　　　　　　　　　　　　　　　　　　　　lift - ed me!

366 This Is like Heaven to Me

J. E. French, 20th Century   J. E. French, 20th Century

1. We find man-y peo-ple who can't un-der-stand Why we are so
2. So when we are hap-py we sing and we shout. Some don't un-der-
3. We've heard the sweet mu-sic, the heav-en-ly chord, From glo-ry-land
4. We're look-ing for Je-sus with glo-ry to come; 'Tis Je-sus who

hap-py and free. We've crossed o-ver Jor-dan to Ca-naan's fair land,
stand us, I see. We're filled with the Spir-it, there is-n't a doubt,
o-ver the sea: A soul-thrill-ing mes-sage from Je-sus, our Lord,
died on the tree. A cloud of bright an-gels to car-ry me home—

REFRAIN

1-3. And this is like heav-en to me. Oh, this is like heav-en to
4. Oh, that will be heav-en to me! Oh, that will be heav-en to

me. Yes, this is like heav-en to me. I've crossed o-ver
me. Yes, that will be heav-en to me. A cloud of bright
to me.   to me.

Jor-dan to Ca-naan's fair land, And this is like heav-en to me.
an-gels to car-ry me home, Yes, that will be heav-en to me.
                                                              to me.

367 Jesus Is All the World to Me

ELIZABETH

Will L. Thompson, 1847-1909

Will L. Thompson, 1847-1909

1. Je - sus is all the world to me: My Life, my Joy, my All.
2. Je - sus is all the world to me, My Friend in tri - als sore.
3. Je - sus is all the world to me, And true to Him I'll be.
4. Je - sus is all the world to me; I want no bet - ter friend.

He is my Strength from day to day; With - out Him I would fall.
I go to Him for bless - ings, and He gives them o'er and o'er.
Oh, how could I this Friend de-ny When He's so true to me?
I trust Him now; I'll trust Him when Life's fleet-ing days shall end.

When I am sad, to Him I go; No oth - er one can cheer me
He sends the sun-shine and the rain; He sends the har - vest's gold-en
Fol - low-ing Him I know I'm right. He watch-es o'er me day and
Beau- ti - ful life with such a Friend; Beau - ti - ful life that has no

so. When I am sad, He makes me glad. He's my Friend.
grain: Sun-shine and rain, har-vest of grain— He's my Friend.
night. Fol- low - ing Him by day and night, He's my Friend.
end! E - ter - nal life, e - ter - nal joy, He's my Friend!

368

I've Found a Friend

James G. Small, 1817-1888

George C. Stebbins, 1846-1945

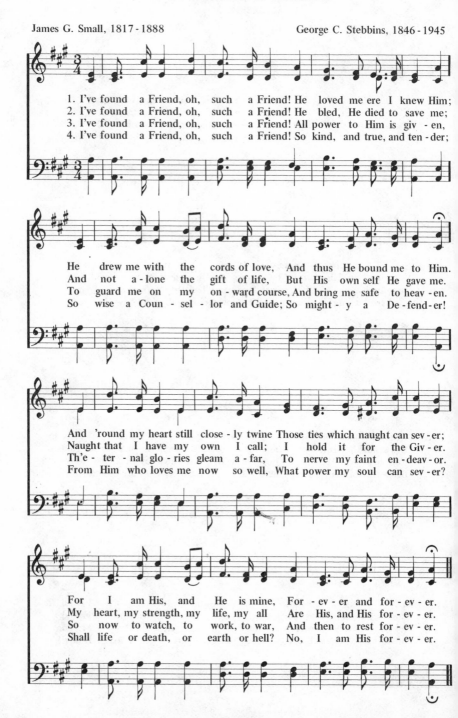

1. I've found a Friend, oh, such a Friend! He loved me ere I knew Him;
2. I've found a Friend, oh, such a Friend! He bled, He died to save me;
3. I've found a Friend, oh, such a Friend! All power to Him is giv - en,
4. I've found a Friend, oh, such a Friend! So kind, and true, and ten - der;

He drew me with the cords of love, And thus He bound me to Him.
And not a - lone the gift of life, But His own self He gave me.
To guard me on my on - ward course, And bring me safe to heav - en.
So wise a Coun - sel - lor and Guide; So might - y a De - fend - er!

And 'round my heart still close - ly twine Those ties which naught can sev - er;
Naught that I have my own I call; I hold it for the Giv - er.
Th'e - ter - nal glo - ries gleam a - far, To nerve my faint en - deav - or.
From Him who loves me now so well, What power my soul can sev - er?

For I am His, and He is mine, For - ev - er and for - ev - er.
My heart, my strength, my life, my all Are His, and His for - ev - er.
So now to watch, to work, to war, And then to rest for - ev - er.
Shall life or death, or earth or hell? No, I am His for - ev - er.

369 Then I Met Jesus

Byron M. Carmony, 1916-
Byron M. Carmony, 1916-

Slow with expression

1. I wan-dered o'er life's stor-my road, No hope in sight for me.
2. I tried the things that seemed a joy; They did not sat - is - fy.
3. I need - ed one to share my cares, To lead when dark the way;

My eyes were blind-ed by my tears; I could no shel-ter see.
So bur - dened was my heart with sin, "O save me!" was my cry.
I prayed for one to take my hand And guide me ev - 'ry day.

REFRAIN

Then I met Je - sus, won - der-ful Friend! He loved and

saved me, love with-out end._____ Now I am walk-ing

close by His side. Storms may sur-round me; in Him I hide.

370 Springs of Living Water

John W. Peterson, 1921 -   John W. Peterson, 1921 -

1. I thirst - ed in the bar - ren land of sin and shame, And
2. How sweet the liv - ing wa - ter from the hills of God! It
3. O sin - ner, won't you come to - day to Cal - va - ry? A

noth-ing sat - is - fy - ing there I found; But to the bless-ed cross of
makes me glad and hap - py all the way. Now glo - ry, grace, and bless-ing
foun-tain there is flow - ing deep and wide. The Sav -iour now invites you

Christ one day I came, Where springs of liv - ing wa - ter did a-bound.
mark the path I've trod. I'm shout - ing, "Hal - le - lu - jah!" ev - 'ry day.
to the wa - ter free, Where thirst - ing spir - its can be sat - is - fied.

REFRAIN

Drink-ing at the springs of liv - ing wa - ter,   Hap - py now am
                                                    Hap - py

I;   My soul they sat - is - fy.   Drink-ing at th
now am I; My soul they sat - is - fy. I'm

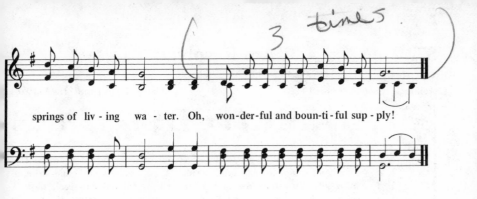

springs of liv - ing wa - ter. Oh, won-der-ful and boun-ti-ful sup - ply!

371   Still, Still with Thee

CONSOLATION

Harriet B. Stowe, 1812 - 1896   Felix Mendelssohn, 1809 - 1847

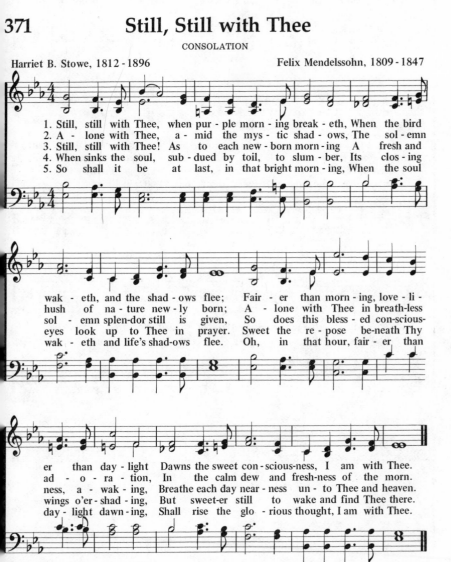

1. Still, still with Thee, when pur - ple morn - ing break - eth, When the bird
2. A - lone with Thee, a - mid the mys - tic shad - ows, The sol - emn
3. Still, still with Thee! As to each new - born morn - ing A fresh and
4. When sinks the soul, sub - dued by toil, to slum - ber, Its clos - ing
5. So shall it be at last, in that bright morn - ing, When the soul

wak - eth, and the shad - ows flee; Fair - er than morn - ing, love - li -
hush of na - ture new - ly born; A - lone with Thee in breath-less
sol - emn splen-dor still is given, So does this bless - ed con-scious-
eyes look up to Thee in prayer. Sweet the re - pose be-neath Thy
wak - eth and life's shad-ows flee. Oh, in that hour, fair - er than

er than day - light Dawns the sweet con - scious-ness, I am with Thee.
ad - o - ra - tion, In the calm dew and fresh-ness of the morn.
ness, a - wak - ing, Breathe each day near - ness un - to Thee and heaven.
wings o'er - shad - ing, But sweet-er still to wake and find Thee there.
day - light dawn-ing, Shall rise the glo - rious thought, I am with Thee.

372 I Am Resolved

RESOLUTION

Palmer Hartsough, 1844-1932

James H. Fillmore, 1849-1936

1. I am re-solved no lon - ger to lin - ger, Charmed by the world's de-light;
2. I am re-solved to go to the Sav - iour, Leav - ing my sin and strife.
3. I am re-solved to fol - low the Sav - iour, Faith - ful and true each day,
4. I am re-solved to en - ter the King-dom, Leav - ing the paths of sin.

Things that are high-er, things that are no - bler, These have al-lured my sight.
He is the true One; He is the just One; He hath the words of life.
Heed what He say - eth, do what He will - eth; He is the liv - ing Way.
Friends may oppose me, foes may be-set me; Still will I en - ter in.

REFRAIN

I will has-ten to Him, Has-ten so glad and free.

I will has - ten,

Hasten glad and free.

Je - sus, Great - est, High - est, I will come to Thee.

Je - sus, Je - sus,

373 Give Him the Glory

Elisha A. Hoffman, 1839 - 1929

Elisha A. Hoffman, 1839 - 1929

1. It was down at the feet of Je - sus— Oh, the hap - py,
2. It was down at the feet of Je - sus, Where I found such
3. It was down at the feet of Je - sus, Where I brought my

hap - py day!— That my soul found peace in be - liev - ing,
per - fect rest, Where the light first dawned on my spir - it,
guilt and sin, That He can - celed all my trans - gres - sions,

And my sins were washed a - way.
And my soul was tru - ly blest.
And sal - va - tion en - tered in.

REFRAIN

Let me tell the old, old sto - ry Of His grace so full and free; For I feel like giv - ing Him the glo - ry For His won - drous love to me.

374 Sweeter as the Years Go By

Lelia N. Morris, 1862-1929

Lelia N. Morris, 1862-1929

1. Of Je - sus' love that sought me When I was lost in sin; Of wondrou
2. He trod in old Ju - de - a Life's path-way long a - go; The peo-ple
3. 'Twas wondrous love which led Him For us to suf-fer loss—To bear with

grace that brought me Back to His fold a - gain; Of heights and depths of
thronged a-bout Him, His sav - ing grace to know. He healed the bro - ken-
out a mur - mur The an-guish of the Cross. With saints re-deemed in

mer - cy, Far deep - er than the sea, And high - er than the heav-ens
heart-ed, And caused the blind to see; And still His great heart yearnet
glo - ry, Let us our voic - es raise, Till heav'n and earth re - ech - o

REFRAIN

My theme shall ev - er be.
In love for e - ven me. Sweet-er as the years go by,_____
With our Re - deem-er's praise. Sweet - er as the years go by, 'Tis

Sweet - er as the years go by;_____ Rich - er, full-er, deep - er,
Sweet - er as the years go by;

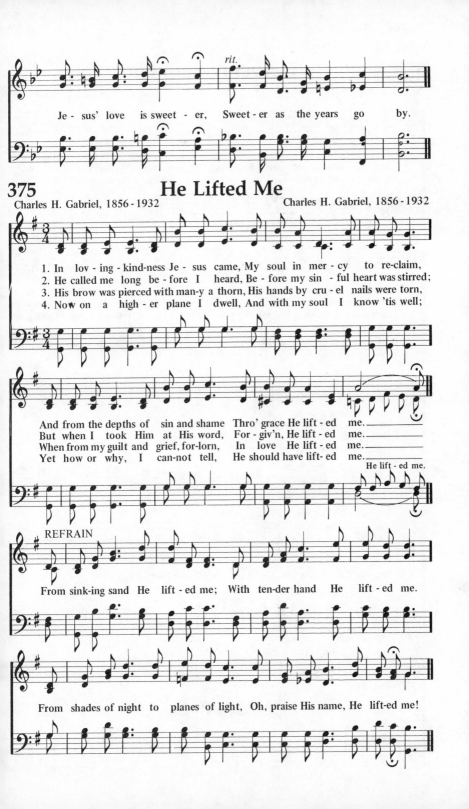

Je - sus' love is sweet - er, Sweet - er as the years go by.

375   **He Lifted Me**

Charles H. Gabriel, 1856 - 1932   Charles H. Gabriel, 1856 - 1932

1. In lov - ing - kind-ness Je - sus came, My soul in mer - cy to re-claim,
2. He called me long be - fore I heard, Be - fore my sin - ful heart was stirred;
3. His brow was pierced with man-y a thorn, His hands by cru - el nails were torn,
4. Now on a high - er plane I dwell, And with my soul I know 'tis well;

And from the depths of sin and shame Thro' grace He lift - ed me.
But when I took Him at His word, For - giv'n, He lift - ed me.
When from my guilt and grief, for-lorn, In love He lift - ed me.
Yet how or why, I can-not tell, He should have lift - ed me.

He lift - ed me.

REFRAIN

From sink-ing sand He lift - ed me; With ten-der hand He lift - ed me.

From shades of night to planes of light, Oh, praise His name, He lift-ed me!

376 Heavenly Sunlight

Henry J. Zelley, 1859-1942

George H. Cook, 20th Century

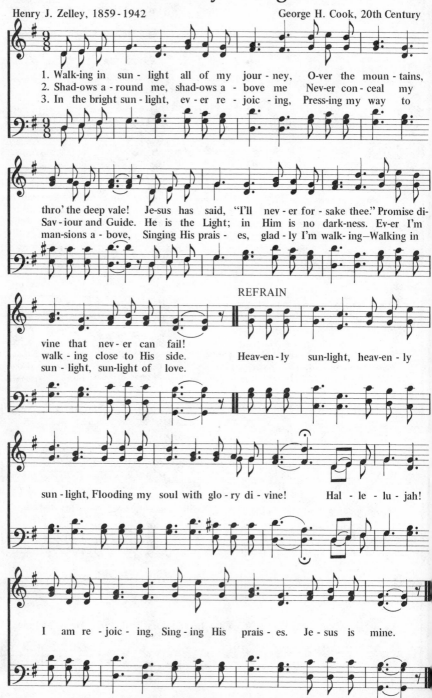

1. Walk-ing in sun - light all of my jour - ney, O-ver the moun - tains,
2. Shad-ows a - round me, shad-ows a - bove me Nev-er con - ceal my
3. In the bright sun - light, ev - er re - joic - ing, Press-ing my way to

thro' the deep vale! Je-sus has said, "I'll nev - er for - sake thee." Promise di-
Sav-iour and Guide. He is the Light; in Him is no dark-ness. Ev-er I'm
man-sions a - bove, Singing His prais - es, glad - ly I'm walk-ing—Walking in

vine that nev - er can fail!
walk - ing close to His side.
sun - light, sun-light of love.

REFRAIN

Heav-en - ly sun-light, heav-en - ly

sun - light, Flooding my soul with glo - ry di - vine! Hal - le - lu - jah!

I am re - joic - ing, Sing-ing His prais - es. Je - sus is mine.

377 A Child of the King

Harriet E. Buell, 1834-1910   *Arr. by John B. Sumner, 1838-1918*

1. My Fa-ther is rich in hous-es and lands; He hold-eth the
2. My Fa-ther's own Son, the Sav-iour of men, Once wandered o'er
3. I once was an out-cast stran-ger on earth, A sin-ner by
4. A tent or a cot-tage, why should I care? They're build-ing a

wealth of the world in His hands! Of ru-bies and dia-monds, of
earth as the poor-est of them; But now He is reign-ing for-
choice, an al-ien by birth! But I've been a-dopt-ed; my
pal-ace for me o-ver there! Tho' ex-iled from home, yet

sil-ver and gold, His cof-fers are full— He has rich-es un-told.
ev-er on high, And will give me a home in heav'n by and by.
name's written down. I'm heir to a man-sion, a robe, and a crown!
still I may sing: "All glo-ry to God, I'm a child of the King!"

REFRAIN

I'm a child of the King! A child of the King!

With Je-sus, my Sav-iour, I'm a child of the King!

378   He Took My Sins Away

Margaret J. Harris, 20th Century   Margaret J. Harris, 20th Century

1. I came to Je - sus, wea - ry, worn, and sad. He took my sins a - way;
2. The load of sin was more than I could bear. He took them all a - way;
3. No con - dem - na - tion have I in my heart. He took my sins a - way;
4. If you will come to Je - sus Christ to - day, He'll take your sins a - way,

He took my sins a - way. And now His love has made my heart so glad.
He took them all a - way. And now on Him I roll my ev - 'ry care.
He took my sins a - way. His per - fect peace He did to me im - part.
He'll take your sins a - way, And keep you hap - py in His love each day.

REFRAIN

He took my sins a - way.
He took my sins a - way.
He took my sins a - way.
He'll take your sins a - way.

He took my sins a - way,

He took my sins a - way, And keeps me sing - ing ev - 'ry day!

I'm so glad He took my sins a - way. He took my sins a - way.

379 Saved to the Uttermost

William J. Kirkpatrick, 1838-1921

William J. Kirkpatrick, 1838-1921

1. Saved to the ut-ter-most! I am the Lord's. Je-sus, my
2. Saved to the ut-ter-most! Je-sus is near; Keep-ing me
3. Saved to the ut-ter-most! This I can say, "Once all was
4. Saved to the ut-ter-most! Cheer-ful-ly sing Loud hal-le-

Sav-iour, sal - va-tion af-fords; Gives me His Spir - it, a
safe-ly, He cast-eth out fear. Trust-ing His prom-is-es,
dark-ness, but now it is day; Beau-ti-ful vi - sions of
lu - jahs to Je-sus, my King. Ran-somed and par-doned, re-

wit - ness with-in, Whis-p'ring of par-don and sav-ing from sin.
now I am blest. Lean - ing up - on Him, how sweet is my rest!
glo-ry I see, Je - sus in bright-ness re-vealed un-to me."
deemed by His blood, Cleansed from un-righ-teous-ness—glo-ry to God!

REFRAIN

Saved, saved, saved to the ut-ter-most! Saved, saved by pow-er di-vine!

Saved, saved, saved to the ut-ter-most! Je-sus, the Sav-iour, is mine!

380

It Is Mine

Elisha A. Hoffman, 1839-1929

William Edie Marks, 20th Century

1. God's a - bid - ing peace is in my soul to - day. Yes, I feel it
2. He has wrought in me a sweet and per-fect rest; In my rap - tured
3. He has giv - en me a nev - er - fail - ing joy. Oh, I have it
4. Oh, the love of God is com-fort-ing my soul, For His love is

now; yes, I feel it now. He has tak - en all my doubts and fears a-
heart I can feel it now. He each pass - ing mo-ment keeps me saved and
now! Oh, I have it now! To His praise I will my ransomed pow'rs em-
mine; yes, His love is mine! Waves of joy and glad-ness o'er my spir - it

REFRAIN

way, Tho' I can - not tell you how.
blest, Floods with light my heart and brow.
ploy, And re - new my grate - ful vow.   It is   mine,   mine,
roll, Thrill-ing me with life di - vine.   It is   mine, this priceless treasure, ever

bless - ed be His name! He has giv - en peace, per - fect peace to me. It is

mine,   mine,   bless-ed be His name! Mine for all e - ter - ni - ty!
mine, this priceless treasure, ever

381 He Brought Me Out

Henry J. Zelley, 1859-1942
Chorus by Henry L. Gilmour, 1837-1920

Henry L. Gilmour, 1837-1920

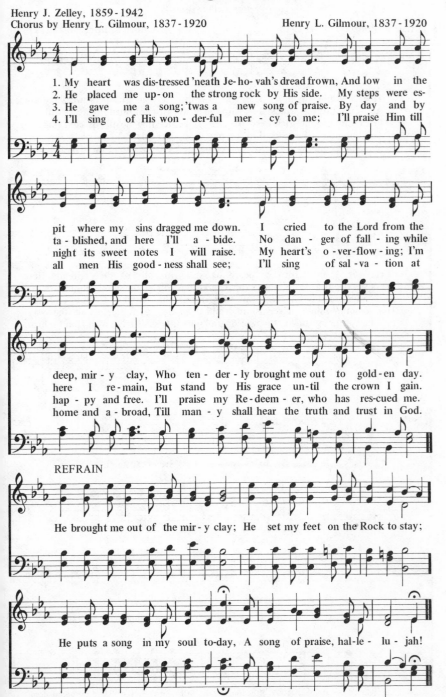

1. My heart was dis-tressed 'neath Je-ho-vah's dread frown, And low in the
2. He placed me up-on the strong rock by His side. My steps were es-
3. He gave me a song; 'twas a new song of praise. By day and by
4. I'll sing of His won-der-ful mer-cy to me; I'll praise Him till

pit where my sins dragged me down. I cried to the Lord from the
ta-blished, and here I'll a-bide. No dan-ger of fall-ing while
night its sweet notes I will raise. My heart's o-ver-flow-ing; I'm
all men His good-ness shall see; I'll sing of sal-va-tion at

deep, mir-y clay, Who ten-der-ly brought me out to gold-en day.
here I re-main, But stand by His grace un-til the crown I gain.
hap-py and free. I'll praise my Re-deem-er, who has res-cued me.
home and a-broad, Till man-y shall hear the truth and trust in God.

REFRAIN

He brought me out of the mir-y clay; He set my feet on the Rock to stay;

He puts a song in my soul to-day, A song of praise, hal-le-lu-jah!

382 He Keeps Me Singing

SWEETEST NAME

Luther B. Bridgers, 1884-1948   Luther B. Bridgers, 1884-1948

1. There's within my heart a mel - o - dy. Je - sus whis-pers sweet and low:
2. All my life was wrecked by sin and strife; Discord filled my heart with pain.
3. Feast - ing on the rich - es of His grace, Resting 'neath His shelt'ring wing,
4. Tho' sometimes He leads thro' wa-ters deep, Tri - als fall a - cross the way,
5. Soon He's com-ing back to wel - come me Far be - yond the star - ry sky.

"Fear not, I am with thee; peace, be still," In all of life's ebb and flow.
Je - sus swept a - cross the bro - ken strings, Stirred the slumb'ring chords again.
Al - ways look-ing on His smil - ing face, That is why I shout and sing.
Tho' sometimes the path seems rough and steep, See His footprints all the way.
I shall wing my flight to worlds un-known; I shall reign with Him on high.

REFRAIN

Je - sus, Je - sus, Je - sus,— Sweet-est name I know,

Fills my ev - 'ry long - ing, Keeps me sing-ing as I go.

383 Saved, Saved!

RAPTURE

Jack P. Schofield, 1882-   Jack P. Schofield, 1882-

1. I've found a Friend who is all to me; His love is ev-er true. I love to tell how He lift-ed me, And what His grace can do for you.
2. He saved me from ev-'ry sin and harm, Se-cures my soul each day. I'm lean-ing strong on His might-y arm; I know He'll guide me all the way.
3. When poor and need-y and all a-lone, In love He said to me, "Come un-to Me and I'll lead you home, To live with Me e-ter-nal-ly."

REFRAIN

Saved by His pow'r di-vine! Saved to new life sub-lime!
Saved by His pow'r, Saved to new life,

Life now is sweet and my joy is com-plete, For I'm saved, saved, saved!

384 Constantly Abiding

Anne S. Murphy, 20th Century   Anne S. Murphy, 20th Century

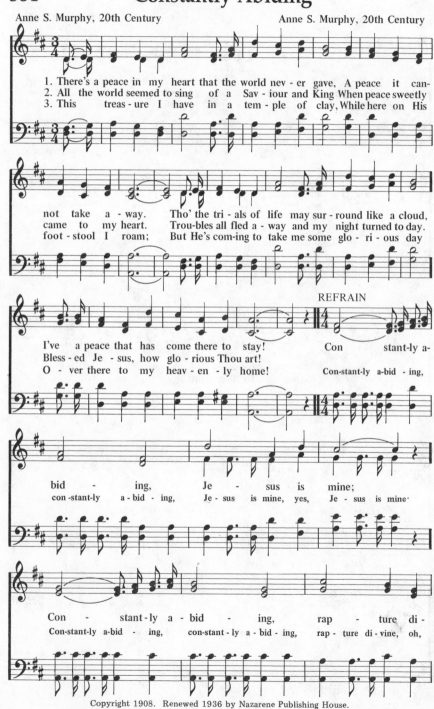

1. There's a peace in my heart that the world nev-er gave, A peace it can-
2. All the world seemed to sing of a Sav-iour and King When peace sweetly
3. This treas-ure I have in a tem-ple of clay, While here on His

not take a-way. Tho' the tri-als of life may sur-round like a cloud,
came to my heart. Trou-bles all fled a-way and my night turned to day.
foot-stool I roam; But He's com-ing to take me some glo-ri-ous day

REFRAIN

I've a peace that has come there to stay!   Con-stant-ly a-
Bless-ed Je-sus, how glo-rious Thou art!   Con-stant-ly a-bid-ing,
O-ver there to my heav-en-ly home!

bid-ing,   Je-sus is mine;
con-stant-ly a-bid-ing, Je-sus is mine, yes, Je-sus is mine·

Con-stant-ly a-bid-ing,   rap-ture di-
Con-stant-ly a-bid-ing, con-stant-ly a-bid-ing, rap-ture di-vine, oh,

vine! He nev-er leaves me lone - ly; whis-pers,
rap- ture di-vine! He nev -er leaves me, nev -er leaves me lone - ly; whis-pers,

oh, so kind: "I will nev-er leave thee." Je - sus is mine!
whis-pers, oh, so kind: nev-er leave thee." Je - sus, Je - sus is mine.

385
Jesus Is Mine
LUNDIE

Catherine J. Bonar, 1821 - 1884

Theodore E. Perkins, 1831 - 1912

1. Fade, fade each earth - ly joy; Je - sus is mine! Break ev - 'ry
2. Tempt not my soul a - way; Je - sus is mine! Here would I
3. Fare - well, ye dreams of night; Je - sus is mine! Lost in this
4. Fare - well, mor-tal - i - ty; Je - sus is mine! Wel-come, e-

ten - der tie; Je - sus is mine! Dark is the wil - der-ness;
ev - er stay; Je - sus is mine! Per - ish-ing things of clay,
dawn-ing light, Je - sus is mine! All that my soul has tried
ter - ni - ty; Je - sus is mine! Wel-come, O loved and blest!

Earth has no rest-ing place. Je - sus a - lone can bless; Je - sus is mine!
Born for but one brief day, Pass from my heart a-way. Je - sus is mine!
Left but a dis-mal void. Je - sus has sat - is - fied; Je - sus is mine!
Wel-come,sweet scenes of rest! Wel-come,my Saviour's breast! Je - sus is mine!

386 My Burden Is Gone

Haldor Lillenas, 1885-1959

Haldor Lillenas, 1885-1959

1. One day I trav-eled a toil-some road O-ver the
2. Gone is the night with its shad-ows drear; Morn-ing hath
3. No more the bur-den of guilt is mine; No more in

hills of de-spair; One day I car-ried a wea-ry load,
dawned up-on me. Gone is the bur-den of anx-ious fear;
bond-age I dwell. Un-to my glo-ri-ous King di-vine

REFRAIN

Cum-bered with toil and with care.
Free-dom my por-tion shall be. The bur-den that once I
Ju-bi-lant prais-es shall swell.

car-ried Is gone, is gone. Of all of my sins there re-
Is gone, is gone.

main-eth Not one, not one. Je-sus, the Saviour, hath
Not one, not one.

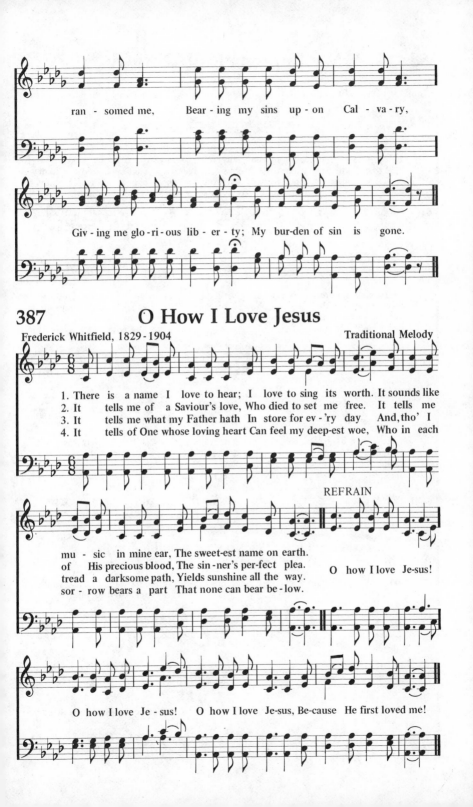

ran - somed me, Bear - ing my sins up - on Cal - va - ry,

Giv - ing me glo - ri - ous lib - er - ty; My bur-den of sin is gone.

387 **O How I Love Jesus**

Frederick Whitfield, 1829 - 1904

Traditional Melody

1. There is a name I love to hear; I love to sing its worth. It sounds like
2. It tells me of a Saviour's love, Who died to set me free. It tells me
3. It tells me what my Father hath In store for ev - 'ry day And, tho' I
4. It tells of One whose loving heart Can feel my deep-est woe, Who in each

REFRAIN

mu - sic in mine ear, The sweet-est name on earth.
of His precious blood, The sin -ner's per-fect plea.   O how I love Je-sus!
tread a darksome path, Yields sunshine all the way.
sor - row bears a part That none can bear be - low.

O how I love Je - sus! O how I love Je-sus, Be-cause He first loved me!

388   My Burdens Rolled Away

Minnie A. Steele, 20th Century   Minnie A. Steele, 20th Century

1. I re-mem-ber when my bur-dens rolled a-way; I had car-ried them for
2. I re-mem-ber when my bur-dens rolled a-way, That I feared would nev-er
3. I re-mem-ber when my bur-dens rolled a-way, That had hin-dered me for
4. I am sing-ing since my bur-dens rolled a-way; There's a song with-in my

years, night and day. When I sought the blessed Lord, and I took Him at His
leave night or day. Je-sus showed to me the loss, so I left them at the
years, night and day. As I sought the throne of grace, just a glimpse of Je-sus'
heart night and day. I am liv-ing for my King, and with joy I shout and

REFRAIN

word, Then at once all my bur-dens rolled a-way. Rolled a-way, rolled a-
Cross; I was glad when my bur-dens rolled a-way.
face, And I knew that my bur-dens could not stay.
sing. Hal-le-lu-jah! all my bur-dens rolled a-way!   Rolled a-way,

way,   I am hap-py since my bur-dens rolled a-way.   Rolled a-
rolled a-way,   since my bur-dens rolled a-way.

way.   rolled a-way,   I am hap-py since my burdens rolled a-way.
Rolled a-way,   rolled a-way,

389 My Sins Are Blotted Out, I Know!

Merrill Dunlop, 1905-

Merrill Dunlop, 1905-

1. What a won-drous mes-sage in God's Word! My sins are blot-ted out, I know! If I trust in His re-deem-ing blood, My sins are blot-ted out, I know!

2. Once my heart was black but now, what joy! My sins are blot-ted out, I know! I have peace that noth-ing can de-stroy. My sins are blot-ted out, I know!

3. I shall stand some-day be-fore my King. My sins are blot-ted out, I know! With the ran-somed host I then shall sing: "My sins are blot-ted out, I know!"

REFRAIN

My sins are blot-ted out, I know! My sins are blot-ted out, I know! They are bur-ied in the depths of the deep-est sea. My sins are blot-ted out, I know!

I know! I know! I know!

390 I've Anchored in Jesus

Lewis E. Jones, 1865 - 1936   Lewis E. Jones, 1865 - 1936

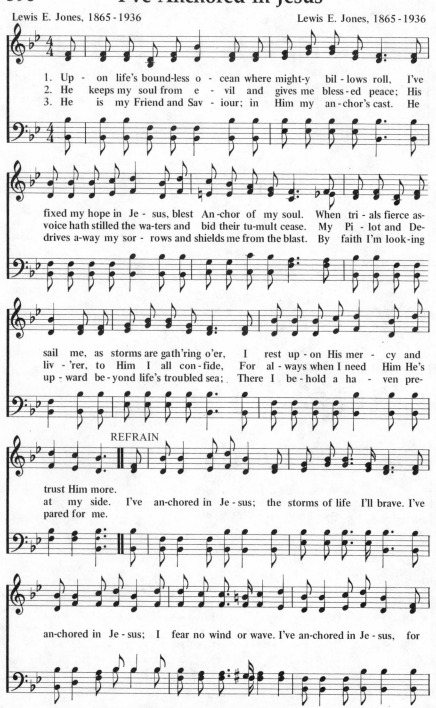

1. Up - on life's bound-less o - cean where might-y bil - lows roll, I've
2. He keeps my soul from e - vil and gives me bless - ed peace; His
3. He is my Friend and Sav - iour; in Him my an - chor's cast. He

fixed my hope in Je - sus, blest An-chor of my soul. When tri - als fierce as-
voice hath stilled the wa-ters and bid their tu-mult cease. My Pi - lot and De-
drives a-way my sor - rows and shields me from the blast. By faith I'm look-ing

sail me, as storms are gath'ring o'er, I rest up - on His mer - cy and
liv - 'rer, to Him I all con-fide, For al - ways when I need Him He's
up - ward be-yond life's troubled sea; There I be-hold a ha - ven pre-

REFRAIN

trust Him more.
at my side. I've an-chored in Je - sus; the storms of life I'll brave. I've
pared for me.

an-chored in Je - sus; I fear no wind or wave. I've an-chored in Je - sus, for

He hath pow'r to save. I've an-chored in the Rock of A - ges.

391
At Calvary

William R. Newell, 1868 - 1956

Daniel B. Towner, 1850 - 1919

1. Years I spent in van - i - ty and pride, Car - ing not my Lord was
2. By God's Word at last my sin I learned; Then I trem-bled at the
3. Now I've giv'n to Je - sus ev - 'ry - thing; Now I glad - ly own Him
4. Oh, the love that drew sal - va - tion's plan! Oh, the grace that bro't it

cru - ci - fied, Know-ing not it was for me He died On Cal - va - ry.
law I'd spurned, Till my guilt - y soul im - plor-ing turned To Cal - va - ry.
as my King; Now my rap - tured soul can on - ly sing Of Cal - va - ry.
down to man! Oh, the might - y gulf that God did span At Cal - va - ry.

REFRAIN

Mer - cy there was great and grace was free; Par - don there was mul - ti -

plied to me; There my bur-dened soul found lib-er - ty, At Cal - va - ry.

392 Still Sweeter Every Day

W. C. Martin, 19th Century

C. Austin Miles, 1868-1946

1. To Je - sus ev - 'ry day I find my heart is clos - er drawn; He's
2. His glo - ry broke up-on me when I saw Him from a - far; He's
3. My heart is some-times heav-y, but He comes with sweet re - lief; He

fair - er than the glo - ry of the gold and pur - ple dawn; He's all my
fair - er than the lil - y, bright - er than the morn - ing star. He fills and
folds me to His bos - om when I droop with blighting grief. I love the

fan - cy pic - tures in its fair - est dreams and more.
sat - is - fies my long-ing spir - it o'er and o'er. Each day He grows still
Christ, who all my bur - dens in His bod - y bore.

REFRAIN

sweet - er than He was the day be -fore. The half_____ can-not be
The half can - not be fan-cied on this

fan - cied this side_____ the gold-en shore. Oh,
side the gold - en shore. The half can-not be fan-cied on this side the gold-en shore. Oh,

there_____ He'll be still sweet - er than He ev - er was be-fore.
there He'll be still sweeter than He ev - er was be-fore, than He

393   Where Jesus Is, 'Tis Heaven

C. F. Butler, 19th Century   James M. Black, 1856 - 1938

1. Since Christ my soul from sin set free, This world has been a heav'n to me;
2. Once heav-en seemed a far-off place, Till Je - sus showed His smil-ing face.
2. What mat-ters where on earth we dwell? On mountain-top or in the dell,

And mid earth's sor - rows and its woe 'Tis heav'n my Je - sus here to know.
Now it's be - gun with-in my soul; 'Twill last while endless a - ges roll.
In cot - tage or a man-sion fair, Where Je-sus is, 'tis heav-en there.

REFRAIN

Oh, hal - le - lu - jah, yes, 'tis heav'n, 'Tis heav'n to know my sins for - giv'n!

On land or sea, what mat-ters where? Where Je-sus is, 'tis heav-en there.

394 The Crystal Fountain

Floyd W. Hawkins, 1904 -

Floyd W. Hawkins, 1904 -

1. So long of thirst my wea-ry soul did lan-guish, And naught of
2. I tried the world with its al-lur-ing pleas-ure. It mocked my
3. Dear faint-ing heart, oh, do not lon-ger tar-ry. Come now to

earth my soul could sat-is-fy; But when to Christ I turned in
soul, all bur-den'd down with care. But grace and help in bless-ed,
Christ and drink, your soul re-new. He knows your need, the heav-y

bit-ter an-guish, I found in Him the an-swer to my cry.
bound-less meas-ure I've found in Christ, the Fount of Life, so fair.
load you car-ry. This bless-ed Fount is o-pen now for you.

REFRAIN

Oh, I have found it, ____ the Crys-tal Foun-tain, Where all my

life's deep needs have been sup-plied; So free-ly flow-ing from Calv'ry's

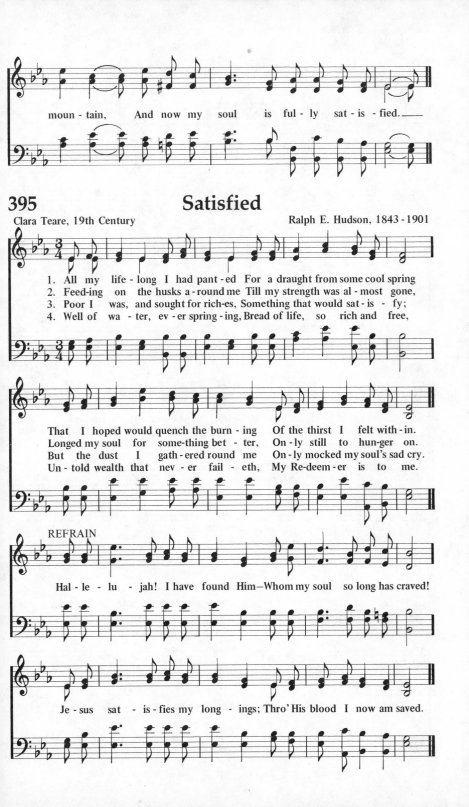

moun - tain, And now my soul is ful - ly sat - is - fied.___

395 **Satisfied**

Clara Teare, 19th Century   Ralph E. Hudson, 1843 - 1901

1. All my life - long I had pant - ed For a draught from some cool spring
2. Feed-ing on the husks a - round me Till my strength was al - most gone,
3. Poor I was, and sought for rich-es, Something that would sat - is - fy;
4. Well of wa - ter, ev - er spring - ing, Bread of life, so rich and free,

That I hoped would quench the burn - ing Of the thirst I felt with - in.
Longed my soul for some-thing bet - ter, On - ly still to hun-ger on.
But the dust I gath-ered round me On - ly mocked my soul's sad cry.
Un - told wealth that nev - er fail - eth, My Re-deem - er is to me.

REFRAIN

Hal - le - lu - jah! I have found Him—Whom my soul so long has craved!

Je - sus sat - is - fies my long - ings; Thro' His blood I now am saved.

396   He's Everything to Me

Kate Byron, 20th Century

Hampton H. Sewell, 1874 - 1937

1. In sin I once had wan - dered, all wea - ry, sad, and lone, Till Je - sus
2. In sin no more I'll wan - der; He's Pi - lot, Friend, and Guide. He brings me
3. No lon - ger will I stray from His ten - der, lov - ing care; Like Him to

thro' His mer - cy a - dopt - ed me His own. E'er since I learned to
joy and sing - ing. His Spir - it doth a - bide. A bless - ed, lov - ing
be my pur - pose, my aim, my con - stant prayer. And when He bids me

trust Him, His grace doth make me free, And now I feel His par - don.
Sav - iour, the Lamb of Cal - va - ry! He pur-chased my re - demp - tion.
wel-come thro'-out e - ter - ni - ty, I'll praise His name for - ev - er.

REFRAIN

He's ev - 'ry-thing to me. He's ev -'ry-thing to me.___ From sin He
          He's all   to me.

sets me free;___ His peace and love my por - tion thro' all e - ter - ni-
He   sets me free;   e-

ty!_____ He's ev-'ry-thing to me,_____ More than I dreamed could
ter - ni - ty!   He's all   to me,

be._____ Oh, praise His name for-ev-er!   He's ev - 'ry-thing to me.
could be.

397   Where He Leads Me

E. W. Blandly, 19th Century   John S. Norris, 1844 - 1907

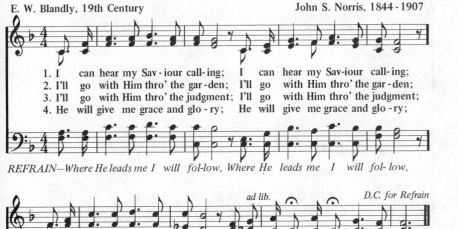

1. I   can hear my Sav-iour call-ing;   I   can   hear my Sav-iour call-ing;
2. I'll   go   with Him thro' the gar-den;   I'll   go   with Him thro' the gar-den;
3. I'll   go   with Him thro' the judgment;   I'll   go   with Him thro' the judgment;
4. He   will   give   me grace and glo-ry;   He   will   give me grace and glo-ry;

REFRAIN—*Where He leads me I   will   fol-low, Where He   leads me   I   will fol-low,*

ad lib.   *D.C. for Refrain*

I   can   hear   my Sav-iour   call - ing, "Take thy cross, and fol-low, fol - low Me."
I'll go   with Him thro' the   gar - den.   I'll go   with Him, with Him all the   way.
I'll go   with Him thro' the   judgment.   I'll go   with Him, with Him all the   way.
He will give me grace and glo - ry,   And go   with me, with me all the   way.

Where He leads me I   will   fol - low; I'll go with Him, with Him all the   way.

398 Jesus Is the Joy of Living

Alfred H. Ackley, 1887-1960

Alfred H. Ackley, 1887-1960

1. I have found a won-drous Sav - iour, Je - sus Christ, the Soul's De-light;
2. Life is grow-ing rich with beau - ty; Toil has lost its wea - ry strain;
3. Heav'nly wis-dom He pro - vides me, Grace to keep my spir - it free;
4. Oh, what Splen-dor, oh, what Glo - ry, Oh, what matchless Pow'r di - vine

Ev - 'ry bless-ing of His fa - vor   Fills my heart with hope so bright.
Now a ha - lo crowns each du - ty,   And I sing a glad re - frain.
In His own sweet way He guides me   When the path I can - not see.
Is the Christ of gos - pel sto - ry!   Christ, the Sav-iour, who is mine!

REFRAIN

Je - sus is the Joy of Liv - ing; He's the King of Life to me.___

of Life to me.

Un - to Him my all I'm giv - ing, His for - ev - er-more to be (to be).

I will do what He com-mands me; An - y-where He leads I'll go (I'll go).

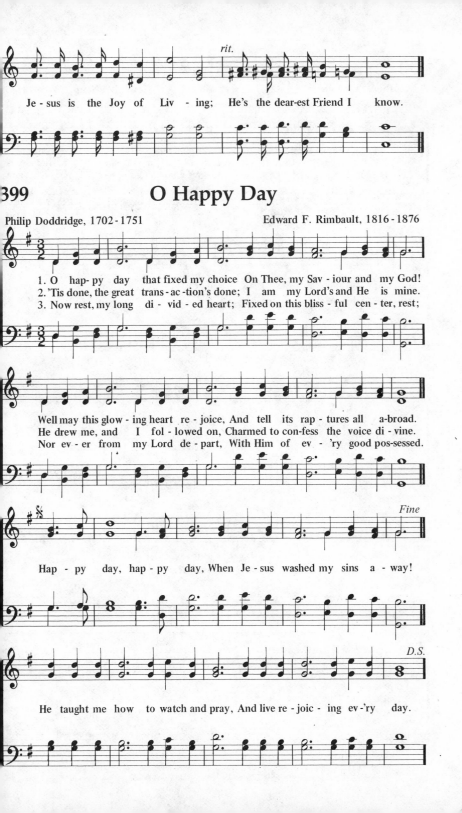

Je - sus is the Joy of Liv - ing; He's the dear-est Friend I know.

399 O Happy Day

Philip Doddridge, 1702-1751

Edward F. Rimbault, 1816-1876

1. O hap- py day that fixed my choice On Thee, my Sav - iour and my God!
2. 'Tis done, the great trans - ac -tion's done; I am my Lord's and He is mine.
3. Now rest, my long di - vid - ed heart; Fixed on this bliss - ful cen - ter, rest;

Well may this glow - ing heart re - joice, And tell its rap - tures all a-broad.
He drew me, and I fol - lowed on, Charmed to con-fess the voice di - vine.
Nor ev - er from my Lord de - part, With Him of ev - 'ry good pos-sessed.

Hap - py day, hap - py day, When Je - sus washed my sins a - way!

He taught me how to watch and pray, And live re - joic - ing ev -'ry day.

400 Love Lifted Me

James Rowe, 1865-1933   Howard E. Smith, 1863-1918

1. I was sink-ing deep in sin, Far from the peace-ful shore, Ver-y deep-ly
2. All my heart to Him I give; Ev - er to Him I'll cling, In His blessed
3. Souls in dan-ger, look a - bove; Je - sus com-plete-ly saves. He will lift you

stained with-in, Sink-ing to rise no more. But the Mas - ter of the sea
pres - ence live, Ev - er His prais-es sing. Love so might - y and so true
by His love Out of the an - gry waves. He's the Mas - ter of the sea;

Heard my de-spair-ing cry, From the wa - ters lift - ed me; Now safe am I.
Mer-its my soul's best songs; Faith - ful, lov - ing ser - vice, too, To Him be-longs.
Bil - lows His will o - bey. He your Sav-iour wants to be—Be saved to-day.

REFRAIN

Love lift - ed me!   Love lift - ed me!   When noth-ing
e - ven me!   e - ven me!

1
else could help, Love lift - ed me.

2
Love lift - ed me.

401 He's a Wonderful Saviour to Me

Virgil P. Brock, 20th Century

Blanche Kerr Brock, 20th Century

1. I was lost in sin but Je-sus res-cued me;
2. He's a Friend so true, so pa-tient, and so kind;
3. He is al-ways near to com-fort and to cheer;
4. Dear-er grows the love of Je-sus day by day;

He's a won-der-ful Sav-iour to me.
So won-der-ful!

I was bound by fear but Je-sus set me free;
Ev-'ry-thing I need in Him I al-ways find;
He for-gives my sins; He dries my ev-'ry tear.
Sweeter is His grace while pressing on my way;

He's a won-der-ful Sav-iour to me.
So wonderful!

REFRAIN

For He's a won-der-ful Sav-iour to me;
wonderful!

He's a won-der-ful Sav-iour to me.
wonderful!

I was lost in sin, but Je-sus took me in; He's a won-der-ful Sav-iour to me.

402   Since Jesus Came into My Heart

R. H. McDaniel, 20th Century   Charles H. Gabriel, 1856 - 1932

1. What a won-der - ful change in my life has been wrought Since Je-sus came
2. I have ceased from my wand'ring and go - ing a - stray Since Je-sus came
3. I'm pos-sessed of a hope that is stead-fast and sure, Since Je-sus came
4. There's a light in the val - ley of death now for me, Since Je-sus came
5. I shall go there to dwell in that cit - y I know, Since Je-sus came

in - to my heart! I have light in my soul for which long I had sought
in - to my heart; And my sins which were man-y are all washed a - way,
in - to my heart; And no dark clouds of doubt now my pathway ob-scure,
in - to my heart; And the gates of the cit - y be - yond I can see,
in - to my heart; And I'm hap-py, so hap - py, as on - ward I go,

REFRAIN

Since Je - sus came in - to my heart.   Since Je - sus came in-to my
                                                         came in,   came

heart,   Since Je-sus came in - to my heart,   Floods of joy o'er my
in-to my heart, Since Je-sus came in,   came   in-to my heart,

soul like the sea bil-lows roll, Since Je-sus came in-to my heart.

403   I Know I Love Thee Better, Lord

Frances R. Havergal, 1836 - 1879   Ralph E. Hudson, 1843 - 1901

1. I know I love Thee bet-ter, Lord, Than an - y earth-ly joy;
2. I know that Thou art near-er still Than an - y earth-ly throng;
3. Thou hast put glad-ness in my heart; Then may I well be glad!
4. O Sav - iour, pre-cious Sav-iour mine! What will Thy pres-ence be,

For Thou hast giv - en me the peace Which noth-ing can de - stroy.
And sweet - er is the tho't of Thee Than an - y love - ly song.
With - out the se - cret of Thy love I could not but be sad.
If such a life of joy can crown Our walk on earth with Thee?

REFRAIN

The half has nev-er yet been told (been told) Of love so full and free!

The half has nev-er yet been told (been told). The Blood—it cleanseth me!

404 The Lily of the Valley

SALVATIONIST

Charles W. Fry, 1837-1882

English Melody
William S. Hays, 1837-1907

1. I've found a Friend in Je - sus. He's ev - 'ry-thing to me. He's the fair - est of ten thou-sand to my soul. The Lil - y of the Val-ley, in Him a - lone I see All I need to cleanse and make me ful - ly whole. In sor - row He's my Com-fort; in trou - ble He's my Stay. He tells me ev - 'ry care on Him to roll. (Hal-le-lu - jah!)

2. He all my griefs has ta - ken, and all my sor - rows borne. In temp-ta - tion He's my strong and might-y Tow'r. I've all for Him for - sa - ken; I've all my i - dols torn From my heart, and now He keeps me by His pow'r. Tho' all the world for-sake me, and Sa - tan tempt me sore, Thro' Je - sus I shall safe - ly reach the goal.

3. He'll nev - er, nev - er leave me, nor yet for - sake me here, While I live by faith and do His bless - ed will. A wall of fire a - bout me, I've noth-ing now to fear. With His man - na He my hun - gry soul shall fill. Then sweep-ing up to glo - ry, I'll see His bless - ed face, Where riv - ers of de - light shall ev - er roll.

D.S. Lil - y of the Val-ley, the Bright and Morning Star. He's the fair - est of ten thou-sand to my soul.

Fine

He's the

D.S.

405   I'd Rather Have Jesus

Rhea F. Miller, 20th Century   George Beverly Shea, 20th Century

1. I'd ra-ther have Je-sus than sil-ver or gold; I'd rath-er be
2. I'd ra-ther have Je-sus than men's ap - plause; I'd rath-er be
3. He's fair-er than lil-lies of rar-est bloom; He's sweet-er than

His than have rich-es un-told; I'd rath-er have Je-sus than
faith-ful to His dear cause; I'd rath-er have Je-sus than
hon-ey from out the comb; He's all that my hun-ger-ing

(small notes, last stanza)

hous-es or lands. I'd rath-er be led by His nail-pierced hand
world-wide fame. I'd rath-er be true to His ho-ly name
spir-it needs. I'd rath-er have Je-sus and let Him lead

Than to be the king of a vast do-main Or be held in sin's dread sway.

I'd rath-er have Je-sus than an-y-thing This world af-fords to-day.

406 Wonderful

Haldor Lillenas, 1885 - 1959

1. Oh, my heart sings to - day, sings for joy and glad - ness. Je - sus saves,
2. Once a slave, now I'm free, free from con - dem - na - tion. Je - sus gives
3. Liv - ing here with my Lord in a ho - ly u - nion, Day by day,

sat - is - fies, takes a - way my sad - ness. Guilt is gone; peace is mine,
lib - er - ty and a full sal - va - tion. Now the sins of the past
all the way hold - ing sweet com - mu - nion; Oh, what change grace hath wrought

peace like to a riv - er. Je - sus is won - der - ful, might - y to de - liv - er.
have been all for - giv - en, And my name is inscribed in the book of heav - en.
in my low - ly sta - tion Since my soul has received full and free sal - va - tion!

REFRAIN

Won - der - ful, won - der - ful, Je - sus is to me! Coun - sel - or,

Prince of Peace, Might - y God is He! Sav - ing me, keep - ing me

from all sin and shame, Won-der-ful is my Re-deem-er, praise His name!

407   'Tis So Sweet to Trust in Jesus

TRUST IN JESUS

Louisa M. R. Stead, 19th Century   William J. Kirkpatrick, 1838-1921

1. 'Tis so sweet to trust in Je-sus, Just to take Him at His Word;
2. Oh, how sweet to trust in Je-sus, Just to trust His cleans-ing blood;
3. Yes, 'tis sweet to trust in Je-sus, Just from sin and self to cease;
4. I'm so glad I learned to trust Thee, Pre-cious Je-sus, Sav-iour, Friend;

Just to rest up-on His prom-ise; Just to know, "Thus saith the Lord."
Just in sim-ple faith to plunge me 'Neath the heal-ing, cleans-ing flood!
Just from Je-sus sim-ply tak-ing Life and rest, and joy and peace.
And I know that Thou art with me, Wilt be with me to the end.

REFRAIN

Je-sus, Je-sus, how I trust Him! How I've proved Him o'er and o'er!

p

Je-sus, Je-sus, pre-cious Je-sus! O for grace to trust Him more!

408 He Ransomed Me

Julia H. Johnston, 1849 - 1919

J. W. Henderson, 20th Century

1. There's a sweet and bless - ed sto - ry Of the Christ who came from glo - ry
2. From the depth of sin and sad - ness To the heights of joy and glad-ness
3. From the throne of heav'n-ly glo - ry— Oh, the sweet and bless - ed sto - ry!–
4. By and by with joy in - creas-ing, And with grat - i - tude un - ceas-ing,

Just to res - cue me from sin and mis - er - y. He in lov-ing-kind-ness sought me,
Je - sus lift - ed me, in mer-cy full and free. With His precious blood He bo't me;
Je - sus came to lift the lost in sin and woe In - to lib - er - ty all- glo-rious,
Lift - ed up with Christ for-ev-er-more to be, I will join the hosts there sing-ing,

And from sin and shame hath bro't me. Hal - le - lu - jah! Je - sus ran-somed me.
When I knew Him not, He sought me, And in love di - vine He ran-somed me.
Tro-phies of His grace vic - to - rious, Ev - er - more re - joic-ing here be - low.
In the an-them ev - er ring - ing, To the King of Love, who ransomed me.

REFRAIN

Hal - le - lu - jah, what a Sav - iour! Who can take a poor lost sin-ner, Lift him

from the mir-y clay and set him free! Hal-le-lu-jah! I will ev - er tell the sto - ry,

Shout-ing,"Glo-ry! Glo - ry! Glo - ry!" Hal - le - lu - jah! Je-sus ran-somed me.

409   Singing I Go

Eliza E. Hewitt, 1851 - 1920   William J. Kirkpatrick, 1838 - 1921

1. The trust - ing heart to Je - sus clings, Nor an - y ill__ fore-bodes,__
2. The pass - ing days bring man - y cares. "Fear not," I hear Him say;__
3. He tells me of my Fa - ther's love, And nev - er-slum -b'ring eye;__
4. When to the throne of grace I flee, I find the prom - ise true;__

But at the cross of Cal - v'ry sings, "Praise God for lift - ed loads!"__
And when my fears are turned to prayers, The bur - dens slip a - way.__
My ev - er-last - ing King a - bove Will all my needs sup-ply.__
The might - y arms up - hold - ing me Will bear my bur - dens too.__

REFRAIN

Sing-ing I go a - long life's road, Prais- ing the Lord, prais - ing the Lord;

rit. ad lib.

Sing-ing I go a - long life's road, For Je - sus has lift - ed my load.__

410   A New Name in Glory

C. Austin Miles, 1868-1946   C. Austin Miles, 1868-1946

1. I was once a sin-ner, but I came Par-don to re-ceive from my Lord.
2. I was hum-bly kneel-ing at the Cross, Fear-ing naught but God's angry frown,
3. In the Book 'tis writ-ten, "Saved by Grace." Oh, the joy that came to my soul!

This was free-ly giv-en, and I found That He al-ways kept His word.
When the heavens o-pened and I saw That my name was writ-ten down.
Now I am for-giv-en, and I know By the Blood I am made whole.

(1) kept His word.

REFRAIN

There's a new name writ-ten down in glo-ry, And it's mine.

And it's

Oh, yes, it's mine! And the white-robed an-gels sing the

mine;   yes, it's mine!

sto-ry, "A sin-ner has come home." For there's a

has come home."

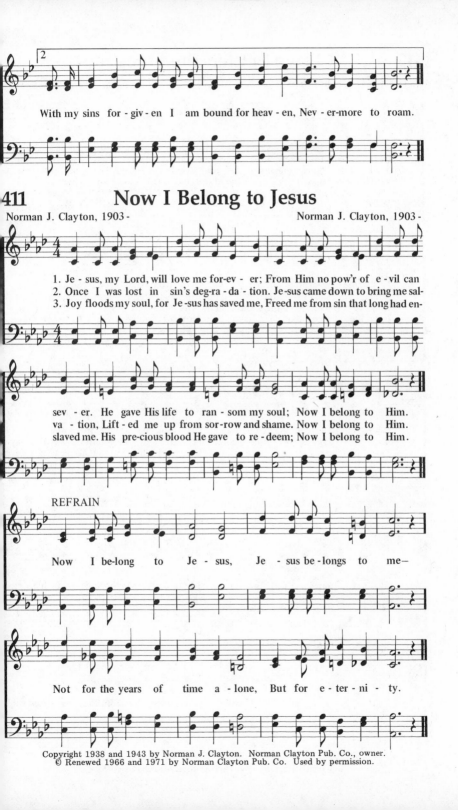

With my sins for-giv-en I am bound for heav-en, Nev-er-more to roam.

411   Now I Belong to Jesus

Norman J. Clayton, 1903 -   Norman J. Clayton, 1903 -

1. Je - sus, my Lord, will love me for-ev - er; From Him no pow'r of e - vil can
2. Once I was lost in sin's deg-ra - da - tion. Je-sus came down to bring me sal-
3. Joy floods my soul, for Je-sus has saved me, Freed me from sin that long had en-

sev - er. He gave His life to ran - som my soul; Now I belong to Him.
va - tion, Lift - ed me up from sor-row and shame. Now I belong to Him.
slaved me. His pre-cious blood He gave to re - deem; Now I belong to Him.

REFRAIN

Now I be-long to Je - sus, Je - sus be-longs to me—

Not for the years of time a - lone, But for e - ter - ni - ty.

412   I Have Settled the Question

Haldor Lillenas, 1885 - 1959   Haldor Lillenas, 1885 - 1959

1. I re - mem - ber when the Lord spoke to my soul (to my soul).
2. I no lon - ger walk the ways of sin - ful - ness (sin - ful - ness),
3. I will choose the ho - ly joys that al - ways last (al - ways last),
4. Oth - ers may de - ny the Lord and live in sin (live in sin),

I could feel the heav - y bur - den from me roll (from me roll)
But I dai - ly tread the paths of righ - teous - ness (righ - teous - ness)
And re - ject sin's pleas - ures that will soon be past (soon be past).
But the race that I have en - tered I must win (I must win).

When He spoke the gra - cious words,"Wilt thou be whole?"(be whole?)Then I
Since the day the Lord has come my life to bless (to bless). I have
To the treas - ures of true worth I'm hold - ing fast (hold-ing fast). I have
Thro' the pearl - y gates I mean to en - ter in (en - ter in). I have

REFRAIN

set - tled the question for - ev - er. I have set-tled the ques-tion, hal - le -

lu - jah! I will nev - er turn back from the nar - row way.
lu - jah! hal - le - lu - jah!

Copyright 1919. Renewed 1947 by Nazarene Publishing House.

I am go-ing thro' with Je-sus, hal-le-lu - jah!
hal - le - lu - jah! hal - le - lu - jah!

Till I reach the gates of glo - ry some sweet day (some sweet day).

413 **Faith of Our Fathers**

ST. CATHERINE

Frederick W. Faber, 1814 - 1863

Henri F. Hemy, 1818 - 1888
Adapt. by James G. Walton, 1821 - 1905

1. Faith of our fa - thers, liv - ing still   In spite of dun-geon, fire, and sword!
2. Our fa-thers, chained in pris-ons dark, Were still in heart and conscience free.
3. Faith of our fa - thers! we will love Both friend and foe in all   our strife;

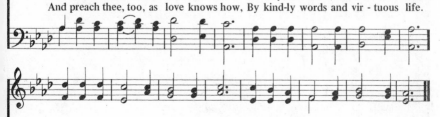

Oh, how our hearts beat high with joy When-e'er we hear that glo -rious word!
How sweet would be their children's fate   If they, like them, could die for   thee!
And preach thee, too, as love knows how, By kind-ly words and vir - tuous life.

Faith of our   fa - thers! ho - ly   faith! We will be true to   thee   till death!

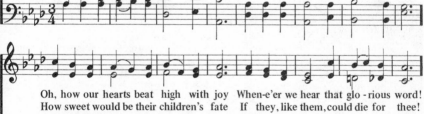

414 It's Just like His Great Love

Edna R. Worrell, 20th Century

Clarence B. Strouse, 20th Century

1. A Friend I have, called Je-sus, Whose love is strong and true And
2. Some-times the clouds of trouble Be-dim the sky a-bove. I
3. When sor-row's clouds o'er-take me And break up-on my head, When
4. Oh, I could sing for-ev-er Of Je-sus' love di-vine, Of

nev-er fails, how-e'er 'tis tried, No mat-ter what I do. I've sinned a-
can-not see my Sav-iour's face; I doubt His won-drous love. But He, from
life seems worse than use-less And earth-ly hopes are dead, I take my
all His care and ten-der-ness For this poor life of mine. His love is

gainst this love of His; But when I knelt to pray, Con-fess-ing all my
heav-en's mer-cy seat, Be-hold-ing my de-spair, In pit-y bursts the
grief to Je-sus then; Nor do I go in vain, For heav'n-ly hope He
in and o-ver all, And wind and waves o-bey When Je-sus whis-pers,

REFRAIN

guilt to Him, The sin-clouds rolled a-way.
clouds be-tween, And shows me He is there.
gives that cheers Like sun-shine af-ter rain.
"Peace, be still!" And rolls the clouds a-way.

It's just like Je-sus to

roll the clouds a-way. It's just like Je - sus to keep me day by day.

It's just like Je - sus all a-long the way. It's just like His great love.

415 There Is a Name I Love to Hear

EVAN

Frederick Whitfield, 1829 - 1904

William H. Havergal, 1793 - 1870

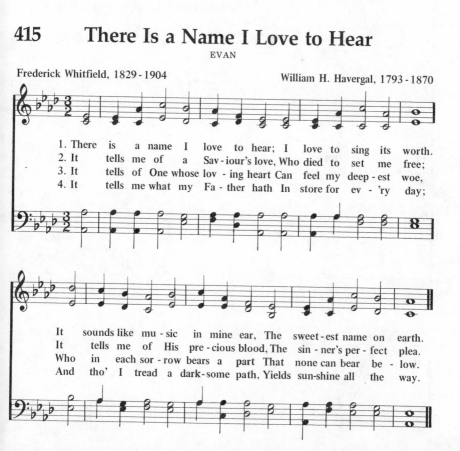

1. There is a name I love to hear; I love to sing its worth.
2. It tells me of a Sav - iour's love, Who died to set me free;
3. It tells of One whose lov - ing heart Can feel my deep - est woe,
4. It tells me what my Fa - ther hath In store for ev - 'ry day;

It sounds like mu - sic in mine ear, The sweet - est name on earth.
It tells me of His pre - cious blood, The sin - ner's per - fect plea.
Who in each sor - row bears a part That none can bear be - low.
And tho' I tread a dark-some path, Yields sun-shine all the way.

416 Hidden Peace

John S. Brown, 19th Century

L. O. Brown, 19th Century

1. I can-not tell thee whence it came, This peace with-in my breast;
2. Be-neath the toil and care of life This hid - den stream flows on;
3. I can-not tell the half of love, Un-feigned, su-preme, di - vine,
4. I can-not tell thee why He chose To suf - fer and to die;

But this I know, there fills my soul A strange and tran-quil rest.
My wea - ry soul no lon - ger thirsts, Nor am I sad and lone.
That caused my dark - est, in - most self With beams of hope to shine.
But if I suf - fer here with Him I'll reign with Him on high.

REFRAIN

There's a deep, set - tled peace in my soul.
in my soul.
There's a deep, set - tled peace in my soul.
in my soul.
Tho' the bil - lows of sin near me roll, He a - bides; Christ a - bides.

417 Sweet Peace, the Gift of God's Love

SWEET PEACE

Peter P. Bilhorn, 1865-1936   Peter P. Bilhorn, 1865-1936

1. There comes to my heart one sweet strain (sweet strain), A glad and a joy-ous re-frain (re-frain); I sing it a-gain and a-gain: Sweet peace,
2. Thro' Christ on the Cross peace was made (was made); My debt by His death was all paid (all paid). No oth-er foun-da-tion is laid For peace,
3. When Je-sus as Lord I had crowned (had crowned), My heart with this peace did a-bound (a-bound). In Him the rich bless-ing I found, Sweet peace,
4. In Je-sus for peace I a-bide (a-bide); And as I keep close to His side (His side), There's noth-ing but peace doth be-tide, Sweet peace,

the gift of God's love.

REFRAIN

Peace, peace, sweet peace! Won-der-ful gift from a-bove! a-bove! Oh, won-der-ful, won-der-ful peace! Sweet peace, the gift of God's love!

418 Wonderful Peace

Haldor Lillenas, 1885 - 1959

Haldor Lillenas, 1885 - 1959

1. Com - ing to Je - sus, my Sav - iour, I found
2. Peace like a riv - er so deep and so broad,
3. Peace like a ho - ly and in - fi - nite calm,
4. Gone is the bat - tle that once raged with - in.

Won - der - ful peace,

won - der - ful peace. Storms in their fu - ry may rage all a - round;
won - der - ful peace! Rest - ing my soul on the bos - om of God,
won - der - ful peace; Like to the strains of an eve - ning psalm,
won - der - ful peace! Je - sus has saved me and cleansed me from sin;

I have peace, sweet peace.
won - der - ful, won - der - ful, glo - ri - ous peace.

REFRAIN

Peace, peace,

won - der - ful peace! Peace, peace, glo - ri - ous peace! Since my Re-

poco rit.

deem - er has ran - somed my soul I have peace, sweet peace.
won - der - ful peace.

419 "Thou Wilt Keep Him in Perfect Peace"

Vivian A. Kretz, 20th Century
Stanzas 2 and 3 by Floyd W. Hawkins, 1904-

Vivian A. Kretz, 20th Century
Arr. by Floyd W. Hawkins, 1904-

1. "Thou wilt keep him in per-fect peace, Whose mind is
2. In the shad-ow of the might-y Rock I lay me
3. 'Tis the prom-ise of the Ho-ly One, "My peace I

stayed on thee." When the shad-ows come and dark-ness falls, He
down to sleep; He who watch-es o-ver Is-ra-el So
give to thee." Tho' the storms of life in fu-ry rage, Thy

REFRAIN

giv - eth in-ward peace.
faith - ful-ly will keep. Oh, He is the on-ly per-fect
Ref - uge sure is He.

Rest-ing Place! He giv-eth per-fect peace. "Thou wilt keep him in

1-2 Last

per-fect peace, whose mind is stayed on thee." stayed on thee."

420 The Peace That Jesus Gives

Haldor Lillenas, 1885-1959   Haldor Lillenas, 1885-1959

1. Like the sun - shine af - ter rain, Like a rest that fol - lows pain,
2. Like the soft, re - fresh - ing dew, Like a ro - sy day-break new,
3. Like a riv - er deep and long, With its cur - rent cease - less, strong,

Like a hope re - turned a-gain, Is the peace that Je - sus gives.
Like a friend-ship ten - der, true, Is the peace that Je - sus gives.
Like the ca - dence of a song, Is the peace that Je - sus gives.

REFRAIN

Oh, the peace that Je - sus gives   Nev-er dies; it al - ways lives.

Je-sus gives,   ev-er lives.

Like the mu - sic of a psalm, Like a glad, e - ter - nal calm,

Is the peace that Je - sus gives,   Is the peace that Je - sus gives.

Je - sus gives,

421 Wonderful Peace

W. D. Cornell, Alt.,19th Century

W. G. Cooper, 19th Century

1. Far a - way in the depths of my spir - it to - night Rolls a
2. What a treas - ure I have in this won - der - ful peace, Bur -ied
3. I am rest - ing to-night in this won - der - ful peace, Rest-ing
4. And me-thinks when I rise to that cit - y of peace, Where the
5. Ah! soul, are you here with-out com - fort or rest, March-ing

mel - o - dy sweet -er than psalm; In ce - les - tial-like strains it un-
deep in the heart of my soul, So se - cure that no pow - er can
sweet - ly in Je - sus' con - trol; For I'm kept from all dan - ger by
Au - thor of peace I shall see, That one strain of the song which the
down the rough path-way of time? Make Je - sus your Friend ere the

ceas - ing - ly falls O'er my soul like an in - fi - nite calm.
mine it a - way While the years of e - ter - ni - ty roll!
night and by day, And His glo - ry is flood-ing my soul.
ran - somed will sing In that heav - en - ly King-dom shall be:
shad - ows grow dark. Oh, ac - cept this sweet peace so sub-lime!

REFRAIN

Peace! peace! won-der-ful peace, Coming down from the Fa-ther a - bove! Sweep

o - ver my spir- it for - ev-er, I pray, In fath-om-less bil-lows of love.

422 Joy Unspeakable

B. E. Warren, 20th Century   B. E. Warren, 20th Century

1. I have found His grace in all com-plete; He sup-pli-eth ev-'ry need.
2. I have found the pleas-ure I once craved; It is joy and peace with-in.
3. I have found that hope so bright and clear, Liv-ing in the realm of grace.
4. I have found the joy no tongue can tell. How its waves of glo-ry roll!

While I sit and learn at Je-sus' feet, I am free, yes, free in-deed.
What a won-drous bless-ing! I am saved From the aw-ful gulf of sin.
Oh, the Sav-iour's pres-ence is so near, I can see His smil-ing face.
It is like a great o'er-flow-ing well Springing up with-in my soul.

REFRAIN

It is joy un-speak-a-ble and full of glo-ry, Full of glo-ry, full of glo-ry. It is joy un-speak-a-ble and full of glo-ry. Oh, the half has nev-er yet been told!

423 Sunlight, Sunlight

Judson W. Van DeVenter, 1855-1939   Winfield S. Weeden, 1847-1908

1. I wan-dered in the shades of night Till Je-sus came to me,
2. Tho' clouds may gath-er in the sky, And bil-lows 'round me roll,
3. While walk-ing in the light of God, I sweet com-mu-nion find;
4. I cross the wide-ex-tend-ed fields, I jour-ney o'er the plain,
5. Soon I shall see Him as He is, The Light that came to me;

And with the sun-light of His love Bid all my dark-ness flee.
How-ev-er dark the world may be, I've sun-light in my soul.
I press with ho-ly vig-or on, And leave the world be-hind.
And in the sun-light of His love I reap the gold-en grain.
Be-hold the bright-ness of His face Thro'-out e-ter-ni-ty.

REFRAIN

Sun-light, sun-light in my soul to day! (to-day, yes,) Sun-light, sun-light

all a-long the way! (nar-row way!) Since the Sav-iour found me, took a-way my

sin, (load of sin,) I have had the sun-light of His love with-in.

424   # Heaven Came Down

John W. Peterson, 1921 -
John W. Peterson, 1921 -

1. Oh, what a won-der-ful, won-der-ful day— Day I will nev-er for-get!
2. Born of the Spir-it with life from a-bove In - to God's fam-'ly di - vine;
3. Now I've a hope that will sure-ly en-dure Af - ter the pass-ing of time.

Af - ter I'd wandered in dark-ness a-way, Je - sus, my Sav-iour, I met.
Jus - ti-fied ful-ly thru Cal - va-ry's love, Oh, what a stand-ing is mine!
I have a fu - ture in heav-en for sure, There in those mansions sub-lime.

Oh, what a ten-der, com-pas-sion-ate Friend! He met the need of my heart;
And the transaction so quick-ly was made; When as a sin - ner I came,
And it's because of that won-der-ful day When at the Cross I be - lieved;

Shad-ows dispelling, with joy I am tell-ing, He made all the darkness de - part!
Took of the of - fer of grace He did proffer, He saved me. Oh, praise His dear name!
Rich - es e - ter - nal and blessings supernal From His precious hand I re - ceived.

REFRAIN

Heav - en came down and glo - ry filled my soul,
filled my soul,

When at the Cross the Sav-iour made me whole.

made me whole. My

sins were washed a - way, And my night was turned to day.

Heav-en came down and glo - ry filled my soul!

filled my soul!

425 The King of Love My Shepherd Is

DIMINUS REGUT ME

From Psalms 23
Henry W. Baker, 1821 - 1877

John B. Dykes, 1823 - 1876

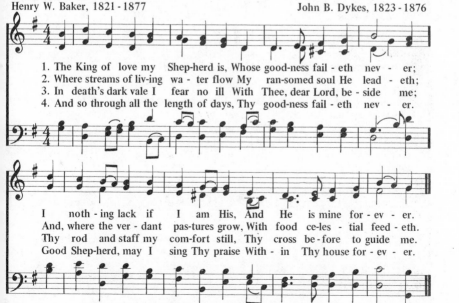

1. The King of love my Shep-herd is, Whose good-ness fail - eth nev - er;
2. Where streams of liv-ing wa - ter flow My ran-somed soul He lead - eth;
3. In death's dark vale I fear no ill With Thee, dear Lord, be - side me;
4. And so through all the length of days, Thy good-ness fail - eth nev - er.

I noth - ing lack if I am His, And He is mine for - ev - er.
And, where the ver - dant pas-tures grow, With food ce-les - tial feed - eth.
Thy rod and staff my com-fort still, Thy cross be - fore to guide me.
Good Shep-herd, may I sing Thy praise With - in Thy house for - ev - er.

426 Ring the Bells of Heaven

William O. Cushing, 1823-1902

George F. Root, 1820-1895

1. Ring the bells of heav - en! there is joy to - day For a soul return - ing from the wild! See the Fa-ther meets him out up - on the way,
Wel - com-ing His wea - ry, wan - d'ring child.

2. Ring the bells of heav - en! there is joy to - day, For the wan - d'rer
now is rec - on - ciled. Yes, a soul is res - cued from his sin - ful way,
And is born a - new a ran-somed child.

3. Ring the bells of heav - en! spread the feast to-day! An - gels, swell the
glad, tri - um-phant strain! Tell the joy - ful tid - ings; bear it far a - way!
For a pre-cious soul is born a - gain.

REFRAIN

Glo - ry! glo-ry! how the an - gels sing! Glo - ry! glo - ry! how the loud harps ring! 'Tis the ran-somed ar - my, like a might - y sea, Peal - ing forth the an-them of the free.

427 In My Heart There Rings a Melody

Elton M. Roth, 1891 - 1951   Elton M. Roth, 1891 - 1951

1. I have a song that Je - sus gave me; It was sent from
2. I love the Christ who died on Cal - v'ry, For He washed my
3. 'Twill be my end - less theme in glo - ry; With the an - gels

heav'n a - bove. There nev-er was a sweet-er mel - o - dy; 'Tis a
sins a - way. He put with-in my heart a mel - o - dy, And I
I will sing. 'Twill be a song with glo - rious har - mo - ny When the

REFRAIN

mel - o - dy of love.
know it's there to stay.   In my heart there rings a mel - o - dy, There
courts of heav - en ring.

rings a mel - o - dy with heav - en's har-mo - ny.   In my heart there

rings a mel - o - dy, There rings a mel - o - dy of love.

428 Sunshine in My Soul

SUNSHINE

Eliza E. Hewitt, 1851-1920

John R. Sweney, 1837-1899

1. There's sun-shine in my soul to-day, More glo-ri-ous and bright
2. There's mu-sic in my soul to-day, A car-ol to my King;
3. There's spring-time in my soul to-day; For when the Lord is near
4. There's glad-ness in my soul to-day, And hope and praise and love,

Than glows in an-y earth-ly sky, For Je-sus is my Light.
And Je-sus, lis-ten-ing, can hear The songs I can-not sing.
The dove of peace sings in my heart, The flow'rs of grace ap-pear.
For bless-ings which He gives me now, For joys "laid up" a-bove.

REFRAIN

Oh, there's sun - shine, bless - ed sun - shine,
sun-shine in my soul, sun-shine in my soul,

While the peace-ful, hap-py mo-ments roll.
hap-py mo-ments roll.

When Je-sus shows His smil-ing face, There is sun-shine in my soul.

429 You May Have the Joy-bells

J. Edward Ruark, 19th Century

William J. Kirkpatrick, 1838-1921

1. You may have the joy - bells ring - ing in your heart, And a peace that
2. Love of Je - sus in its full - ness you may know, And this love to
3. You will meet with tri - als as you jour - ney home; Grace suf-fi - cient
4. Let your life speak well of Je - sus ev - 'ry day; Own His right to

from you nev - er will de - part. Walk the straight and nar - row way;
those a - round you sweet - ly show. Words of kind - ness al - ways say;
He will give to o - ver - come. Tho' un - seen by mor - tal eye,
ev - 'ry ser - vice you can pay. Sin - ners you can help to win

Fine

Live for Je - sus ev - 'ry day. He will keep the joy-bells ringing in your heart.
Deeds of mer - cy do each day. Then He'll keep the joy-bells ringing in your heart.
He is with you ev - er nigh, And He'll keep the joy-bells ringing in your heart.
If your life is pure and clean, And you keep the joy-bells ringing in your heart.

D.S.—He will keep the joy-bells ringing in your heart.

REFRAIN

Joy - bells ring-ing in your heart! Joy - bells
Ring-ing in your heart,
You may have the joy - bells

D.S.

ring-ing in your heart! Take the Saviour here below With you ev'rywhere you go;

430 Glorious Freedom

Haldor Lillenas, 1885-1959

Alfred Judson, 20th Century

1. Once I was bound by sin's gall-ing fet - ters; Chained like a slave, I
2. Free-dom from all the car - nal af - fec - tions; Free-dom from en - vy,
3. Free-dom from pride and all sin - ful fol - lies; Free-dom from love and
4. Free-dom from fear with all of its tor - ments; Free-dom from care with

strug - gled in vain. But I re - ceived a glo - ri - ous free - dom
ha - tred, and strife; Free-dom from vain and world-ly am - bi - tions;
glit - ter of gold; Free-dom from e - vil tem - per and an - ger—
all of its pain; Free-dom in Christ, my bless - ed Re - deem - er,

REFRAIN

When Je - sus broke my fet - ters in twain.
Free-dom from all that sad-dened my life!
Glo - ri - ous free - dom, rap - ture un - told!   Glo - ri - ous free-dom!
He who has rent my fet - ters in twain!

Won-der-ful free-dom! No more in chains of sin I re - pine! Je-sus, the

glo - rious E-man-ci - pa - tor! Now and for-ev - er He shall be mine.

431   Victory All the Time

Lelia N. Morris, 1862-1929   Lelia N. Morris, 1862-1929

1. They who know the Sav-iour shall in Him be strong, Might-y in the
2. In the midst of bat-tle be thou not dis-mayed, Tho' the pow'rs of
3. Brave to bear life's test-ing, strong the foe to meet, Walk-ing like a

conflict of the right 'gainst wrong. This the blessed promise giv-en in God's Word,
darkness 'gainst thee are arrayed. God, thy Strength, is with thee, causing thee to stand;
he-ro midst the fur-nace heat, Doing wondrous exploits with the Spirit's Sword,

REFRAIN

Do-ing won-drous ex-ploits, they who know the Lord.   Vic-to-ry! vic-to-ry!
Heaven's al-lied ar-mies wait at thy com-mand.
Winning souls for Je-sus, praise, oh, praise the Lord!   Vic-to-ry! yes, vic-to-ry!

blessed, Blood-bo't vic-to-ry! Vic-to-ry! vic-to-ry! vict'ry all the time! As Jehovah
Vic-to-ry! yes, vic-to-ry!

liv-eth, strength divine He giv-eth Unto those who know Him, vict'ry all the time.

My Anchor Holds

432

W. C. Martin, Alt., 20th Century

Daniel B. Towner, 1850 - 1919

1. Tho' the an - gry sur - ges roll On my tem - pest-driv - en soul,
2. Might-y tides a - bout me sweep; Per - ils lurk with-in the deep;
3. I can feel the an - chor fast As I meet each sud - den blast,
4. Troub-les al - most 'whelm the soul; Griefs like bil - lows o'er me roll;

I am peace - ful, for I know, Wild - ly though the winds may blow,
An - gry clouds o'er-shade the sky, And the tem - pest ris - es high.
And the ca - ble, though un - seen, Bears the heav - y strain be - tween.
Tempters seek to lure a - stray; Storms ob-scure the light of day.

I've an an - chor safe and sure, That can ev - er-more en - dure.
Still I stand the tem-pest's shock, For my an - chor grips the Rock.
Thro' the storm I safe - ly ride, Till the turn - ing of the tide.
But in Christ I can be bold; I've an an - chor that shall hold.

REFRAIN

And it holds, my an - chor holds; Blow your wild - est, then, O
And it holds, my an - chor holds; Blow your wild - est,

gale, On my bark so small and frail. By His grace I shall not
then, O gale,

fail, For my an - chor holds, my an - chor holds.
For my an - chor holds. It firm - ly holds;

433   I Would Not Be Denied

Charles P. Jones, 20th Century   Charles P. Jones, 20th Century

1. When pangs of fear seized on my soul, Un - to the Lord I cried.
2. As Ja - cob in the days of old, I wres - tled with the Lord;
3. Old Sa - tan said my Lord was gone And would not hear my prayer.

Till Je - sus came and made me whole, I would not be de - nied.
And in - stant - ly with cour - age bold, I stood up - on His Word.
But praise the Lord! the work is done, And Christ the Lord is here.

REFRAIN

I would not be de - nied. I would not be de - nied.
de-nied. de-nied.

Till Je - sus came and made me whole, I would not be de - nied.
de-nied.

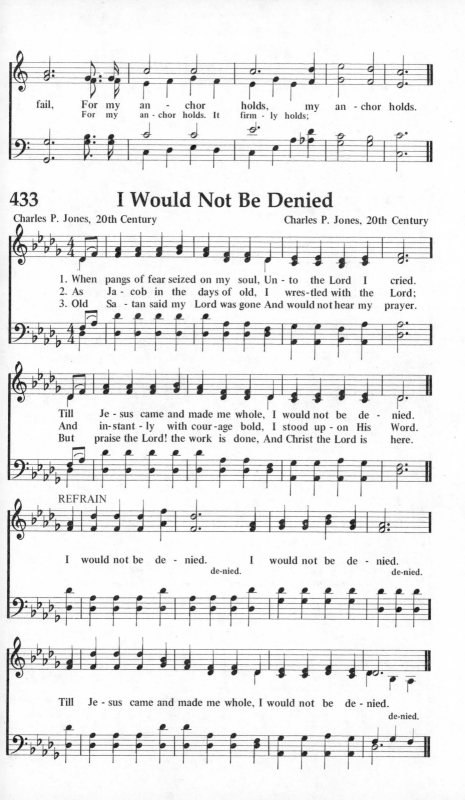

434

Victory in Jesus

Eugene M. Bartlett, 1885 - 1941   Eugene M. Bartlett, 1885 - 1941

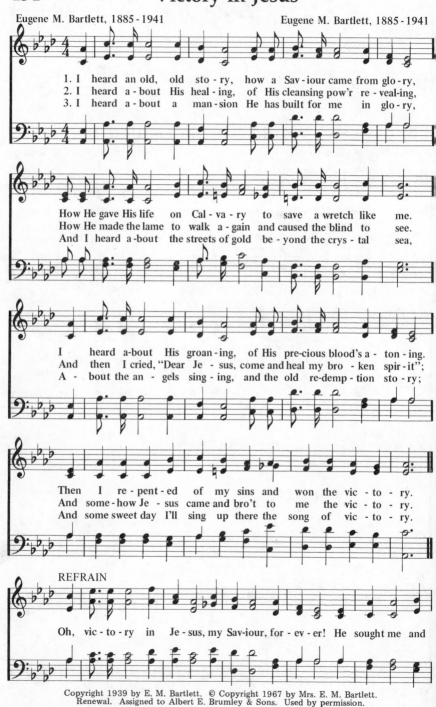

1. I heard an old, old sto - ry, how a Sav - iour came from glo - ry,
2. I heard a - bout His heal - ing, of His cleansing pow'r re - veal - ing,
3. I heard a - bout a man - sion He has built for me in glo - ry,

How He gave His life on Cal - va - ry to save a wretch like me.
How He made the lame to walk a - gain and caused the blind to see.
And I heard a - bout the streets of gold be - yond the crys - tal sea,

I heard a - bout His groan - ing, of His pre - cious blood's a - ton - ing.
And then I cried, "Dear Je - sus, come and heal my bro - ken spir - it";
A - bout the an - gels sing - ing, and the old re - demp - tion sto - ry;

Then I re - pent - ed of my sins and won the vic - to - ry.
And some - how Je - sus came and bro't to me the vic - to - ry.
And some sweet day I'll sing up there the song of vic - to - ry.

REFRAIN

Oh, vic - to - ry in Je - sus, my Sav - iour, for - ev - er! He sought me and

bought me with His re-deem-ing blood. He loved me ere   I knew Him, and all my

love   is   due Him. He plunged me to vic - to-ry be-neath the cleansing flood.

435   Jesus Never Fails

Arthur A. Luther, 1891 - 1960   Arthur A. Luther, 1891 - 1960

1. Earth - ly friends may prove un - true, Doubts and fears as - sail;   One still
2. Tho' the sky be dark and drear, Fierce and strong the gale,   Just re-
3. In life's dark and bit - ter hour Love will still pre - vail.   Trust His

REFRAIN

loves and cares for you, One who will not   fail.
mem - ber He is near, And He will not   fail.   Je -sus nev-er fails.
ev - er - last - ing pow'r; Je - sus will not   fail.

Je-sus nev-er fails. Heav'n and earth may pass a-way, But   Je-sus nev-er fails.

Yield Not to Temptation

PALMER

Horatio R. Palmer, 1834 - 1907   Horatio R. Palmer, 1834 - 1907

1. Yield not to temp - ta - tion, For yield-ing is sin. Each vic - t'ry will
2. Shun e - vil com - pan-ions; Bad lan-guage dis- dain. God's name hold in
3. To him that o'er-com-eth God giv - eth a crown. Thro' faith we shall

help you Some oth-er to win. Fight man - ful - ly on - ward;
rev - 'rence, Nor take it in vain. Be thought-ful and ear - nest,
con - quer, Though of - ten cast down. He who is our Sav - iour

Dark pas - sions sub - due.
Kind - heart - ed and true. Look ev-er to Je - sus; He'll car-ry you through.
Our strength will re - new.

REFRAIN

Ask the Sav - iour to help you, Com - fort, strength-en, and keep you.

He is will - ing to aid you; He will car - ry you through.

437 Blessed Assurance

ASSURANCE

Fanny J. Crosby, 1820-1915

Phoebe Palmer Knapp, 1839-1908

1. Bless-ed as-sur-ance, Je - sus is mine! Oh, what a fore - taste of
2. Per-fect sub-mis - sion, per-fect de - light! Vi - sions of rap - ture now
3. Per-fect sub-mis - sion, all is at rest. I in my Sav - iour am

glo - ry di - vine! Heir of sal - va - tion, pur-chase of God, Born of His
burst on my sight! An-gels de-scend-ing bring from a - bove Ech - oes of
hap- py and blest; Watching and wait - ing, look-ing a - bove, Filled with His

REFRAIN

Spir - it, washed in His blood! This is my sto - ry, this is my
mer - cy, whis - pers of love.
good-ness, lost in His love.

song, Prais - ing my Sav - iour all the day long. This is my

sto - ry, this is my song, Prais - ing my Sav - iour all the day long.

438   He Giveth More Grace

Annie Johnson Flint, 20th Century   Hubert Mitchell, 20th Century

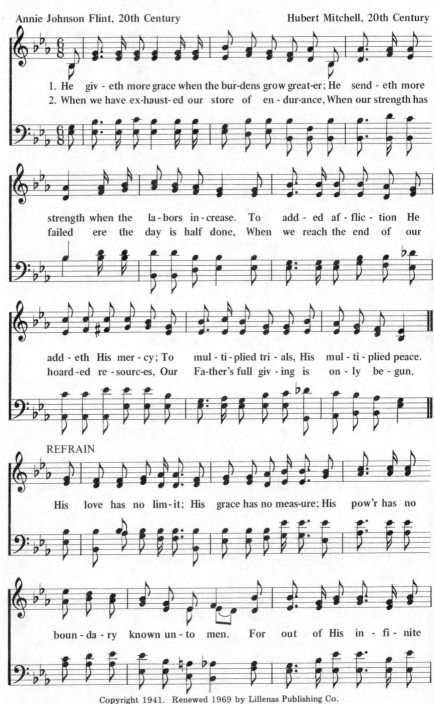

1. He giv - eth more grace when the bur-dens grow great-er; He send - eth more
2. When we have ex-haust-ed our store of en - dur-ance, When our strength has

strength when the la - bors in - crease. To add - ed af - flic - tion He
failed ere the day is half done, When we reach the end of our

add - eth His mer - cy; To mul - ti - plied tri - als, His mul - ti - plied peace.
hoard-ed re - sourc-es, Our Fa-ther's full giv - ing is on - ly be - gun.

REFRAIN

His love has no lim - it; His grace has no meas-ure; His pow'r has no

boun - da - ry known un - to men. For out of His in - fi - nite

rich - es in Je - sus, He giv - eth, and giv - eth, and giv - eth a - gain!

439 Have You Any Room for Jesus?

Source Unknown
Arr. by Daniel W. Whittle, 1840-1901

C. C. Williams, 19th Century

1. Have you an - y room for Je - sus, He who bore your load of sin?
2. Room for pleasure, room for busi - ness, But for Christ, the cru - ci - fied,
3. Have you an - y room for Je - sus, As in grace He calls a - gain?
4. Room and time now give to Je - sus. Soon will pass God's day of grace;

As He knocks and asks ad - mis - sion, Sin - ner, will you let Him in?
Not a place that He can en - ter, In the heart for which He died?
Oh, to - day is time ac - cept - ed; To-mor - row you may call in vain.
Soon thy heart left cold and si - lent, And Thy Sav-iour's plead-ing cease.

REFRAIN

Room for Je - sus, King of glo - ry! Has - ten now, His word o - bey.

Swing the heart's door wide-ly o - pen; Bid Him en - ter while you may.

We Have an Anchor

440

ANCHOR

Priscilla J. Owens, 1829-1907

William J. Kirkpatrick, 1838-1921

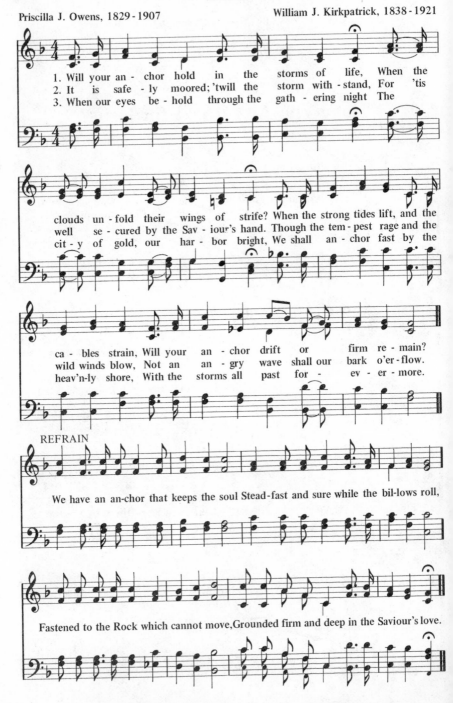

1. Will your an-chor hold in the storms of life, When the
2. It is safe-ly moored; 'twill the storm with-stand, For 'tis
3. When our eyes be-hold through the gath-ering night The

clouds un-fold their wings of strife? When the strong tides lift, and the
well se-cured by the Sav-iour's hand. Though the tem-pest rage and the
cit-y of gold, our har-bor bright, We shall an-chor fast by the

ca-bles strain, Will your an-chor drift or firm re-main?
wild winds blow, Not an an-gry wave shall our bark o'er-flow.
heav'n-ly shore, With the storms all past for-ev-er-more.

REFRAIN

We have an-chor that keeps the soul Stead-fast and sure while the bil-lows roll,

Fastened to the Rock which cannot move, Grounded firm and deep in the Saviour's love.

441 I Know God's Promise Is True

Lelia N. Morris, 1862-1929

Lelia N. Morris, 1862-1929

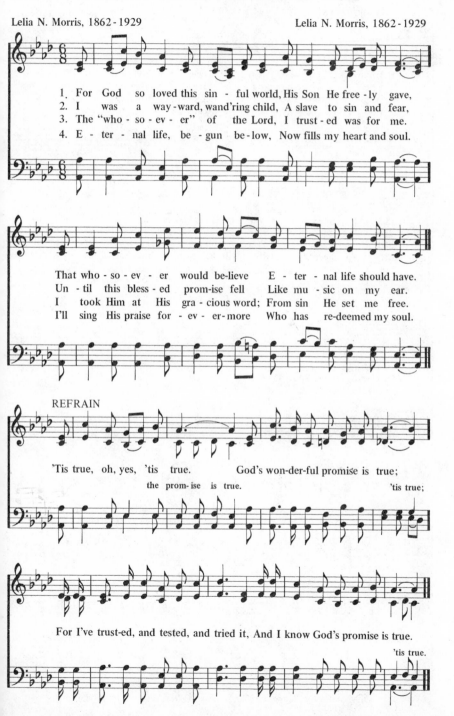

1. For God so loved this sin - ful world, His Son He free - ly gave,
2. I was a way - ward, wand'ring child, A slave to sin and fear,
3. The "who - so - ev - er" of the Lord, I trust - ed was for me.
4. E - ter - nal life, be - gun be - low, Now fills my heart and soul.

That who - so - ev - er would be - lieve E - ter - nal life should have.
Un - til this bless - ed prom - ise fell Like mu - sic on my ear.
I took Him at His gra - cious word; From sin He set me free.
I'll sing His praise for - ev - er - more Who has re - deemed my soul.

REFRAIN

'Tis true, oh, yes, 'tis true. God's won - der - ful promise is true;
the prom - ise is true. 'tis true;

For I've trust - ed, and tested, and tried it, And I know God's promise is true.
'tis true.

442 Jesus Is All I Need

James Rowe, 1865-1933

Adger M. Pace, 20th Century

1. When I am bur-dened, or wea-ry and sad, Je-sus is all I need. Nev-er He fails to up-lift and make glad. Je-sus is all I need.
2. When I am tempt-ed and fear I may fall, Je-sus is all I need. He nev-er fails to re-spond to my call. Je-sus is all I need.
3. When I am swept by the tem-pests of life, Je-sus is all I need. Peace He im-parts, what-so-ev-er the strife. Je-sus is all I need.
4. When thro' the val-ley He calls me to go, Je-sus is all I'll need. He will be with me to cheer me, I know. Je-sus is all I'll need.

REFRAIN

need. All that I need He will al-ways be, All that I need till His face I see, All that I need thro' e-ter-ni-ty. Je-sus is all I need.

443   He Never Has Failed Me Yet

W. J. Henry, 20th Century   W. J. Henry, 20th Century

1. When I trav-el the path-way so rug-ged and steep, When I pass thro' the
2. So I walk by His side thro' the heat of the day. Where He leads me I
3. Then I'll dread not the fu-ture, and fear not the foe. I am safe in His

val - ley so dark and so deep, And when snares for my soul by my
fol - low; His will I o - bey. And He makes me to con - quer the
keep - ing wher-ev - er I go; For no soul that has trust - ed Him

REFRAIN

foes have been set, Je-sus nev - er has failed me yet. He nev-er has
ills that be-set, For He nev - er has failed me yet.
will He for-get, For He nev - er has failed me yet.

failed me yet. He nev-er has failed me yet. I have prov-en Him

true; what He says He will do. He nev - er has failed me yet.

444 **His Yoke Is Easy**

From Psalms 23
Ralph E. Hudson, 1843 - 1901

Ralph E. Hudson, 1843 - 1901

1. The Lord is my Shep - herd; I shall not want. He mak - eth me down to
2. My soul cri - eth out: "Re - store me a - gain, And give me the strength to
3. Yea, tho' I should walk the val - ley of death, Yet why should I fear from

lie In pas - tures green. He lead - eth me The qui - et wa - ters by.
take The nar - row path of righ - teous-ness, E'en for His own name's sake."
ill? For Thou art with me, and Thy rod And staff me com-fort still.

REFRAIN

His yoke is eas - y; His bur-den is light. I've found it so; I've found it so.

He lead - eth me by day and by night Where liv - ing wa - ters flow.

445 **O for a Faith That Will Not Shrink**

AZMON
William H. Bathurst, 1796 - 1877

Carl G. Glaser, 1784 - 1829

1. O for a faith that will not shrink, Tho' pressed by ev - 'ry foe,
2. That will not mur - mur nor com-plain Be - neath the chast'ning rod
3. A faith that shines more bright and clear When tem-pests rage with-out;
4. Lord, give us such a faith as this; And then, what - e'er may come,

447   Yesterday, Today, Forever

Albert B. Simpson, 1843 - 1919   J. H. Burke, 19th Century

1. Oh, how sweet the glo - rious mess - age Sim - ple faith may claim:
2. Him who par - don'd err - ing Pe - ter, Nev - er need'st thou fear;
3. He who mid the rag - ing bil - lows Walk'd up - on the sea
4. As of old He walk'd to Em-ma-us, With them to a - bide,

Yes - ter - day, to - day, for - ev - er, Je - sus is the same!
He that came to faith - less Thom-as All thy doubt will clear.
Still can hush our wild - est tem - pest, As on Gal - i - lee.
So thro' all life's way He walk - eth, Ev - er near our side.

Still He loves to save the sin - ful, Heal the sick and lame,
He who let the lov'd dis-ci - ple On His bos - om rest
He who wept and pray'd in an - guish, In Geth-sem - a - ne,
Soon a - gain shall we be - hold Him. Has- ten, Lord, the day!

Cheer the mourn - er, still the tem - pest. Glo - ry to His name!
Bids thee still, with love as ten - der, Lean up-on His breast.
Drinks with us each cup of trem - bling, In our ag - o - ny.
But 'twill still be "this same Je - sus," As He went a - way.

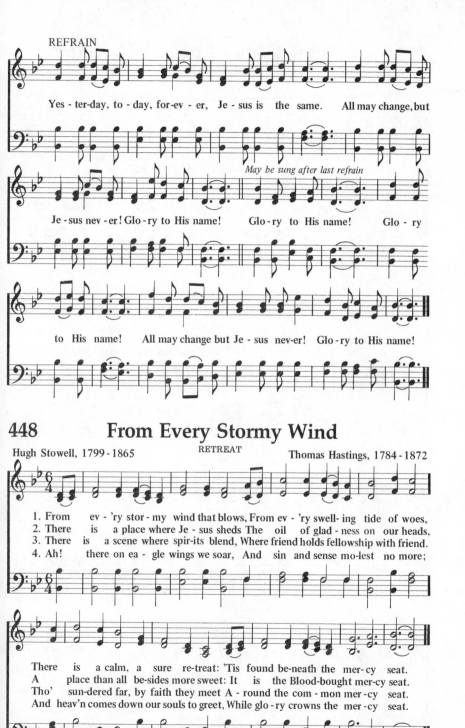

REFRAIN

Yes - ter-day, to - day, for-ev - er, Je - sus is the same. All may change, but

Je - sus nev - er! Glo-ry to His name! Glo-ry to His name! Glo - ry

May be sung after last refrain

to His name! All may change but Je - sus nev-er! Glo-ry to His name!

448   From Every Stormy Wind

RETREAT

Hugh Stowell, 1799 - 1865   Thomas Hastings, 1784 - 1872

1. From ev - 'ry stor - my wind that blows, From ev - 'ry swell- ing tide of woes,
2. There is a place where Je - sus sheds The oil of glad - ness on our heads,
3. There is a scene where spir-its blend, Where friend holds fellowship with friend.
4. Ah! there on ea - gle wings we soar, And sin and sense mo-lest no more;

There is a calm, a sure re-treat: 'Tis found be-neath the mer-cy seat.
A place than all be-sides more sweet: It is the Blood-bought mer-cy seat.
Tho' sun-dered far, by faith they meet A - round the com - mon mer -cy seat.
And heav'n comes down our souls to greet, While glo - ry crowns the mer-cy seat.

449 I Know Whom I Have Believed

EL NATHAN

Daniel W. Whittle, 1840-1901

James McGranahan. 1840-1907

1. I know not why God's won-drous grace To me He hath made known;
2. I know not how this sav-ing faith To me He did im-part,
3. I know not how the Spir-it moves, Con-vinc-ing men of sin,
4. I know not what of good or ill May be re-served for me,
5. I know not when my Lord may come, At night or noon-day fair,

Nor why, un-wor-thy, Christ in love Re-deemed me for His own.
Nor how be-liev-ing in His Word Wrought peace within my heart.
Re-veal-ing Je-sus thro' the Word, Cre-at-ing faith in Him.
Of wea-ry ways or gold-en days, Be-fore His face I see.
Nor if I'll walk the vale with Him, Or meet Him in the air.

REFRAIN

But "I know whom I have be-liev-ed, And am per-suad-ed that He is

a-ble To keep that which I've com-mit-ted Un-to Him a-gainst that day."

450 God Will Take Care of You

Civilla D. Martin, 1869 - 1948

W. Stillman Martin, 1862 - 1935

1. Be not dis-mayed what - e'er be-tide; God will take care of you.
2. Thro' days of toil when heart doth fail; God will take care of you;
3. All you may need He will pro-vide; God will take care of you.
4. No mat-ter what may be the test, God will take care of you.

Be - neath His wings of love a-bide; God will take care of you.
When dan - gers fierce your path as-sail, God will take care of you.
Noth-ing you ask will be de-nied; God will take care of you.
Lean, wea - ry one, up - on His breast; God will take care of you.

REFRAIN

God will take care of you, Thro' ev-'ry day, O'er all the way.

He will take care of you; God will take care of you.

take care of you.

451 Under His Wings

William O. Cushing, 1823-1902   Ira D. Sankey, 1840-1908

1. Un - der His wings   I am   safe - ly   a - bid - ing.   Tho' the night
2. Un - der His wings,   what a   ref - uge in sor - row!   How the heart
3. Un - der His wings,   oh, what pre - cious en - joy-ment!   There will I

deep-ens and   tem-pests are   wild,   Still   I   can trust Him; I
yearn-ing - ly   turns to His   rest!   Of - ten when earth has no
hide till life's   tri - als are   o'er;   Shel - tered, pro - tect - ed,   no

know He   will keep me.   He has re-deemed me, and   I   am His child.
balm for   my heal - ing,   There I find com-fort, and there I   am blest.
e - vil   can harm me.   Rest-ing in Je - sus, I'm   safe ev - er - more.

REFRAIN

Un - der His wings,   un-der His wings, Who from His love   can   sev - er?

Un - der His wings my soul shall a - bide, Safe-ly a - bide   for - ev - er.

452 Hiding in Thee

HIDING

William O. Cushing, 1823 - 1902

Ira D. Sankey, 1840 - 1908

1. Oh, safe to the Rock that is high - er than I,
2. In the calm of the noon - tide, in sor - row's lone hour,
3. How oft in the con - flict, when pressed by the foe,

My soul in its con - flicts and sor - rows would fly. So
In times when temp - ta - tion casts o'er me its pow'r; In the
I have fled to my Ref - uge and breathed out my woe! How

sin - ful, so wea - ry, Thine, Thine would I be. Thou
tem - pests of life, on its wide, heav - ing sea, Thou
of - ten, when tri - als like sea bil - lows roll, Have I

REFRAIN

blest "Rock of A - ges," I'm hid - ing in Thee.
blest "Rock of A - ges," I'm hid - ing in Thee. Hid - ing in Thee,
hid - den in Thee, O Thou Rock of my soul!

Hid - ing in Thee; Thou blest "Rock of A - ges," I'm hid - ing in Thee.

453 Come, Ye Disconsolate

CONSOLATION

Thomas Moore, 1779-1852
Alt. by Thomas Hastings, 1784-1872

Samuel Webbe, 1740-1816

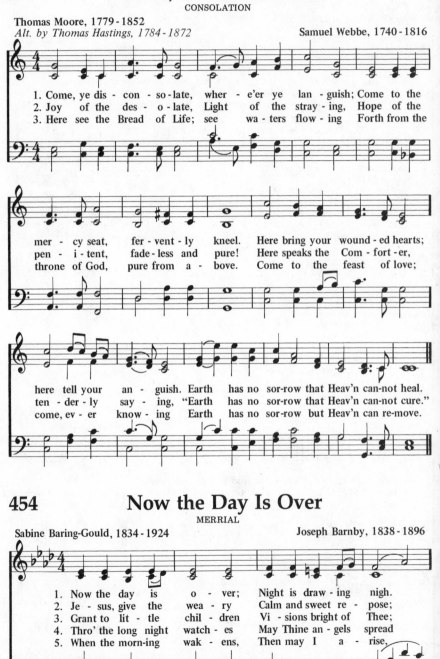

1. Come, ye dis - con - so - late, wher - e'er ye lan - guish; Come to the
2. Joy of the des - o - late, Light of the stray - ing, Hope of the
3. Here see the Bread of Life; see wa - ters flow - ing Forth from the

mer - cy seat, fer - vent - ly kneel. Here bring your wound - ed hearts;
pen - i - tent, fade - less and pure! Here speaks the Com - fort - er,
throne of God, pure from a - bove. Come to the feast of love;

here tell your an - guish. Earth has no sor-row that Heav'n can-not heal.
ten - der - ly say - ing, "Earth has no sor-row that Heav'n can-not cure."
come, ev - er know - ing Earth has no sor-row but Heav'n can re-move.

454 Now the Day Is Over

MERRIAL

Sabine Baring-Gould, 1834-1924

Joseph Barnby, 1838-1896

1. Now the day is o - ver; Night is draw - ing nigh.
2. Je - sus, give the wea - ry Calm and sweet re - pose;
3. Grant to lit - tle chil - dren Vi - sions bright of Thee;
4. Thro' the long night watch - es May Thine an - gels spread
5. When the morn - ing wak - ens, Then may I a - rise,

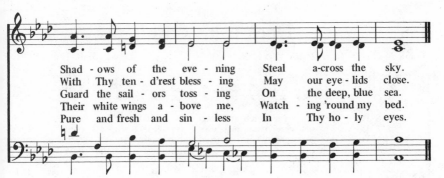

Shad - ows of the eve - ning   Steal   a-cross the   sky.
With Thy ten - d'rest bless - ing May   our eye - lids close.
Guard the sail - ors toss - ing On   the deep, blue sea.
Their white wings a - bove me, Watch - ing 'round my bed.
Pure   and fresh and sin - less In   Thy ho - ly   eyes.

455   In the Hour of Trial

PENITENCE

James Montgomery, 1771 - 1854
Alt. by Frances A. Hutton, 1811 - 1877
                                            Spencer Lane, 1843 - 1903

1. In the hour of tri - al, Je - sus, plead for me, Lest by base de -
2. With for-bid - den pleas - ures Would this vain world charm, Or its sor - did
3. Should Thy mer -cy send me Sor - row, toil, and woe, Or should pain at-
4. When my last hour com - eth, Fraught with strife and pain, When my dust re-

ni - al   I de - part from Thee. When Thou seest me wa - ver, With a
treas-ures Spread to work me harm. Bring to my re - mem -brance Sad Geth-
tend me   On my path be - low, Grant that I may nev - er Fail Thy
turn - eth To the dust a - gain, On Thy truth re - ly - ing, Thro' that

look re - call, Nor for fear or fa - vor Suf - fer me to fall.
sem - a - ne, Or, in dark - er sem-blance, Cross-crowned Cal-va-ry.
hand to see; Grant that I may ev - er Cast my care on Thee.
mor - tal strife, Je - sus, take me, dy - ing, To e - ter - nal life.

456 Does Jesus Care?

Frank E. Graeff, 1860 - 1919

J. Lincoln Hall, 1866 - 1930

1. Does Je - sus care when my heart is pained Too deep - ly for
2. Does Je - sus care when my way is dark With a name - less
3. Does Je - sus care when I've tried and failed To re - sist some temp-
4. Does Je - sus care when I've said, "Good-by," To the dear - est on

mirth and song, As the bur - dens press, and the cares dis-tress, And the
dread and fear? As the day - light fades in - to deep night shades,Does He
ta - tion strong; When for my deep grief I find no re - lief, Tho' my
earth to me, And my sad heart aches till it near - ly breaks? Is it

REFRAIN

way grows wea-ry and long?
care e - nough to be near?
tears flow all the night long?
aught to Him? Does He see?

Oh, yes, He cares; I know He cares. His

heart is touched with my grief.___ When the days are wea-ry, the

rit.

long nights drea-ry, I know my Sav - iour cares.

He cares.

457 Trusting Jesus

Edgar Page Stites, 1836 - 1921

Ira D. Sankey, 1840 - 1908

1. Sim - ply trust - ing ev - 'ry day, Trust - ing thro' a storm - y way;
2. Bright-ly doth His Spir - it shine In - to this poor heart of mine.
3. Sing - ing if my way is clear; Pray - ing if the path be drear;
4. Trust-ing Him while life shall last, Trust - ing Him till earth be past,

E - ven when my faith is small, Trust - ing Je - sus, that is all.
While He leads I can - not fall; Trust - ing Je - sus, that is all.
If in dan - ger, for Him call; Trust - ing Je - sus, that is all.
Till with-in the jas - per wall: Trust - ing Je - sus, that is all.

REFRAIN

Trust - ing as the mo - ments fly; Trust - ing as the days go by;

Trust - ing Him what - e'er be - fall; Trust - ing Je - sus, that is all.

458 The Rock That Is Higher than I

Erastus Johnson, 1826 - 1909

William G. Fischer, 1835 - 1912

1. Oh, some-times the shad-ows are deep, And rough seems the path to the goal;
2. Oh, some-times how long seems the day, And sometimes how wea-ry my feet!
3. Oh, near to the Rock let me keep If bless-ings or sor-rows prevail,

And sor - rows, sometimes how they sweep Like tempests down o-ver the soul!
But toil - ing in life's dust-y way, The Rock's blessed shadow, how sweet!
Or climb-ing the moun-tain way steep, Or walk-ing the shad-ow-y vale.

REFRAIN

Oh, then to the Rock let me fly,
let me fly,
To the Rock that is

high - er than I!
is high - er than I!
Oh, then to the Rock let me

fly,
let me fly,
To the Rock that is high - er than I!

459 Just When I Need Him Most

William C. Poole, 1875-1949

Charles H. Gabriel, 1856-1932

1. Just when I need Him, Je-sus is near, Just when I fal - ter, just when I fear; Read - y to help me, read - y to cheer, Just when I need Him most.
2. Just when I need Him, Je-sus is true, Nev - er for - sak - ing all the way thro'; Giv - ing for bur - dens pleas - ures a - new, Just when I need Him most.
3. Just when I need Him, Je-sus is strong, Bear - ing my bur - dens all the day long; For all my sor - row giv - ing a song, Just when I need Him most.
4. Just when I need Him, He is my All, An-swer - ing when up - on Him I call; Ten - der - ly watch - ing lest I should fall, Just when I need Him most.

REFRAIN

Just when I need Him most, Just when I need Him most; Je - sus is near to com - fort and cheer, Just when I need Him most.

460 No One Understands like Jesus

John W. Peterson, 1921 -   John W. Peterson, 1921 -

1. No one un-der-stands like Je - sus; He's a Friend be-yond com-pare.
2. No one un-der-stands like Je - sus; Ev - 'ry woe He sees and feels.
3. No one un-der-stands like Je - sus, When the foes of life as - sail.
4. No one un-der-stands like Je - sus, When you falt-er on the way.

Meet Him at the throne of mer-cy; He is wait-ing for you there.
Ten - der-ly He whis-pers com-fort, And the bro-ken heart He heals.
You should nev - er be dis - cour-aged; Je - sus cares and will not fail.
Tho' you fail Him, sad - ly fail Him, He will par-don you to - day.

REFRAIN

No one un - der-stands like Je - sus, When the days are dark and grim.

No one is so near, so dear as Je - sus; Cast your ev'ry care on Him.

461 Sweetly Resting

Mary D. James, 19th Century

W. Warren Bently, 19th Century

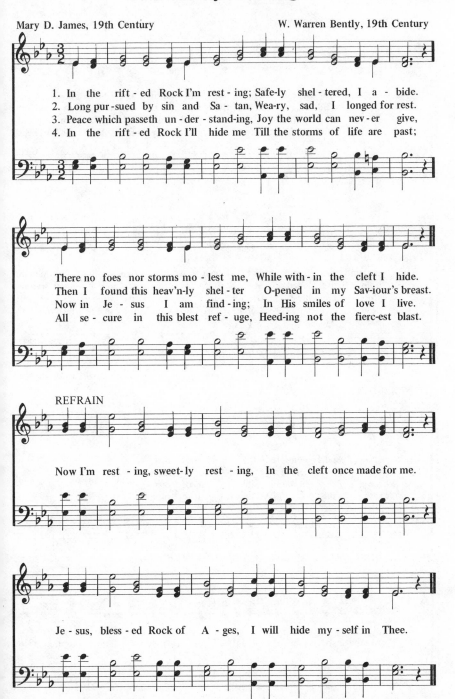

1. In the rift-ed Rock I'm rest-ing; Safe-ly shel-tered, I a-bide.
2. Long pur-sued by sin and Sa-tan, Wea-ry, sad, I longed for rest.
3. Peace which passeth un-der-stand-ing, Joy the world can nev-er give,
4. In the rift-ed Rock I'll hide me Till the storms of life are past;

There no foes nor storms mo-lest me, While with-in the cleft I hide.
Then I found this heav'n-ly shel-ter O-pened in my Sav-iour's breast.
Now in Je-sus I am find-ing; In His smiles of love I live.
All se-cure in this blest ref-uge, Heed-ing not the fierc-est blast.

REFRAIN

Now I'm rest-ing, sweet-ly rest-ing, In the cleft once made for me.

Je-sus, bless-ed Rock of A-ges, I will hide my-self in Thee.

462   The Haven of Rest

Henry L. Gilmour, 1837-1920

George D. Moore, 19th Century

1. My soul in sad ex-ile was out on life's sea, So bur-dened with
2. I yield-ed my-self to His ten-der em-brace, And faith tak-ing
3. The song of my soul, since the Lord made me whole, Has been the old
4. Oh, come to the Sav-iour. He pa-tient-ly waits To save by His

sin and dis-trest, Till I heard a sweet voice say-ing,"Make Me your
hold of the Word, My fet-ters fell off, and I an-chored my
sto-ry so blest, Of Je-sus, who'll save who-so-ev-er will
pow-er di-vine. Come, an-chor your soul in the ha-ven of

D.S: tem-pest may sweep o'er the wild, storm-y

choice,"And I en-tered the ha-ven of rest.
soul. The Ha-ven of Rest is my Lord.
have A home in the ha-ven of rest.
rest, And say,"My Be-lov-ed is mine."

REFRAIN

I've an-chored my soul

deep; In Je-sus I'm safe ev-er-more.

in the ha-ven of rest. I'll sail the wide seas no more. The

D.S.

463 God Be with You

Jeremiah E. Rankin, 1828 - 1904

William G. Tomer, 1833 - 1896

1. God be with you till we meet a - gain;   By   His counsels guide, uphold you;
2. God be with you till we meet a - gain, 'Neath His wings protecting   hide you,
3. God be with you till we meet a - gain;   When life's per-ils thick con-found you,
4. God be with you till we meet a - gain,   Keep love's banner floating   o'er you,

With His sheep se - cure-ly   fold   you.
Dai - ly man - na still pro - vide   you.   God be with you till we meet a-gain.
Put His arms un - fail - ing round   you.
Smite death's threat'ning wave before you.

REFRAIN

Till we meet,—   till we meet,   Till we meet at Je - sus'   feet;
   Till we meet,   till we meet,   till we meet;

Till we meet,—   till we   meet,   God be with you till we meet a-gain.
   Till we meet,   till we meet,

464 No, Not One!

EVANGELINE

Johnson Oatman, Jr., 1856-1922

George C. Hugg, 1848-1907

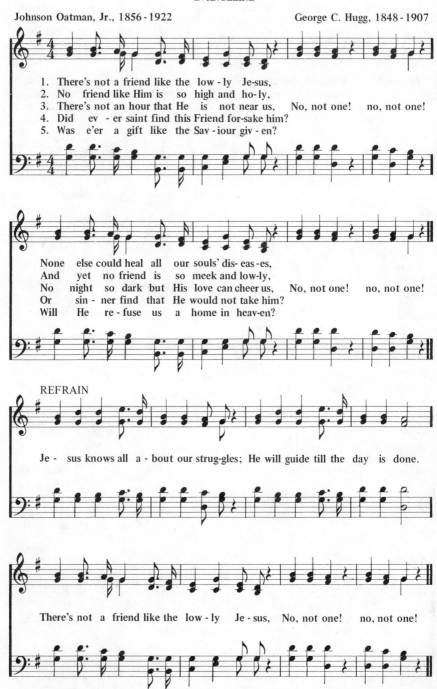

1. There's not a friend like the low-ly Je-sus,
2. No friend like Him is so high and ho-ly,
3. There's not an hour that He is not near us, No, not one! no, not one!
4. Did ev - er saint find this Friend for-sake him?
5. Was e'er a gift like the Sav-iour giv-en?

None else could heal all our souls' dis-eas-es,
And yet no friend is so meek and low-ly,
No night so dark but His love can cheer us, No, not one! no, not one!
Or sin - ner find that He would not take him?
Will He re - fuse us a home in heav-en?

REFRAIN

Je - sus knows all a - bout our strug-gles; He will guide till the day is done.

There's not a friend like the low-ly Je-sus, No, not one! no, not one!

465 Trust and Obey

John H. Sammis, 1849-1919

Daniel B. Towner, 1850-1919

1. When we walk with the Lord In the light of His Word, What a glo - ry He
2. Not a shad - ow can rise, Not a cloud in the skies, But His smile quickly
3. Not a bur - den we bear, Not a sor - row we share But our toil He doth
4. But we nev - er can prove The de-lights of His love Un - til all on the
5. Then in fel - low-ship sweet We will sit at His feet, Or we'll walk by His

sheds on our way! While we do His good will, He a - bides with us still,
drives it a - way. Not a doubt nor a fear, Not a sigh nor a tear
rich - ly re - pay. Not a grief nor a loss, Not a frown nor a cross
al - tar we lay; For the fa - vor He shows And the joy He be-stows
side in the way. What He says we will do; Where He sends we will go;

REFRAIN

And with all who will trust and o - bey.
Can a - bide while we trust and o - bey.
But is blest if we trust and o - bey. Trust and o - bey, For there's
Are for them who will trust and o - bey.
Nev - er fear, on - ly trust and o - bey.

no oth - er way To be hap-py in Je - sus But to trust and o - bey.

466 Faith Is the Victory

John H. Yates, 1837-1900

Ira D. Sankey, 1840-1908

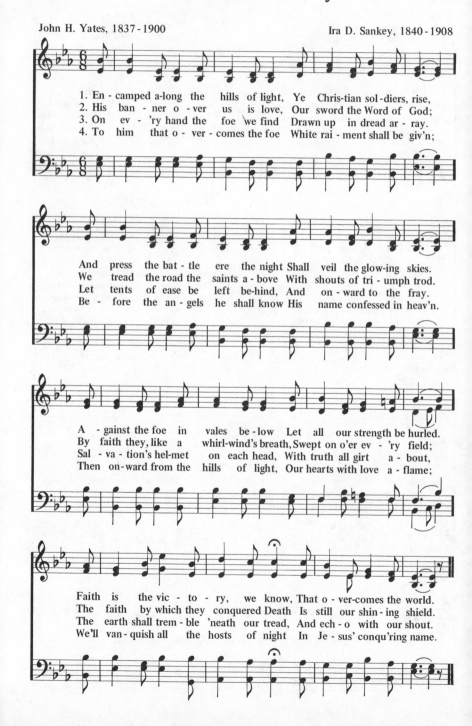

1. En - camped a-long the hills of light, Ye Chris-tian sol -diers, rise,
2. His ban - ner o - ver us is love, Our sword the Word of God;
3. On ev - 'ry hand the foe we find Drawn up in dread ar - ray.
4. To him that o - ver - comes the foe White rai - ment shall be giv'n;

And press the bat - tle ere the night Shall veil the glow-ing skies.
We tread the road the saints a - bove With shouts of tri - umph trod.
Let tents of ease be left be-hind, And on - ward to the fray.
Be - fore the an - gels he shall know His name confessed in heav'n.

A - gainst the foe in vales be - low Let all our strength be hurled.
By faith they, like a whirl-wind's breath, Swept on o'er ev - 'ry field;
Sal - va - tion's hel-met on each head, With truth all girt a - bout,
Then on-ward from the hills of light, Our hearts with love a - flame;

Faith is the vic - to - ry, we know, That o - ver-comes the world.
The faith by which they conquered Death Is still our shin - ing shield.
The earth shall trem - ble 'neath our tread, And ech - o with our shout.
We'll van - quish all the hosts of night In Je - sus' conqu'ring name.

REFRAIN

Faith_____ is the vic - to - ry! Faith_____ is the vic - to - ry!
Faith   Faith

Oh, glo - ri - ous vic - to - ry That o - ver -comes the world!

467 **I Would Be True**
PEEK

Howard Arnold Walter, 1883 - 1918
Author of third stanza unknown

Joseph Yates Peek, 1843 - 1911

1. I would be true, for there are those who trust me. I would be pure, for there
2. I would be friend of all— the foe, the friend-less. I would be giv - ing, and
3. I would be prayerful thro' each bus - y mo - ment. I would be con - stant- ly

are those who care. I would be strong, for there is much to suf - fer. I would be
for - get the gift. I would be hum - ble, for I know my weak-ness. I would look
in touch with God. I would be tuned to hear His slightest whis-per. I would have

brave, for there is much to dare. I would be brave, for there is much to dare.
up, and laugh, and love, and lift. I would look up, and laugh, and love, and lift.
faith to keep the path Christ trod. I would have faith to keep the path Christ trod.

468 Living by Faith

James Wells, 20th Century
4th stanza, R. E. Winsett, 20th Century

J. L. Heath, 20th Century

1. I care not to-day what the morrow may bring, If shadow or sunshine or rain.
2. Tho' tempests may blow and storm clouds arise, Obscuring the brightness of life,
3. I know that He safe-ly will car-ry me thro', No mat-ter what e-vils be - tide.
4. Our Lord will return to this earth some sweet day; Our troubles will then all be o'er.

The Lord, I know, rul-eth o'er ev - er - y-thing, And all of my wor-ry is vain.
I'm nev - er a-larmed at the o-ver-cast skies; The Master looks on at the strife.
Why should I then care, tho' the tempest may blow, If Jesus walks close to my side?
The Mas-ter so gent-ly will lead us a - way, Beyond that blest heavenly shore.

REFRAIN

Liv - ing by faith_____ in Je - sus a - bove; _____
Yes, liv - ing by faith   in Je - sus a - bove;

Trust-ing, con-fid - ing in His great love; _____
Trust-ing, con-fid - ing   yes, in His great love;

Safe from all harm_____ in His shel-ter-ing arm,
I'm safe from all harm   His shel - ter - ing arm;

Copyright renewed 1946 in "His Voice in Song" by R. E. Winsett.

I'm liv-ing by faith_____ and feel no a - larm._____

I'm liv - ing by faith   *feel no a-larm.*

469   # I Must Tell Jesus
ORWIGSBURG

Elisha A. Hoffman, 1839 - 1929   Elisha A. Hoffman, 1839 - 1929

1. I must tell Je - sus all of my tri - als; I can - not bear these
2. I must tell Je - sus all of my trou - bles; He is a kind, com-
3. Tempt-ed and tried, I need a great Sav - iour, One who can help my

bur - dens a - lone.   In my dis - tress He kind - ly will help me;
pas - sion - ate Friend.   If I but ask Him, He will de - liv - er,
bur - dens to bear.   I must tell Je - sus, I must tell Je - sus;

D.S: I must tell Je - sus! I must tell Je - sus;

REFRAIN

He ev - er loves and cares for His own.   I must tell Je - sus!
Make of my trou - bles quick - ly an end.
He all my cares and sor - rows will share.

Je-sus can help me, Je-sus a - lone.

D.S.

I must tell Je - sus! I can - not bear my bur - dens a - lone.

470 I Need Jesus

George O. Webster, 1866-1942

Charles H. Gabriel, 1856-1932

1. I need Je-sus; my need I now con-fess. No friend like Him in times of deep dis-tress! I need Je-sus; the need I glad-ly own. Tho' some may bear their load a-lone, Yet I need Je-sus.

2. I need Je-sus; I need a Friend like Him, A Friend to guide when paths of life are dim. I need Je-sus when foes my soul as-sail. A-lone, I know I can but fail, So I need Je-sus.

3. I need Je-sus; I need Him to the end. No one like Him— He is the sin-ners' Friend. I need Je-sus; no oth-er friend will do. So con-stant, kind, so strong and true—Yes, I need Je-sus.

REFRAIN

I need Je-sus; I need Je-sus. I need Jesus ev-'ry day.
I need Je-sus with me; I need Je-sus al-ways.
ev-'ry day.
Need Him in the sunshine hour, need Him when the

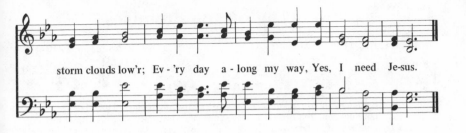

storm clouds low'r; Ev - 'ry day a - long my way, Yes, I need Je-sus.

471 Near to the Heart of God

Cleland B. McAfee, 1866 - 1944   Cleland B. McAfee, 1866 - 1944

1. There is a place of qui - et rest, Near to the heart of God;
2. There is a place of com-fort sweet, Near to the heart of God;
3. There is a place of full re - lease, Near to the heart of God;

A place where sin can - not mo - lest, Near to the heart of God.
A place where we our Sav - iour meet, Near to the heart of God.
A place where all is joy and peace, Near to the heart of God.

REFRAIN

O Je - sus, blest Re - deem - er, Sent from the heart of God,

Hold us, who wait be - fore Thee, Near to the heart of God.

472   Standing on the Promises

R. Kelso Carter, 1849-1928

PROMISES

R. Kelso Carter, 1849-1928

1. Stand-ing on the prom-is-es of Christ, my King! Thro' e-ter-nal
2. Stand-ing on the prom-is-es that can-not fail! When the howl-ing
3. Stand-ing on the prom-is-es I now can see Per-fect, pres-ent
4. Stand-ing on the prom-is-es of Christ, the Lord, Bound to Him e-
5. Stand-ing on the prom-is-es I can-not fall, Lis-t'ning ev-'ry

a-ges let His prais-es ring. "Glo-ry in the high-est!" I will shout and sing,
storms of doubt and fear assail, By the liv-ing Word of God I shall pre-vail,
cleansing in the Blood for me; Stand-ing in the lib-er-ty where Christ makes free,
ter-nal-ly by love's strong cord, O-ver-com-ing dai-ly with the Spirit's Sword,
mo-ment to the Spir-it's call, Rest-ing in my Sav-iour as my All in All,

Stand-ing on the prom-is-es of God.

REFRAIN

Stand-ing, stand-
Standing on the prom-is-es, Standing on the

ing, Stand-ing on the prom-is-es of God, my Sav-iour; Stand-
prom-is-es, Standing on the

ing, stand-ing, I'm standing on the promises of God.
prom-is-es, Stand-ing on the prom-is-es,

473 Blessed Hour of Prayer

Fanny J. Crosby, 1820-1915

William H. Doane, 1832-1915

1. 'Tis the bless-ed hour of prayer, when our hearts low-ly bend, And we
2. 'Tis the bless-ed hour of prayer, when the Sav-iour draws near With a
3. 'Tis the bless-ed hour of prayer, when the tempt-ed and tried To the
4. At the bless-ed hour of prayer, trust-ing Him, we be-lieve That the

gath-er to Je-sus, our Sav-iour and Friend. If we come to Him in
ten-der com-pas-sion His chil-dren to hear, When He tells us we may
Sav-iour, who loves them, their sor-row con-fide. With a sym-pa-thiz-ing
bless-ings we're need-ing we'll sure-ly re-ceive. In the full-ness of this

faith, His pro-tec-tion to share,
cast at His feet ev-'ry care.
heart He re-moves ev-'ry care.
trust we shall lose ev-'ry care.

What a balm for the wea-ry! Oh, how

REFRAIN

sweet to be there! Bless-ed hour of prayer! Bless-ed hour of

prayer! What a balm for the wea-ry! Oh, how sweet to be there!

474 Tell It to Jesus

Jeremiah E. Rankin, 1828-1904

Edmund S. Lorenz, 1854-1942

1. Are you wea - ry, are you heav-y-heart-ed?
2. Do the tears flow down your cheeks un-bid-den?
3. Do you fear the gath-'ring clouds of sor-row?
4. Are you trou-bled at the tho't of dy-ing?

Tell it to Je - sus; Tell it to Je - sus.

Are you griev - ing o - ver joys de-part-ed?
Have you sins that to men's eyes are hid-den?
Are you anx - ious what shall be to-mor-row?
For Christ's com-ing king-dom are you sigh-ing?

REFRAIN

Tell it to Je - sus a - lone. Tell it to Je - sus; tell it to Je - sus.

He is a Friend that's well - known. You've no oth - er

such a friend or broth - er. Tell it to Je - sus a - lone.

475 Sweet Hour of Prayer

SWEET HOUR

Attrib. to William W. Walford, 1772-1850   William B. Bradbury, 1816-1868

1. Sweet hour of prayer, sweet hour of prayer, That calls me from a world of care
2. Sweet hour of prayer, sweet hour of prayer, The joy I feel, the bliss I share,
3. Sweet hour of prayer, sweet hour of prayer, Thy wings shall my pe-ti-tion bear

And   bids me at my   Fa-ther's throne Make all my wants and wishes known!
Of   those whose anx-ious spir-its burn With strong desires for thy re-turn!
To   Him whose truth and faith-ful-ness En-gage the wait-ing soul to bless;

In   sea-sons of dis-tress and grief My soul has of-ten found relief,
With such I has-ten to the place Where God, my Saviour, shows His face,
And   since He bids me seek His face, Be-lieve His word, and trust His grace,

And   oft es-caped the tempter's snare, By thy return, sweet hour of prayer.
And   glad-ly take my sta-tion there, And wait for thee, sweet hour of prayer.
I'll   cast on Him my ev-'ry care, And wait for thee, sweet hour of prayer.

476 I Need Thee Every Hour

NEED

Annie S. Hawks, 1835-1918

Robert Lowry, 1826-1899

1. I need Thee ev-'ry hour, Most gra-cious Lord; No ten-der voice like
2. I need Thee ev-'ry hour; Stay Thou near-by. Temp-ta-tions lose their
3. I need Thee ev-'ry hour, In joy or pain; Come quick-ly and a-
4. I need Thee ev-'ry hour, Most Ho-ly One. Oh, make me Thine in-

REFRAIN

Thine Can peace af-ford.
pow'r When Thou art nigh.
bide, Or life is vain.
deed, Thou bless-ed Son!

I need Thee; oh, I need Thee! Ev-'ry hour I

need Thee! Oh, bless me now, my Sav-iour; I come to Thee!

477 Not My Will, but Thine

Hugh C. Benner, 1899-

Hugh C. Benner, 1899-

Slowly

Not my will, but Thine; not my will, but Thine; Not my will, but

Thy will, be done, Lord, in me. May Thy Spir-it di-vine fill this be - ing of mine. Not my will, but Thy will, be done, Lord, in me.

478 Saviour, More than Life
EVERY DAY AND HOUR

Fanny J. Crosby, 1820 - 1915

William H. Doane, 1832 - 1915

1. Sav-iour, more than life to me, I am cling-ing, cling-ing close to Thee.
2. Thro' this chang-ing world be - low Lead me gent-ly, gent-ly as I go.
3. Let me love Thee more and more Till this fleet-ing, fleet-ing life is o'er;

Let Thy pre - cious blood ap - plied Keep me ev - er, ev - er near Thy side.
Trusting Thee, I can - not stray; I can nev-er, nev-er lose my way.
Till my soul is lost in love In a bright-er, bright-er world a - bove.

REFRAIN

Ev - 'ry day, ev - 'ry hour, Let me feel Thy cleansing pow'r.
Ev - 'ry day and hour, ev - 'ry day and hour,

May Thy ten - der love to me Bind me clos-er, clos-er, Lord, to Thee.

479 # Did You Think to Pray?

Mrs. M. A. Kidder, 1825-1905

William O. Perkins, 19th Century

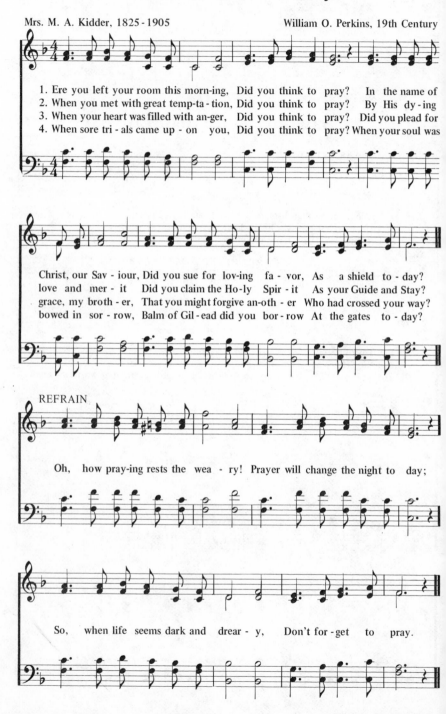

1. Ere you left your room this morn-ing, Did you think to pray? In the name of
2. When you met with great temp-ta-tion, Did you think to pray? By His dy-ing
3. When your heart was filled with an-ger, Did you think to pray? Did you plead for
4. When sore tri-als came up-on you, Did you think to pray? When your soul was

Christ, our Sav-iour, Did you sue for lov-ing fa-vor, As a shield to-day?
love and mer-it Did you claim the Ho-ly Spir-it As your Guide and Stay?
grace, my broth-er, That you might forgive an-oth-er Who had crossed your way?
bowed in sor-row, Balm of Gil-ead did you bor-row At the gates to-day?

REFRAIN

Oh, how pray-ing rests the wea-ry! Prayer will change the night to day;

So, when life seems dark and drear-y, Don't for-get to pray.

480 God Leads Us Along

G. A. Young, 19th Century   G. A. Young, 19th Century

1. In shad-y green pas-tures so rich and so sweet, God leads His dear
2. Sometimes on the mount where the sun shines so bright, God leads His dear
3. Tho' sor-rows be-fall us and Sa-tan op-pose, God leads His dear
4. A-way from the mire, and a-way from the clay, God leads His dear

chil-dren a-long. Where the wa-ter's cool flow bathes the wea-ry one's feet,
chil-dren a-long. Some-times in the val-ley in the dark-est of night,
chil-dren a-long. Through grace we can con-quer, de-feat all our foes.
chil-dren a-long. A-way up in glo-ry, e-ter-ni-ty's day,

REFRAIN

God leads His dear children a-long. Some thro' the waters, some thro' the flood,

Some thro' the fire, but all thro' the Blood. Some thro' great sor-row, but

rit.

God gives a song In the night sea-son and all the day long.

481 It Is Glory Just to Walk with Him

Avis M. Burgeson, 20th Century

Haldor Lillenas, 1885-1959

1. It is glo - ry just to walk with Him whose blood has ransomed me;
2. It is glo - ry when the shad - ows fall to know that He is near.
3. 'Twill be glo - ry when I walk with Him on heav - en's gold - en shore,

It is rap - ture for my soul each day. It is joy di - vine to
Oh! what joy to sim - ply trust and pray! It is glo - ry to a -
Nev - er from His side a - gain to stray. 'Twill be glo - ry, wondrous

feel Him near where'er my path may be. Bless the Lord, it's glo-ry all the way!
bide in Him when skies a-bove are clear. Yes, with Him, it's glo-ry all the way!
glo - ry with the Sav-iour ev - er-more, Ev - er - last-ing glo-ry all the way!

REFRAIN

It is glo - ry just to walk with Him.
walk with Him.
It is

glo - ry just to walk with Him.
walk with Him.
He will guide my steps a - right,

483 Moment by Moment

MOMENT

Daniel W. Whittle, 1840-1901

May Whittle Moody, 1870-1963

1. Dy - ing with Je - sus, by death reckoned mine; Liv-ing with Je -sus a
2. Nev - er a tri - al that He is not there, Nev-er a burden that
3. Nev - er a heartache and nev - er a groan, Nev-er a tear-drop and
4. Nev - er a weakness that He doth not feel, Nev-er a sick-ness that

new life di - vine; Looking to Je-sus till glo -ry doth shine, Mo-ment by
He doth not bear, Nev-er a sor-row that He doth not share; Mo-ment by
nev - er a moan, Nev-er a dan-ger but there on the throne, Mo-ment by
He can-not heal; Mo-ment by mo-ment, in woe or in weal, Je - sus, my

REFRAIN

mo-ment, O Lord, I am Thine.
mo-ment, I'm un - der His care.
mo-ment, He thinks of His own.   Mo-ment by mo-ment I'm kept in His love;
Sav-iour, a - bides with me still.

Mo-ment by mo-ment I've life from a - bove.   Look-ing to Je - sus till

glo - ry doth shine,   Mo - ment by mo-ment, O Lord, I am   Thine.

484 He Leadeth Me

Joseph H. Gilmore, 1834-1918

William B. Bradbury, 1816-1868

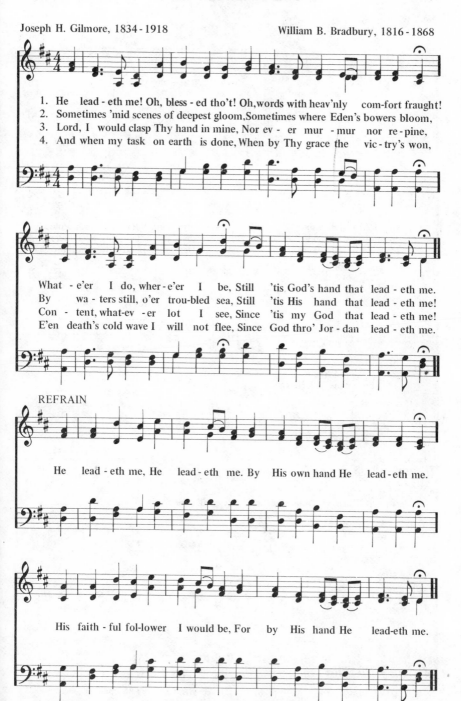

1. He lead-eth me! Oh, bless-ed tho't! Oh, words with heav'nly com-fort fraught!
2. Sometimes 'mid scenes of deepest gloom, Sometimes where Eden's bowers bloom,
3. Lord, I would clasp Thy hand in mine, Nor ev-er mur-mur nor re-pine,
4. And when my task on earth is done, When by Thy grace the vic-try's won,

What-e'er I do, wher-e'er I be, Still 'tis God's hand that lead-eth me.
By wa-ters still, o'er trou-bled sea, Still 'tis His hand that lead-eth me!
Con-tent, what-ev-er lot I see, Since 'tis my God that lead-eth me!
E'en death's cold wave I will not flee, Since God thro' Jor-dan lead-eth me.

REFRAIN

He lead-eth me, He lead-eth me. By His own hand He lead-eth me.

His faith-ful fol-lower I would be, For by His hand He lead-eth me.

485 Surely Goodness and Mercy

John W. Peterson, 1921 -
Alfred B. Smith, 1916 -

John W. Peterson, 1921 -

1. A pilgrim was I and a - wand'ring. In the cold night of
2. He re - stor - eth my soul when I'm wea-ry; He giv - eth me
3. When I walk thro' the dark, lone-some val-ley, My Sav - iour will

sin I did roam, When Je - sus, the kind Shep-herd, found me,
strength day by day. He leads me be - side the still wa - ters;
walk with me there; And safe - ly His great hand will lead me

REFRAIN

And now I am on my way home.
He guards me each step of the way. Sure - ly good-ness and mer-cy shall
To the man-sions He's gone to pre - pare.

fol - low me All the days, all the days of my life.

Sure - ly good - ness and mer - cy shall fol - low me All the days,

all the days of my life. And I shall dwell in the house of the

Lord for - ev - er, And I shall feast at the ta - ble spread for me.

486   The Lord's My Shepherd

Francis Rous, 1579-1659   CRIMOND   Jessie Seymour Irvine, 1836-1887

1. The Lord's my Shep - herd; I'll not want. He
2. My soul He doth re - store a - gain, And
3. Yea, tho' I walk in death's dark vale, Yet
4. My ta - ble Thou hast fur - nish - ed In
5. Good - ness and mer - cy all my life Shall

makes me down to lie In pas - tures green; He
me to walk doth make With - in the paths of
will I fear no ill; For Thou art with me,
pres - ence of my foes; My head Thou dost with
sure - ly fol - low me, And in God's house for-

lead - eth me The qui - et wa - ters by.
righ - teous - ness, E'en for His own name's sake.
and Thy rod And staff me com - fort still.
oil a - noint, And my cup o - ver - flows.
ev - er - more My dwell - ing place shall be.

487   The Lord Is My Shepherd

James Montgomery, 1771-1854   Thomas Koschat, 1845-1914

1. The Lord is my Shep-herd; no want shall I know. I feed in green
2. Thro' the val-ley and shad-ow of death though I stray, Since Thou art my
3. In the midst of af-flic-tion my ta-ble is spread; With blessings un-
4. Let good-ness and mer-cy, my boun-ti-ful God, Still fol-low my

pas-tures; safe-fold-ed I rest. He lead-eth my soul where the
Guard-ian, no e-vil I fear. Thy rod shall de-fend me, Thy
meas-ured my cup run-neth o'er; With per-fume and oil Thou a-
steps till I meet Thee a-bove. I seek by the path which my

still wa-ters flow, Re-stores me when wan-dering, re-deems when op-
staff be my stay. No harm can be-fall, with my Com-fort-er
noint-est my head. Oh, what shall I ask of Thy prov-i-dence
fore-fa-thers trod, Thro' the land of their so-journ, Thy king-dom of

pressed; Re-stores me when wan-dering, re-deems when op-pressed.
near; No harm can be-fall, with my Com-fort-er near.
more? Oh, what shall I ask of Thy prov-i-dence more?
love; Thro' the land of their so-journ, Thy king-dom of love.

488   Jesus Will Walk with Me

Haldor Lillenas, 1885-1959   Haldor Lillenas, 1885-1959

1. Je-sus will walk with me down thro' the val-ley; Je-sus will walk with me
2. Je-sus will walk with me when I am tempt-ed, Giv-ing me strength as my
3. Je-sus will walk with me, guarding me ev-er, Giv-ing me vic-t'ry thro'
4. Je-sus will walk with me in life's fair morning, And when the shadows of

o - ver the plain. When in the shad-ow or when in the sun-shine,
need may de - mand. When in af - flic-tion His pres-ence is near me;
storm and thro' strife. He is my Com-fort-er, Coun-sel - or, Lead-er,
eve-ning must come. Liv - ing or dy-ing, He will not for-sake me.

REFRAIN

If He goes with me I shall not com-plain.
I am up-held by His al-might-y hand. Je - - sus will
O - ver the un - e - ven jour-ney of life.
Je - sus will walk with me all the way home. Je - sus, my Sav - iour, will

walk with me. He will talk with me; He will walk with me. In joy or in

sor-row, to - day and to - mor-row, I know He will walk with me.
will walk with me.

489 Saviour, like a Shepherd Lead Us

BRADBURY

Ascribed to Dorothy A. Thrupp, 1779-1847

William B. Bradbury, 1816-1868

1. Sav - iour, like a shep-herd lead us; Much we need Thy ten-der care.
2. We are Thine; do Thou be-friend us; Be the Guard-ian of our way.
3. Thou hast promised to re - ceive us, Poor and sin - ful tho' we be;
4. Ear - ly let us seek Thy fa - vor; Ear - ly let us do Thy will.

In Thy pleas-ant pas-tures feed us; For our use Thy folds pre-pare.
Keep Thy flock; from sin de - fend us; Seek us when we go a - stray.
Thou hast mer - cy to re - lieve us, Grace to cleanse, and power to free.
Bless - ed Lord and on - ly Sav - iour, With Thy love our bos-oms fill.

Bless - ed Je - sus, bless-ed Je - sus! Thou hast bought us; Thine we are.
Bless - ed Je - sus, bless-ed Je - sus! Hear, O hear us, when we pray.
Bless - ed Je - sus, bless-ed Je - sus! We will ear - ly turn to Thee.
Bless - ed Je - sus, bless-ed Je - sus! Thou hast loved us; love us still.

Bless - ed Je - sus, bless-ed Je - sus! Thou hast bought us; Thine we are.
Bless - ed Je - sus, bless-ed Je - sus! Hear, O hear us, when we pray.
Bless - ed Je - sus, bless-ed Je - sus! We will ear - ly turn to Thee.
Bless - ed Je - sus, bless-ed Je - sus! Thou hast loved us; love us still.

490 All the Way My Saviour Leads

ALL THE WAY

Fanny J. Crosby, 1820-1915

Robert Lowry, 1826-1899

1. All the way my Sav-iour leads me. What have I to ask be - side?
2. All the way my Sav-iour leads me, Cheers each wind-ing path I tread,
3. All the way my Sav-iour leads me. Oh, the full - ness of His love!

Can I doubt His ten-der mer - cy Who thro' life has been my Guide?
Gives me grace for ev - 'ry tri - al, Feeds me with the liv - ing bread.
Per-fect rest to me is prom-ised In my Fa -ther's house a - bove.

Heav'nly peace, di - vin - est com - fort, Here by faith in Him to dwell!
Tho' my wea - ry steps may fal - ter, And my soul a - thirst may be,
When my spir - it, clothed, im-mor - tal, Wings its flight to realms of day.

For I know, what-e'er be - fall me, Je - sus do - eth all things well.
Gush-ing from the Rock be - fore me, Lo! a spring of joy I see.
This my song thro' end-less a - ges— Je- sus led me all the way;

For I know, what-e'er be - fall me, Je - sus do - eth all things well.
Gush-ing from the Rock be - fore me, Lo! a spring of joy I see.
This my song thro' end - less a - ges— Je- sus led me all the way.

491 Lead, Kindly Light

LUX BENIGNA

John H. Newman, 1801-1890

John B. Dykes, 1823-1876

1. Lead, kind-ly Light, a - mid th'en-cir-cling gloom; Lead Thou me on!
2. I was not ev - er thus, nor prayed that Thou Shouldst lead me on;
3. So long Thy power hath blest me, sure it still Will lead me on

The night is dark, and I am far from home; Lead Thou me on!
I loved to choose and see my path, but now Lead Thou me on!
O'er moor and fen, o'er crag and tor-rent, till The night is gone,

Keep Thou my feet; I do not ask to see - - - -
I loved the gar - ish day, and, spite of fears, - - -
And with the morn those an - gel fac - es smile - - -

The dis - tant scene; one step e - nough for me.
Pride ruled my will. Re - mem-ber not past years.
Which I have loved long since and lost a - while!

492 Jesus Loves Even Me

GLADNESS

Philip P. Bliss, 1838-1876   Philip P. Bliss, 1838-1876

1. I am so glad that our Fa-ther in heav'n Tells of His love in the
2. Tho' I for-get Him and wan-der a-way, Still He doth love me wher-
3. Oh, if there's on-ly one song I can sing When in His beau-ty I

Book He has giv'n. Won-der-ful things in the Bi-ble I see;
ev-er I stray. Back to His dear, lov-ing arms would I flee
see the great King, This shall my song in e-ter-ni-ty be:

REFRAIN

This is the dear-est, that Je-sus loves me.
When I re-mem-ber that Je-sus loves me. I am so glad that
"Oh, what a won-der that Je-sus loves me!"

Je-sus loves me, Je-sus loves me, Je-sus loves me!

I am so glad that Je-sus loves me, Je-sus loves e-ven me!

493   Tell Me the Story of Jesus

Fanny J. Crosby, 1820-1915

John R. Sweney, 1837-1899

1. Tell me the sto-ry of Je-sus; Write on my heart ev-'ry word.
2. Fast-ing a-lone in the des-ert, Tell of the days that are past:
3. Tell of the Cross where they nailed Him, Writh-ing in an-guish and pain;

Tell me the sto-ry most pre-cious, Sweet-est that ev-er was heard.
How for our sins He was tempt-ed, Yet was tri-um-phant at last.
Tell of the grave where they laid Him; Tell how He liv-eth a-gain.

Tell how the an-gels, in cho-rus, Sang as they wel-comed His birth:
Tell of the years of His la-bor; Tell of the sor-row He bore.
Love in that sto-ry so ten-der Clear-er than ev-er I see.

"Glo-ry to God in the high-est! Peace and good tid-ings to earth."
He was de-spised and af-flict-ed, Home-less, re-ject-ed, and poor.
Stay, let me weep while you whis-per Love paid the ran-som for me.

REFRAIN

Tell me the sto-ry of Je-sus; Write on my heart ev-'ry word.

Tell me the sto - ry most pre - cious, Sweet-est that ev - er was heard.

494   Jewels

William O. Cushing, 1823 - 1902   George F. Root, 1820 - 1895

1. When He com - eth, when He com - eth To make up His jew - els,
2. He will gath - er, He will gath - er The gems for His king - dom:
3. Lit - tle chil - dren, lit - tle chil - dren Who love their Re - deem - er

All His jew - els, pre-cious jew - els, His loved and His own.
All the pure ones, all the bright ones, His loved and His own.
Are the jew - els, pre-cious jew - els, His loved and His own.

REFRAIN

Like the stars of the morn - ing, His bright crown a - dorn - ing,

They shall shine in their beau - ty, Bright gems for His crown.

495 Our Friendly Church

Elizabeth B. Jones, 20th Century

Hugh C. Benner, 1899-

1. Our church is such a friend-ly place; It's where I
2. Our church is such a hap-py place In ev-'ry-
3. Our church is such a qui-et place When heads are

love to be. I smile at all the friends I meet; I
thing we do. We sing our love and thanks to God; We
bowed for prayer. We whis-per lov-ing words to God; We

smile at all the friends I meet, And they smile back at me.
sing our love and thanks to God, And know He loves us too.
whis-per lov-ing words to God, And thank Him for His care.

Copyright 1945 by Nazarene Publishing House

496 Praise Him, All Ye Little Children

Anonymous

Anonymous

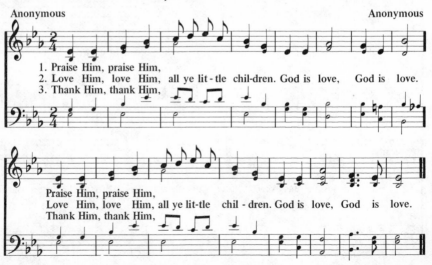

1. Praise Him, praise Him,
2. Love Him, love Him, all ye lit-tle chil-dren. God is love, God is love.
3. Thank Him, thank Him,

Praise Him, praise Him,
Love Him, love Him, all ye lit-tle chil-dren. God is love, God is love.
Thank Him, thank Him,

497 Jesus Loves Me

Anna B. Warner, 1820 - 1915

William B. Bradbury, 1816 - 1868

1. Je - sus loves me! this I know, For the Bi - ble tells me so.
2. Je - sus loves me! He who died Heav-en's gates to o - pen wide.
3. Je - sus, take this heart of mine; Make it pure, and whol-ly Thine.

Lit - tle ones to Him be - long; They are weak but He is strong.
He will wash a - way my sin, Let His lit - tle child come in.
Thou hast bled and died for me; I will henceforth live for Thee.

REFRAIN

Yes, Je-sus loves me. Yes, Je-sus loves me. Yes, Je-sus loves me. The Bi-ble tells me so.

498 Happy the Home When God Is There

Henry Ware, Jr., 1794 - 1843   ST. AGNES   John B. Dykes, 1823 - 1876

1. Hap - py the home when God is there, And love fills ev - 'ry breast;
2. Hap - py the home where Je - sus' name Is sweet to ev - 'ry ear;
3. Hap - py the home where prayer is heard, And praise is wont to rise;
4. Lord, let us in our homes a - gree This bless-ed peace to gain.

When one their wish, and one their prayer, And one their heaven-ly rest.
Where chil - dren ear - ly lisp His fame, And par-ents hold Him dear.
Where par - ents love the sa - cred Word And all its wis - dom prize.
U - nite our hearts in love to Thee, And love to all will reign.

499 A Christian Home

FINLANDIA

Barbara B. Hart, 1916 -

Jean Sibelius, 1865 - 1957

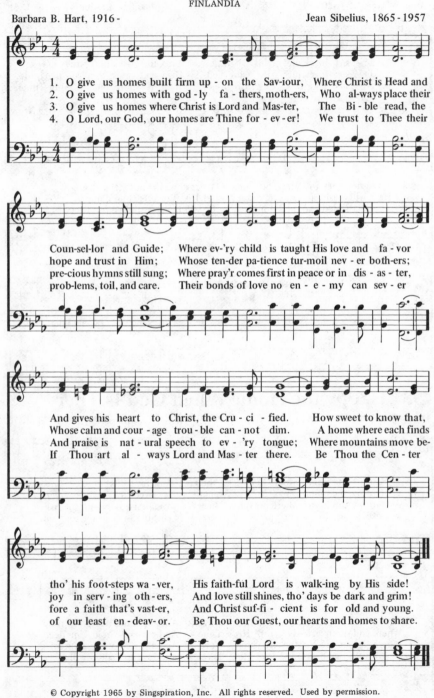

1. O give us homes built firm up - on the Sav-iour, Where Christ is Head and
2. O give us homes with god - ly fa - thers, moth-ers, Who al-ways place their
3. O give us homes where Christ is Lord and Mas-ter, The Bi - ble read, the
4. O Lord, our God, our homes are Thine for - ev - er! We trust to Thee their

Coun-sel-lor and Guide; Where ev-'ry child is taught His love and fa - vor
hope and trust in Him; Whose ten-der pa-tience tur-moil nev - er both-ers;
pre-cious hymns still sung; Where pray'r comes first in peace or in dis - as - ter,
prob-lems, toil, and care. Their bonds of love no en - e - my can sev - er

And gives his heart to Christ, the Cru - ci - fied. How sweet to know that,
Whose calm and cour - age trou - ble can - not dim. A home where each finds
And praise is nat - ural speech to ev - 'ry tongue; Where mountains move be-
If Thou art al - ways Lord and Mas - ter there. Be Thou the Cen - ter

tho' his foot-steps wa - ver, His faith-ful Lord is walk-ing by His side!
joy in serv - ing oth-ers, And love still shines, tho' days be dark and grim!
fore a faith that's vast-er, And Christ suf-fi - cient is for old and young.
of our least en - deav-or. Be Thou our Guest, our hearts and homes to share.

500

O Perfect Love

Dorothy B. Gurney, 1858-1932

Joseph Barnby, 1838-1896

1. O per - fect Love, all hu - man thought tran - scend - ing,
2. O per - fect Life, be Thou their full as - sur - ance
3. Grant them the joy which bright - ens earth - ly sor - row;
4. Hear us, O Fa - ther, gra - cious and for - giv - ing,

Low - ly we kneel in prayer be - fore Thy throne,
Of ten - der char - i - ty and stead - fast faith;
Grant them the peace which calms all earth - ly strife,
Through Je - sus Christ, Thy co - e - ter - nal Word,

That theirs may be the love which knows no end - ing,
Of pa - tient hope, and qui - et, brave en - dur - ance,
And to life's day the glo - rious, un - known mor - row
Who, with the Ho - ly Ghost, by all things liv - ing

Whom Thou for - ev - er - more dost join in one.
With child - like trust that fears nor pain nor death.
That dawns up - on e - ter - nal love and life.
Now and to end - less a - ges art a - dored.

501 The Star-spangled Banner

NATIONAL ANTHEM OF U.S.A.

Francis Scott Key, 1779 - 1843

John Stafford Smith, 1750 - 1836

1. O   say, can you   see,   by the dawn's ear-ly   light, What so
2. On the shore dim - ly   seen   thro' the mists of the   deep, Where the
3. O   thus be it   ev - er when free - men shall stand Be -

proud - ly we   hailed   at the twi - light's last gleaming? Whose broad
foe's haugh - ty   host   in dread si - lence re - pos - es, What is
tween their loved   homes   and the war's des - o - la - tion! Blest with

stripes and bright stars, thro' the per - i - lous fight, O'er the ram-parts we
that which the breeze, o'er the tow - er - ing steep, As it fit - ful - ly
vic - t'ry and peace, may the heav'n-res-cued land Praise the Pow'r that hath

watched,   were so   gal - lant - ly stream - ing? And the rock - et's red
blows,   half con - ceals, half dis - clos - es? Now it catch - es the
made   and pre - served us   a   na - tion! Then   con - quer we

glare,   the bombs burst-ing in   air   Gave   proof thro' the night that our
gleam   of the morn-ing's first beam;   In full glo - ry re - flect - ed, now
must,   when our cause it is   just;   And   this be our mot - to: "In

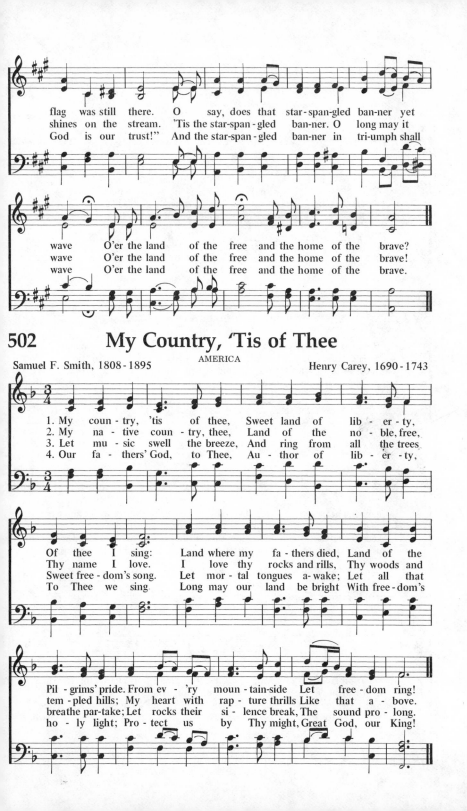

502 My Country, 'Tis of Thee

503 O Canada!

NATIONAL SONG OF CANADA

R. Stanley Weir   Calixa Lavallee

1. O   Can - a - da!   Our   home and   na - tive   land!
2. O   Can - a - da!   Where   pines and   ma - ples   grow,
3. O   Can - a - da!   Be - neath thy   shin - ing   skies
4. Rul - er   Su - preme,   who   hear - est   hum - ble   prayer,

True   pa - triot's   love   in   all   thy   sons com - mand. With
Great   prair - ies   spread,   and   lord - ly   riv - ers   flow, How
May   stal - wart   sons   and   gen - tle   maid - ens   rise, To
Hold   our do - min - ion   in   Thy   lov - ing   care. Help

glow-ing hearts we   see thee rise, The   True North strong and free; And
dear to us   thy   broad do-main, From   East to Wes - tern sea! Thou
keep thee steadfast thro'-out the years From   East to Wes - tern sea, Our
us   to find, O   God, in Thee, A   last - ing, rich re - ward, As

stand on guard, O   Can - a - da, We stand on guard for   thee.
land   of hope for   all   who toil! Thou True North, strong and   free!
own be - lov - ed   na - tive land! Our   True North, strong and   free!
wait - ing for the   bet - ter day, We   ev - er stand on   guard.

REFRAIN

O Can-a-da! Glorious and free! We stand on guard, we stand on

guard for thee. O Can-a-da! We stand on guard for thee.

504   # God Save the Queen

SONG OF THE BRITISH COMMONWEALTH

Henry Carey, 1690-1743

1. God save our gra-cious Queen! Long live our no-ble Queen!
2. Thy choic-est gifts in store, On her be pleased to pour;

God save the Queen! Send her vic-to-ri-ous, Hap-py and
Long may she reign. May she de-fend our laws And ev-er

glo-ri-ous, Long to reign o-ver us. God save the Queen!
give us cause To sing with heart and voice: "God save the Queen!"

505 America, the Beautiful

MATERNA

Katherine Lee Bates, 1859-1929

Samuel A. Ward, 1847-1903

1. O beau - ti - ful for spa - cious skies, For am - ber waves of grain,
2. O beau - ti - ful for pil - grim feet, Whose stern, im-pas-sioned stress
3. O beau - ti - ful for he - roes proved In lib - er - at - ing strife,
4. O beau - ti - ful for pa - triot dream That sees be - yond the years

For pur - ple mountain maj - es - ties A - bove the fruit - ed plain!
A thor - ough-fare for free - dom beat A - cross the wil - der - ness!
Who more than self their coun - try loved, And mer - cy more than life!
Thine al - a - bas - ter cit - ies gleam Un-dimmed by hu - man tears!

A - mer - i - ca! A - mer - i - ca! God shed His grace on thee,
A - mer - i - ca! A - mer - i - ca! God mend thine ev - 'ry flaw,
A - mer - i - ca! A - mer - i - ca! May God thy gold re - fine
A - mer - i - ca! A - mer - i - ca! God shed His grace on thee,

And crown thy good with broth - er - hood From sea to shin - ing sea!
Con - firm thy soul in self - con-trol, Thy lib - er - ty in law!
Till all suc - cess be no - ble - ness And ev - 'ry gain di - vine!
And crown thy good with broth - er - hood From sea to shin - ing sea!

506 Mine Eyes Have Seen the Glory

BATTLE HYMN

Julia Ward Howe, 1819-1910   John William Steffe, 19th Century

1. Mine eyes have seen the glo - ry of the com-ing of the Lord. He is
2. I have seen Him in the watch fires of a hundred circling camps; They have
3. He has sound-ed forth the trumpet that shall nev - er call re-treat; He is
4. In the beau-ty of the lil - ies Christ was born a-cross the sea, With a

tram-pling out the vin - tage where the grapes of wrath are stored; He hath
build - ed Him an al - tar in the eve - ning dews and damps; I can
sift - ing out the hearts of men be - fore His judg - ment seat. Oh, be
glo - ry in His bos - om that trans-fig - ures you and me. As He

loosed the fate - ful light - ning of His ter - ri - ble, swift sword. His truth is
read His righ - teous sen - tence by the dim and flar - ing lamps. His day is
swift, my soul, to an - swer Him! be ju - bi-lant, my feet! Our God is
died to make men ho - ly, let us die to make men free, While God is

REFRAIN

march-ing on. Glo - ry! glo - ry! Hal - le - lu - jah! Glo - ry! glo-ry! Hal-le-

lu - jah! Glo-ry! glo - ry! Hal - le - lu - jah! His truth is march-ing on.

Let the Beauty of the Lord

INVOCATION

Floyd W. Hawkins, 1904 -

Floyd W. Hawkins, 1904 -

Let the beau-ty of the Lord our God be up-

on us in this hour. Let the pres-ence of the

Ho-ly Ghost now a-bide with us in pow'r.
Our Fa-ther,

Hear now our pray'r; Hear now our pray'r.
oh, hear us!

508   Hear Our Prayer, O Lord

George Whelpton, 1847 - 1930

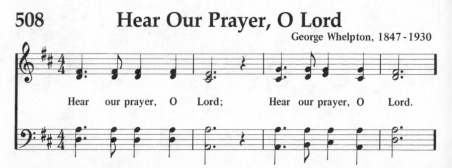

Hear our prayer, O Lord; Hear our prayer, O Lord.

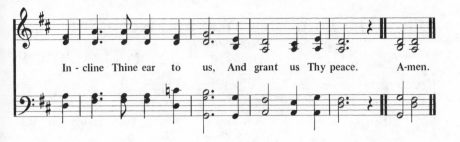

In - cline Thine ear to us, And grant us Thy peace. A-men.

509   Saviour, Again to Thy Dear Name

ELLERS

John Ellerton, 1826 - 1893   Edward J. Hopkins, 1818 - 1901

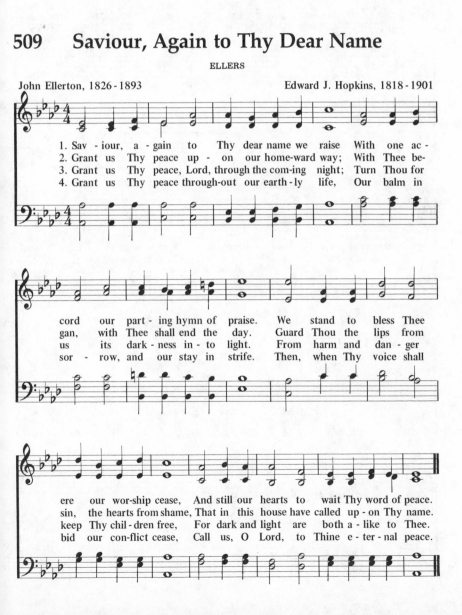

1. Sav - iour, a - gain to Thy dear name we raise With one ac -
2. Grant us Thy peace up - on our home-ward way; With Thee be -
3. Grant us Thy peace, Lord, through the com-ing night; Turn Thou for
4. Grant us Thy peace through-out our earth - ly life, Our balm in

cord our part - ing hymn of praise. We stand to bless Thee
gan, with Thee shall end the day. Guard Thou the lips from
us its dark - ness in - to light. From harm and dan - ger
sor - row, and our stay in strife. Then, when Thy voice shall

ere our wor-ship cease, And still our hearts to wait Thy word of peace.
sin, the hearts from shame, That in this house have called up - on Thy name.
keep Thy chil - dren free, For dark and light are both a - like to Thee.
bid our con-flict cease, Call us, O Lord, to Thine e - ter - nal peace.

510 The Lord Bless You and Keep You

BENEDICTION

Numbers 6:24-26

Peter C. Lutkin, 1858-1931

Scripture Readings

May be used in unison or responsively

Index

511 Calls to Worship

(May be used singly or in combinations)

Praise ye the Lord. Praise God in his sanctuary: praise him in the firmament of his power.

Praise him for his mighty acts: praise him according to his excellent greatness.

Let every thing that hath breath praise the Lord. Praise ye the Lord.

— *Ps. 150:1-2, 6*

Give unto the Lord, O ye mighty, give unto the Lord glory and strength.

Give unto the Lord the glory due unto his name; worship the Lord in the beauty of holiness. — *Ps. 29:1-2*

If my people, which are called by my name, shall humble themselves, and pray, and seek my face, and turn from their wicked ways; then will I hear from heaven, and will forgive their sin, and will heal their land. — *II Chron. 7:14*

But the hour cometh, and now is, when the true worshippers shall worship the Father in spirit and in truth: for the Father seeketh such to worship him.

God is a Spirit: and they that worship him must worship him in spirit and in truth. — *John 4:23-24*

Come unto me, all ye that labour and are heavy laden, and I will give you rest.

Take my yoke upon you, and learn of me; for I am meek and lowly in heart: and ye shall find rest unto your souls.

For my yoke is easy, and my burden is light. — *Matt. 11:28-30*

O come, let us worship and bow down: let us kneel before the Lord our maker.

For he is our God; and we are the people of his pasture, and the sheep of his hand. — *Ps. 95:6-7a*

Enter into his gates with thanksgiving, and into his courts with praise: be thankful unto him, and bless his name.

For the Lord is good; his mercy is everlasting; and his truth endureth to all generations. — *Ps. 100:4-5*

Bless ye the Lord, all ye servants of the Lord, which by night stand in the house of the Lord.

Lift up your hands in the sanctuary, and bless the Lord.

The Lord that made heaven and earth bless thee out of Zion. — *Psalms 134*

512 The Lord's Prayer

Our Father which art in heaven, Hallowed be thy name. Thy kingdom come. Thy will be done in earth, as it is in heaven. Give us this day our daily bread. And forgive us our trespasses, as we forgive those who trespass against us. And lead us not into temptation, but deliver us from evil; for thine is the kingdom, and the power, and the glory, for ever. Amen.

513 The Apostles' Creed

I believe in God the Father Almighty, Maker of heaven and earth;

And in Jesus Christ, His only Son, our Lord; who was conceived by the Holy Spirit, born of the Virgin Mary, suffered under Pontius Pilate, was crucified, dead, and buried; the third day He arose again from the dead; He ascended into heaven, and sitteth at the right hand of God the Father Almighty; from thence He shall come to judge the quick and the dead.

I believe in the Holy Spirit, the holy catholic Church,* the communion of saints, the forgiveness of sins, the resurrection of the body, and the life everlasting. Amen.

*The Church universal.

514 Ten Commandments

And God spake all these words, saying,

I am the Lord thy God, which have brought thee out of the land of Egypt, out of the house of bondage.

Thou shalt have no other gods before me.

Thou shalt not make unto thee any graven image, or any likeness of any thing that is in heaven above, or that is in the earth beneath, or that is in the water under the earth:

Thou shalt not bow down thyself to them, nor serve them; for I the Lord thy God am a jealous God, visiting the iniquity of the fathers upon the children unto the third and fourth generation of them that hate me;

And shewing mercy unto thousands of them that love me, and keep my commandments.

Thou shalt not take the name of the Lord thy God in vain; for the Lord will not hold him guiltless that taketh his name in vain.

Remember the sabbath day, to keep it holy. Six days shalt thou labour, and do all thy work:

But the seventh day is the sabbath of the Lord thy God: in it thou shalt not do any work, thou, nor thy son, nor thy daughter, thy manservant, nor thy maidservant, nor thy cattle, nor thy stranger that is within thy gates:

For in six days the Lord made heaven and earth, the sea, and all that in them is, and rested the seventh day: wherefore the Lord blessed the sabbath day, and hallowed it.

Honour thy father and thy mother: that thy days may be long upon the land which the Lord thy God giveth thee.

Thou shalt not kill.

Thou shalt not commit adultery.

Thou shalt not steal.

Thou shalt not bear false witness against thy neighbor.

Thou shalt not covet thy neighbour's house, thou shalt not covet thy neighbour's wife, nor his manservant, nor his maidservant, nor his ox, nor his ass, nor any thing that is thy neighbour's. — *Exod. 20:1-17*

515 The True Vine

I am the true vine, and my Father is the husbandman. Every branch in me that beareth not fruit he taketh away: and every branch that beareth fruit, he purgeth it, that it may bring forth more fruit.

Now ye are clean through the word which I have spoken unto you.

Abide in me, and I in you. As the branch cannot bear fruit of itself, except it abide in the vine; no more can ye, except ye abide in me.

I am the vine, ye are the branches: He that abideth in me, and I in him, the same bringeth forth much fruit: for without me ye can do nothing.

If a man abide not in me, he is cast forth as a branch, and is withered; and men gather them, and cast them into the fire, and they are burned.

If ye abide in me, and my words abide in you, ye shall ask what ye will, and it shall be done unto you.

Herein is my Father glorified, that ye bear much fruit; so shall ye be my disciples.

As the Father hath loved me, so have I loved you: continue ye in my love.

If ye keep my commandments, ye shall abide in my love; even as I have kept my Father's commandments, and abide in his love.

These things have I spoken unto you, that my joy might remain in you, and that your joy might be full.
— *John 15:1-11*

516 The Shepherd's Psalm

The Lord is my shepherd; I shall not want.

He maketh me to lie down in green pastures: he leadeth me beside the still waters.

He restoreth my soul: he leadeth me in the paths of righteousness for his name's sake.

Yea, though I walk through the valley of the shadow of death, I will fear no evil: for thou art with me; thy rod and thy staff they comfort me.

Thou preparest a table before me in the presence of mine enemies: thou anointest my head with oil; my cup runneth over.

Surely goodness and mercy shall follow me all the days of my life: and I will dwell in the house of the Lord for ever. — *Psalms 23*

517 Strength for the Day

But we have this treasure in earthen vessels, that the excellency of the power may be of God, and not of us.

We are troubled on every side, yet not distressed; we are perplexed, but not in despair;

Persecuted, but not forsaken; cast down, but not destroyed;

Always bearing about in the body the dying of the Lord Jesus, that the life also of Jesus might be made manifest in our body.

For we which live are alway delivered unto death for Jesus' sake, that the life also of Jesus might be made manifest in our mortal flesh.

Knowing that he which raised up the Lord Jesus shall raise up us also by Jesus, and shall present us with you.

For all things are for your sakes, that the abundant grace might through the thanksgiving of many redound to the glory of God.

For which cause we faint not; but though our outward man perish, yet the inward man is renewed day by day.

For our light affliction, which is but for a moment, worketh for us a far more exceeding and eternal weight of glory;

While we look not at the things which are seen, but at the things which are not seen: for the things which are seen are temporal; but the things which are not seen are eternal.
— *II Cor. 4:7-11, 14-18*

518 The Strength of God

To whom then will ye liken me, or shall I be equal? saith the Holy one.

Lift up your eyes on high, and behold who hath created these things, that bringeth out their host by number:

He calleth them all by names by the greatness of his might, for that he is strong in power; not one faileth.

Why sayest thou, O Jacob, and speakest, O Israel, My way is hid from the Lord, and my judgment is passed over from my God?

Has thou not known? hast thou not heard, that the everlasting God, the Lord, the Creator of the ends of the earth, fainteth not, neither is weary? there is no searching of his understanding.

He giveth power to the faint; and to them that have no might he increaseth strength.

Even the youths shall faint and be weary, and the young men shall utterly fall:

But they that wait upon the Lord shall renew their strength; they shall mount up with wings as eagles; they shall run, and not be weary; and they shall walk, and not faint. — *Isa. 40:25-31*

519 The Way of Love

Though I speak with the tongues of men and of angels, and have not charity, I am become as sounding brass, or a tinkling cymbal.

And though I have the gift of prophecy, and understand all mysteries, and all knowledge; and though I have all faith, so that I could remove mountains, and have not charity, I am nothing.

And though I bestow all my goods to feed the poor, and though I give my body to be burned, and have not charity, it profiteth me nothing.

Charity suffereth long, and is kind: charity envieth not:

Charity vaunteth not itself, is not puffed up,

Doth not behave itself unseemly, seeketh not her own, is not easily provoked, thinketh no evil;

Rejoiceth not in iniquity, but rejoiceth in the truth;

Beareth all things, believeth all things, hopeth all things, endureth all things.

Charity never faileth: but whether there be prophecies, they shall fail; whether there be tongues, they shall cease; whether there be knowledge, it shall vanish away.

For we know in part, and we prophesy in part.

But when that which is perfect is come, then that which is in part shall be done away.

When I was a child, I spake as a child, I understood as a child, I thought as a child: but when I became a man, I put away childish things.

For now we see through a glass, darkly; but then face to face: now I know in part; but then shall I know even as also I am known.

And now abideth faith, hope, charity, these three; but the greatest of these is charity. —*I Corinthians 13*

520 The Christian's Hope

But I would not have you to be ignorant, brethren, concerning them which are asleep, that ye sorrow not, even as others which have no hope.

For if we believe that Jesus died and rose again, even so them also which sleep in Jesus will God bring with him.

For this we say unto you by the word of the Lord, that we which are alive and remain unto the coming of the Lord shall not prevent them which are asleep.

For the Lord himself shall descend from heaven with a shout, with the voice of the archangel, and with the trump of God: and the dead in Christ shall rise first:

Then we which are alive and remain shall be caught up together with them in the clouds, to meet the Lord in the air: and so shall we ever be with the Lord.

Wherefore comfort one another with these words.

But of the times and the seasons, brethren, ye have no need that I write unto you.

For yourselves know perfectly that the day of the Lord so cometh as a thief in the night.

For when they shall say, Peace and safety; then sudden destruction cometh upon them, as travail upon a woman with child; and they shall not escape.

But ye, brethren, are not in darkness, that that day should overtake you as a thief.... Therefore let us not sleep, as do others; but let us watch and be sober. —*I Thess. 4:13—5:6*

521 The Comforter

522 Spiritual Victory

And I will pray the Father, and he shall give you another Comforter, that he may abide with you for ever;

Even the Spirit of truth; whom the world cannot receive, because it seeth him not, neither knoweth him: but ye know him; for he dwelleth with you, and shall be in you.

I will not leave you comfortless: I will come to you.

Yet a little while, and the world seeth me no more; but ye see me: because I live, ye shall live also.

At that day ye shall know that I am in my Father, and ye in me, and I in you.

He that hath my commandments, and keepeth them, he it is that loveth me:

And he that loveth me shall be loved of my Father, and I will love him, and will manifest myself to him.

Judas saith unto him, not Iscariot, Lord, how is it that thou wilt manifest thyself unto us, and not unto the world?

Jesus answered and said unto him, If a man love me, he will keep my words: and my Father will love him, and we will come unto him, and make our abode with him.

He that loveth me not, keepeth not my sayings: and the word which ye hear is not mine, but the Father's which sent me.

These things have I spoken unto you, being yet present with you.

But the Comforter, which is the Holy Ghost, whom the Father will send in my name, he shall teach you all things, and bring all things to your remembrance, whatsoever I have said unto you.

— John 14:16-26

There is therefore now no condemnation to them which are in Christ Jesus, who walk not after the flesh, but after the Spirit.

For the law of the Spirit of life in Christ Jesus, hath made me free from the law of sin and death.

For what the law could not do, in that it was weak through the flesh, God sending his own Son in the likeness of sinful flesh, and for sin, condemned sin in the flesh:

That the righteousness of the law might be fulfilled in us, who walk not after the flesh, but after the Spirit.

For they that are after the flesh do mind the things of the flesh, but they that are after the Spirit the things of the Spirit.

For to be carnally minded is death; but to be spiritually minded is life and peace.

Because the carnal mind is enmity against God: for it is not subject to the law of God, neither indeed can be.

So then they that are in the flesh cannot please God.

But ye are not in the flesh, but in the Spirit, if so be that the Spirit of God dwell in you.

Now if any man have not the Spirit of Christ, he is none of his.

And if Christ be in you, the body is dead because of sin; but the Spirit is life because of righteousness.

Therefore, brethren, we are debtors, not to the flesh, to live after the flesh.

For if ye live after the flesh, ye shall die: but if ye through the Spirit do mortify the deeds of the body, ye shall live.

For as many as are led by the Spirit of God, they are the sons of God.

— Rom. 8:1-10, 12-14

523 Pentecost

And when the day of Pentecost was fully come, they were all with one accord in one place.

And suddenly there came a sound from heaven as of a rushing mighty wind, and it filled all the house where they were sitting.

And there appeared unto them cloven tongues like as of fire, and it sat upon each of them.

And they were all filled with the Holy Ghost, and began to speak with other tongues, as the Spirit gave them utterance.

And they were all amazed, and were in doubt, saying one to another, What meaneth this?

Others mocking said, These men are full of new wine.

But Peter, standing up with the eleven, lifted up his voice, and said unto them, Ye men of Judaea, and all ye that dwell at Jerusalem, be this known unto you, and hearken to my words:

For these are not drunken, as ye suppose, seeing it is but the third hour of the day.

But this is that which was spoken by the prophet Joel;

And it shall come to pass in the last days, saith God, I will pour out of my Spirit upon all flesh: and your sons and your daughters shall prophesy, and your young men shall see visions, and your old men shall dream dreams:

And on my servants and on my handmaidens I will pour out in those days of my Spirit; and they shall prophesy:

Now when they heard this, they were pricked in their heart, and said unto Peter and to the rest of the apostles, Men and brethren, what shall we do?

Then Peter said unto them, Repent, and be baptized every one of you in the name of Jesus Christ for the remission of sins, and ye shall receive the gift of the Holy Ghost.

For the promise is unto you, and to your children, and to all that are afar off, even as many as the Lord our God shall call. — Acts 2:1-4, 12-18, 37-39

524 The Sabbath Day

Remember the sabbath day, to keep it holy.

Six days shalt thou labour, and do all thy work:

But the seventh day is the sabbath of the Lord thy God: in it thou shalt not do any work, thou, nor thy son, nor thy daughter, thy manservant, nor thy maidservant, nor thy cattle, nor thy stranger that is within thy gates:

For in six days the Lord made heaven and earth, the sea, and all that in them is, and rested the seventh day: wherefore the Lord blessed the sabbath day, and hallowed it.
— Exod. 20:8-11

And when he was departed thence, he went into their synagogue:

And, behold, there was a man which had his hand withered. And they asked him, saying, Is it lawful to heal on the sabbath days? that they might accuse him.

And he said unto them, What man shall there be among you, that shall have one sheep, and if it fall into a pit on the sabbath day, will he not lay hold on it, and lift it out?

How much then is a man better than a sheep? Wherefore it is lawful to do well on the sabbath days.
— Matt. 12:9-12

And he said unto them, The sabbath was made for man, and not man for the sabbath:

Therefore the Son of man is Lord also of the sabbath. — Mark 2:27-28

525 Trust in God

Preserve me, O God: for in thee do I put my trust.

O my soul, thou hast said unto the Lord, Thou art my Lord: my goodness extendeth not to thee; but to the saints that are in the earth, and to the excellent, in whom is all my delight.

Their sorrows shall be multiplied that hasten after another god: their drink offerings of blood will I not offer, nor take up their names into my lips.

The Lord is the portion of mine inheritance and of my cup: thou maintainest my lot.

The lines are fallen unto me in pleasant places; yea, I have a goodly heritage.

I will bless the Lord, who hath given me counsel: my reins also instruct me in the night seasons.

I have set the Lord always before me: because he is at my right hand, I shall not be moved.

Therefore my heart is glad, and my glory rejoiceth: my flesh also shall rest in hope.

For thou wilt not leave my soul in hell; neither wilt thou suffer thine Holy One to see corruption.

Thou wilt shew me the path of life: in thy presence is fulness of joy; at thy right hand there are pleasures for evermore. — *Psalms 16*

526 The Love of God

Beloved, let us love one another: for love is of God, and every one that loveth is born of God, and knoweth God.

He that loveth not knoweth not God; for God is love.

In this was manifested the love of God toward us, because that God sent his only begotten Son into the world, that we might live through him.

Herein is love, not that we loved God, but that he loved us, and sent his Son to be the propitiation for our sins.

Beloved, if God so loved us, we ought also to love one another.

No man hath seen God at any time.

If we love one another, God dwelleth in us, and his love is perfected in us.

Hereby know we that we dwell in him, and he in us, because he hath given us of his Spirit.

And we have known and believed the love that God hath to us. God is love; and he that dwelleth in love dwelleth in God, and God in him.

Herein is our love made perfect, that we may have boldness in the day of judgment: because as he is, so are we in this world.

If a man say, I love God, and hateth his brother, he is a liar: for he that loveth not his brother whom he hath seen, how can he love God whom he hath not seen?

And this commandment have we from him, That he who loveth God love his brother also.

— *I John 4:7-13, 16-17, 20-21*

527 The Body of Christ

For as the body is one, and hath many members, and all the members of that one body, being many, are one body: so also is Christ.

For by one Spirit are we all baptized into one body, whether we be Jews or Gentiles, whether we be bond or free; and have been all made to drink into one Spirit.

For the body is not one member, but many.

If the foot shall say, Because I am not the hand, I am not of the body; is it therefore not of the body?

And if the ear shall say, Because I am not the eye, I am not of the body; is it therefore not of the body?

If the whole body were an eye, where were the hearing? If the whole were hearing, where were the smelling?

But now hath God set the members every one of them in the body, as it hath pleased him.

And if they were all one member, where were the body?

But now are they many members, yet but one body.

That there should be no schism in the body; but that the members should have the same care one for another.

And whether one member suffer, all the members suffer with it; or one member be honoured, all the members rejoice with it.

Now ye are the body of Christ, and members in particular.

— I Cor. 12:12-20, 25-27

528 The New Birth

There was a man of the Pharisees, named Nicodemus, a ruler of the Jews:

The same came to Jesus by night, and said unto him, Rabbi, we know that thou art a teacher come from God: for no man can do these miracles that thou doest, except God be with him.

Jesus answered and said unto him, Verily, verily, I say unto thee, Except a man be born again, he cannot see the kingdom of God.

Nicodemus saith unto him, How can a man be born when he is old? can he enter the second time into his mother's womb, and be born?

Jesus answered, Verily, verily, I say unto thee, Except a man be born of water and of the Spirit, he cannot enter into the kingdom of God.

That which is born of the flesh is flesh; and that which is born of the Spirit is spirit. Marvel not that I said unto thee, Ye must be born again.

For God so loved the world, that he gave his only begotten Son, that whosoever believeth in him should not perish, but have everlasting life.

For God sent not his Son into the world to condemn the world; but that the world through him might be saved. *— John 3:1-7, 16-17*

529 The Holiness of God

In the year that king Uzziah died I saw also the Lord sitting upon a throne, high and lifted up, and his train filled the temple.

Above it stood the seraphims: each one had six wings; with twain he covered his face, and with twain he covered his feet, and with twain he did fly.

And one cried unto another, and said, Holy, holy, holy, is the Lord of hosts: the whole earth is full of his glory.

And the posts of the door moved at the voice of him that cried, and the house was filled with smoke.

Then said I, Woe is me! for I am undone; because I am a man of unclean lips, and I dwell in the midst of a people of unclean lips: for mine eyes have seen the King, the Lord of hosts.

Then flew one of the seraphims unto me, having a live coal in his hand, which he had taken with the tongs from off the altar:

And he laid it upon my mouth, and said, Lo, this hath touched thy lips; and thine iniquity is taken away, and thy sin purged.

Also I heard the voice of the Lord, saying, Whom shall I send, and who will go for us? Then said I, Here am I; send me. *— Isa. 6:1-8*

530 The People of God

Wherefore laying aside all malice, and all guile, and hypocrisies, and envies, and all evil speakings,

As newborn babes, desire the sincere milk of the word, that ye may grow thereby:

If so be ye have tasted that the Lord is gracious.

To whom coming, as unto a living stone, disallowed indeed of men, but chosen of God, and precious,

Ye also, as lively stones, are built up a spiritual house, an holy priesthood, to offer up spiritual sacrifices, acceptable to God by Jesus Christ.

Wherefore also it is contained in the scripture, Behold, I lay in Sion a chief corner stone, elect, precious: and he that believeth on him shall not be confounded.

Unto you therefore which believe he is precious: but unto them which be disobedient, the stone which the builders disallowed, the same is made the head of the corner,

And a stone of stumbling, and a rock of offence, even to them which stumble at the word, being disobedient: whereunto also they were appointed.

But ye are a chosen generation, a royal priesthood, an holy nation, a peculiar people; that ye should shew forth the praises of him who hath called you out of darkness into his marvellous light:

Submit yourselves to every ordinance of man for the Lord's sake: whether it be to the king, as supreme;

Or unto governors, as unto them that are sent by him for the punishment of evildoers, and for the praise of them that do well.

For so is the will of God, that with well doing ye may put to silence the ignorance of foolish men:

As free, and not using your liberty for a cloak of maliciousness, but as the servants of God.

Honour all men. Love the brotherhood. Fear God. Honour the king.
—I Pet. 2:1-9, 13-17

531 Fellowship in Christ

I therefore, the prisoner of the Lord, beseech you that ye walk worthy of the vocation wherewith ye are called.

With all lowliness and meekness, with longsuffering, forbearing one another in love;

Endeavouring to keep the unity of the Spirit in the bond of peace.

There is one body, and one Spirit, even as ye are called in one hope of your calling;

One Lord, one faith, one baptism,

One God and Father of all, who is above all, and through all, and in you all.

But unto every one of us is given grace according to the measure of the gift of Christ.

And he gave some, apostles; and some, prophets; and some, evangelists; and some, pastors and teachers;

For the perfecting of the saints, for the work of the ministry, for the edifying of the body of Christ:

Till we all come in the unity of the faith, and of the knowledge of the Son of God, unto a perfect man, unto the measure of the stature of the fulness of Christ:

That we henceforth be no more children, tossed to and fro, and carried about with every wind of doctrine, by the sleight of men, and cunning craftiness, whereby they lie in wait to deceive;

But speaking the truth in love, may grow up into him in all things, which is the head, even Christ.
—Eph. 4:1-7, 11-15

532 Christ's Prayer for Us

These words spake Jesus, and lifted up his eyes to heaven, and said, Father, the hour is come; glorify thy Son, that thy Son also may glorify thee:

As thou hast given him power over all flesh, that he should give eternal life to as many as thou hast given him.

I have manifested thy name unto the men which thou gavest me out of the world: thine they were, and thou gavest them me; and they have kept thy word.

Now they have known that all things whatsoever thou hast given me are of thee.

For I have given unto them the words which thou gavest me; and they have received them, and have known surely that I came out from thee, and they have believed that thou didst send me.

I pray for them: I pray not for the world, but for them which thou hast given me; for they are thine.

I pray not that thou shouldest take them out of the world, but that thou shouldest keep them from the evil.

They are not of the world, even as I am not of the world.

Sanctify them through thy truth: thy word is truth.

As thou hast sent me into the world, even so have I also sent them into the world.

And for their sakes I sanctify myself, that they also might be sanctified through the truth.

Neither pray I for these alone, but for them also which shall believe on me through their word;

That they all may be one; as thou, Father, art in me, and I in thee, that they also may be one in us: that the world may believe that thou hast sent me.

And the glory which thou gavest me I have given them; that they may be one, even as we are one.

— John 17:1-2, 6-9, 15-22

533 Stewardship

Will a man rob God? Yet ye have robbed me. But ye say, Wherein have we robbed thee? In tithes and offerings.

Ye are cursed with a curse: for ye have robbed me, even this whole nation.

Bring ye all the tithes into the storehouse, that there may be meat in mine house,

And prove me now herewith, saith the Lord of hosts, if I will not open you the windows of heaven, and pour you out a blessing, that there shall not be room enough to receive it.

— Mal. 3:8-10

Therefore, as ye abound in every thing, in faith, and utterance, and knowledge, and in all diligence, and in your love to us, see that ye abound in this grace also.

I speak not by commandment, but by occasion of the forwardness of others, and to prove the sincerity of your love.

For ye know the grace of our Lord Jesus Christ, that, though he was rich, yet for your sakes he became poor, that ye through his poverty might be rich.

— II Cor. 8:7-9

But this I say, He which soweth sparingly shall reap also sparingly; and he which soweth bountifully shall reap also bountifully.

Every man according as he purposeth in his heart, so let him give; not grudgingly, or of necessity: for God loveth a cheerful giver.

And God is able to make all grace abound toward you; that ye, always having all sufficiency in all things, may abound to every good work.

— II Cor. 9:6-8

534 Basic Commandments

And one of the scribes came, and having heard them reasoning together, and perceiving that he had answered them well, asked him, Which is the first commandment of all?

And Jesus answered him, The first of all the commandments is, Hear, O Israel; The Lord our God is one Lord:

And thou shalt love the Lord thy God with all thy heart, and with all thy soul, and with all thy mind, and with all thy strength: this is the first commandment.

And the second is like, namely this, Thou shalt love thy neighbour as thyself.

There is none other commandment greater than these.

And the scribe said unto him, Well, Master, thou hast said the truth: for there is one God; and there is none other but he:

And to love him with all the heart, and with all the understanding, and with all the soul, and with all the strength, and to love his neighbour as himself, is more than all whole burnt offerings and sacrifices.

And when Jesus saw that he answered discreetly, he said unto him, Thou art not far from the kingdom of God.
                                    — Mark 12:28-34

535 Prayer

And it came to pass, that, as he was praying in a certain place, when he ceased, one of his disciples said unto him, Lord, teach us to pray, as John also taught his disciples.

And he said unto them, When ye pray, say, Our Father which art in heaven, Hallowed be thy name. Thy kingdom come. Thy will be done, as in heaven, so in earth.

Give us day by day our daily bread. And forgive us our sins; for we also forgive every one that is indebted to us. And lead us not into temptation; but deliver us from evil.

And I say unto you, Ask, and it shall be given you; seek, and ye shall find; knock, and it shall be opened unto you.

For every one that asketh receiveth; and he that seeketh findeth; and to him that knocketh it shall be opened.

If a son shall ask bread of any of you that is a father, will he give him a stone? or if he ask a fish, will he for a fish give him a serpent?

Or if he shall ask an egg, will he offer him a scorpion?

If ye then, being evil, know how to give good gifts unto your children: how much more shall your heavenly Father give the Holy Spirit to them that ask him?   *— Luke 11:1-4, 9-13*

536 Overcoming Grace

And we know that all things work together for good, to them that love God, to them who are the called according to his purpose.

What shall we then say to these things? If God be for us, who can be against us?

He that spared not his own Son, but delivered him up for us all, how shall he not with him also freely give us all things?

Who shall lay any thing to the charge of God's elect? It is God that justifieth.

Who is he that condemneth? It is Christ that died, yea rather, that is risen again, who is even at the right hand of God, who also maketh intercession for us.

Who shall separate us from the love of Christ? shall tribulation, or distress, or persecution, or famine, or nakedness, or peril, or sword?

As it is written, For thy sake we are killed all the day long; we are accounted as sheep for the slaughter.

Nay, in all these things we are more than conquerors, through him that loved us.

For I am persuaded, that neither death, nor life, nor angels, nor principalities, nor powers, nor things present, nor things to come,

Nor height, nor depth, nor any other creature, shall be able to separate us from the love of God, which is in Christ Jesus our Lord. — *Rom. 8:28, 31-39*

537 Jesus and the Law

Think not that I am come to destroy the law, or the prophets: I am not come to destroy, but to fulfil.

For verily I say unto you, Till heaven and earth pass, one jot or one tittle shall in no wise pass from the law, till all be fulfilled.

Whosoever therefore shall break one of these least commandments, and shall teach men so, he shall be called the least in the kingdom of heaven: but whosoever shall do and teach them, the same shall be called great in the kingdom of heaven.

For I say unto you, That except your righteousness shall exceed the righteousness of the scribes and Pharisees, ye shall in no case enter into the kingdom of heaven.

Ye have heard that it hath been said, Thou shalt love thy neighbour, and hate thine enemy.

But I say unto you, Love your enemies, bless them that curse you, do good to them that hate you, and pray for them which despitefully use you, and persecute you;

That ye may be the children of your Father which is in heaven: for he maketh his sun to rise on the evil and on the good, and sendeth rain on the just and on the unjust.

For if ye love them which love you,

what reward have ye? do not even the publicans the same?

And if ye salute your brethren only, what do ye more than others? do not even the publicans so?

Be ye therefore perfect, even as your Father which is in heaven is perfect.
— *Matt. 5:17-20, 43-48*

538 The Building of God

At that time ye were without Christ, being aliens from the commonwealth of Israel, and strangers from the covenants of promise, having no hope, and without God in the world:

But now in Christ Jesus ye who sometimes were far off are made nigh by the blood of Christ.

For he is our peace, who hath made both one, and hath broken down the middle wall of partition between us;

Having abolished in his flesh the enmity, even the law of commandments contained in ordinances; for to make in himself of twain one new man, so making peace;

And that he might reconcile both unto God in one body by the cross, having slain the enmity thereby:

And came and preached peace to you which were afar off, and to them that were nigh.

For through him we both have access by one Spirit unto the Father.

Now therefore ye are no more strangers and foreigners, but fellow-citizens with the saints, and of the household of God;

And are built upon the foundation of the apostles and prophets, Jesus Christ himself being the chief corner stone;

In whom all the building fitly framed together groweth unto an holy temple in the Lord: in whom ye also are builded together for an habitation of God through the Spirit. — *Eph. 2:12-22*

539 God's Creation

O Lord our Lord, how excellent is thy name in all the earth! who hast set thy glory above the heavens.

Out of the mouth of babes and sucklings hast thou ordained strength because of thine enemies, that thou mightest still the enemy and the avenger.

When I consider thy heavens, the work of thy fingers, the moon and the stars, which thou hast ordained;

What is man, that thou art mindful of him? and the son of man, that thou visitest him?

For thou hast made him a little lower than the angels, and hast crowned him with glory and honour.

Thou madest him to have dominion over the works of thy hands; thou hast put all things under his feet:

All sheep and oxen, yea, and the beasts of the field; the fowl of the air, and the fish of the sea, and whatsoever passeth through the paths of the seas.

O Lord our Lord, how excellent is thy name in all the earth! — *Psalms 8*

540 The Mind of Christ

If there be therefore any consolation in Christ, if any comfort of love, if any fellowship of the Spirit, if any bowels and mercies,

Fulfil ye my joy, that ye be likeminded, having the same love, being of one accord, of one mind.

Let nothing be done through strife or vainglory; but in lowliness of mind let each esteem other better than themselves.

Look not every man on his own things, but every man also on the things of others.

Let this mind be in you. which was also in Christ Jesus: who, being in the form of God, thought it not robbery to be equal with God:

But made himself of no reputation, and took upon him the form of a servant, and was made in the likeness of men:

And being found in fashion as a man, he humbled himself, and became obedient unto death, even the death of the cross.

Wherefore God also hath highly exalted him, and given him a name which is above every name:

That at the name of Jesus every knee should bow, of things in heaven, and things in earth, and things under the earth;

And that every tongue should confess that Jesus Christ is Lord, to the glory of God the Father. — *Phil. 2:1-11*

541 A Missionary Melody

O sing unto the Lord a new song: sing unto the Lord, all the earth.

Sing unto the Lord, bless his name; shew forth his salvation from day to day.

Declare his glory among the heathen, his wonders among all people. For the Lord is great, and greatly to be praised: he is to be feared above all gods.

For all the gods of the nations are idols: but the Lord made the heavens.

Honour and majesty are before him: strength and beauty are in his sanctuary.

Give unto the Lord, O ye kindreds of the people, give unto the Lord glory and strength.

Give unto the Lord the glory due unto his name: bring an offering, and come into his courts.

O worship the Lord in the beauty of holiness: fear before him, all the earth.

Say among the heathen that the Lord reigneth: the world also shall be established that it shall not be moved: he shall judge the people righteously.

Let the heavens rejoice, and let the earth be glad; let the sea roar, and the fulness thereof.

Let the field be joyful, and all that is therein: then shall all the trees of the wood rejoice

Before the Lord: for he cometh, for he cometh to judge the earth: he shall judge the world with righteousness, and the people with his truth.

—Psalms 96

542 Reconciliation

For the love of Christ constraineth us; because we thus judge, that if one died for all, then were all dead:

And that he died for all, that they which live should not henceforth live unto themselves, but unto him which died for them, and rose again.

Wherefore, henceforth know we no man after the flesh: yea, though we have known Christ after the flesh, yet now henceforth know we him no more.

Therefore if any man be in Christ, he is a new creature: old things are passed away; behold, all things are become new.

And all things are of God, who hath reconciled us to himself by Jesus Christ, and hath given to us the ministry of reconciliation;

To wit, that God was in Christ, reconciling the world unto himself, not imputing their trespasses unto them; and hath committed unto us the word of reconciliation.

Now then we are ambassadors for Christ, as though God did beseech you by us: we pray you in Christ's stead, be ye reconciled to God.

For he hath made him to be sin for us, who knew no sin; that we might be made the righteousness of God in him. *—II Cor. 5:14-21*

543 The Leadership of God

Without faith it is impossible to please him: for he that cometh to God must believe that he is, and that he is a rewarder of them that diligently seek him.

By faith Noah, being warned of God of things not seen as yet, moved with fear, prepared an ark to the saving of his house; by the which he condemned the world, and became heir of the righteousness which is by faith.

By faith Abraham, when he was called to go out into a place which he should after receive for an inheritance, obeyed; and he went out, not knowing whither he went.

By faith he sojourned in the land of promise, as in a strange country, dwelling in tabernacles with Isaac and Jacob, the heirs with him of the same promise:

For he looked for a city which hath foundations, whose builder and maker is God.

Through faith also Sarah herself received strength to conceive seed, and was delivered of a child when she was past age, because she judged him faithful who had promised.

Therefore sprang there even of one, and him as good as dead, so many as the stars of the sky in multitude, and as the sand which is by the sea shore innumerable.

These all died in faith, not having received the promises, but having seen them afar off, and were persuaded of them, and embraced them, and confessed that they were strangers and pilgrims on the earth.

But now they desire a better country, that is, an heavenly:

Wherefore God is not ashamed to be called their God: for he hath prepared for them a city. *—Heb. 11:6-13, 16*

544 The Lord's Supper

Moreover, brethren, I would not that ye should be ignorant, how that all our fathers were under the cloud, and all passed through the sea;

And were all baptized unto Moses in the cloud and in the sea; and did all eat the same spiritual meat;

And did all drink the same spiritual drink: for they drank of that spiritual Rock that followed them: and that Rock was Christ.

The cup of blessing which we bless, is it not the communion of the blood of Christ?

The bread which we break, is it not the communion of the body of Christ?

For we being many are one bread, and one body: for we are all partakers of that one bread. —*I Cor. 10:1-4, 16-17*

For I have received of the Lord that which also I delivered unto you, That the Lord Jesus the same night in which he was betrayed took bread:

And when he had given thanks, he brake it, and said, Take, eat: this is my body, which is broken for you: this do in remembrance of me.

After the same manner also he took the cup, when he had supped, saying, This cup is the new testament in my blood: this do ye, as oft as ye drink it, in remembrance of me.

For as often as ye eat this bread, and drink this cup, ye do shew the Lord's death till he come.

Wherefore whosoever shall eat this bread, and drink this cup of the Lord, unworthily, shall be guilty of the body and blood of the Lord.

But let a man examine himself, and so let him eat of that bread, and drink of that cup. For he that eateth and drinketh unworthily, eateth and drinketh damnation to himself.
—*I Cor. 11:23-29*

545 God's Goodness

Bless the Lord, O my soul: and all that is within me, bless his holy name.

Bless the Lord, O my soul, and forget not all his benefits:

Who forgiveth all thine iniquities; who healeth all thy diseases;

Who redeemeth thy life from destruction; who crowneth thee with lovingkindness and tender mercies;

Who satisfieth thy mouth with good things; so that thy youth is renewed like the eagle's.

The Lord executeth righteousness and judgment for all that are oppressed.

He hath not dealt with us after our sins; nor rewarded us according to our iniquities.

For as the heaven is high above the earth, so great is his mercy toward them that fear him.

As far as the east is from the west, so far hath he removed our transgressions from us.

Like as a father pitieth his children, so the Lord pitieth them that fear him.

For he knoweth our frame; he remembereth that we are dust.

As for man, his days are as grass: as a flower of the field, so he flourisheth.

For the wind passeth over it, and it is gone; and the place thereof shall know it no more.

But the mercy of the Lord is from everlasting to everlasting upon them that fear him, and his righteousness unto children's children;

To such as keep his covenant, and to those that remember his commandments to do them.

Bless the Lord, all his works in all places of his dominion: bless the Lord, O my soul. —*Ps. 103:1-6, 10-18, 22*

546 The Israel of God

Christ hath redeemed us from the curse of the law, being made a curse for us: for it is written, cursed is every one that hangeth on a tree:

That the blessing of Abraham might come on the Gentiles through Jesus Christ; that we might receive the promise of the Spirit through faith.

If there had been a law given which could have given life, verily righteousness should have been by the law.

But the scripture hath concluded all under sin, that the promise by faith of Jesus Christ, might be given to them that believe.

But before faith came, we were kept under the law, shut up unto the faith which should afterwards be revealed.

Wherefore the law was our schoolmaster, to bring us unto Christ, that we might be justified by faith.

But after that faith is come, we are no longer under a schoolmaster.

For ye are all the children of God by faith in Christ Jesus.

For as many of you as have been baptized into Christ have put on Christ.

There is neither Jew nor Greek, there is neither bond nor free, there is neither male nor female: for ye are all one in Christ Jesus.

And if ye be Christ's, then are ye Abraham's seed, and heirs according to the promise. — *Gal. 3:13-14, 21b-29*

For as many as are led by the Spirit of God, they are the sons of God.

For ye have not received the spirit of bondage again to fear; but ye have received the spirit of adoption, whereby we cry, Abba, Father.

The Spirit itself beareth witness with our spirit, that we are the children of God:

And if children, then heirs; heirs of God, and joint-heirs with Christ; if so be that we suffer with him, that we may be also glorified together.

For I reckon that the sufferings of this present time are not worthy to be compared with the glory which shall be revealed in us. — *Rom. 8:14-18*

547 Children

At the same time came the disciples unto Jesus, saying, Who is the greatest in the kingdom of heaven?

And Jesus called a little child unto him, and set him in the midst of them,

And said, Verily I say unto you, Except ye be converted, and become as little children, ye shall not enter into the kingdom of heaven.

Whosoever therefore shall humble himself as this little child, the same is greatest in the kingdom of heaven.

And whoso shall receive one such little child in my name receiveth me.

Take heed that ye despise not one of these little ones; for I say unto you, that in heaven their angels do always behold the face of my Father which is in heaven.

For the Son of man is come to save that which was lost.

How think ye? If a man have an hundred sheep, and one of them be gone astray, doth he not leave the ninety and nine, and goeth into the mountains, and seeketh that which is gone astray?

And if so be that he find it, verily I say unto you, he rejoiceth more of that sheep, than of the ninety and nine which went not astray.

Even so it is not the will of your Father which is in heaven, that one of these little ones should perish.
— *Matt. 18:1-5, 10-14*

548 God's Invitation

Ho, every one that thirsteth, come ye to the waters, and he that hath no money; come ye, buy, and eat; yea, come, buy wine and milk without money and without price.

Wherefore do ye spend money for that which is not bread? and your labour for that which satisfieth not? hearken diligently unto me, and eat ye that which is good, and let your soul delight itself in fatness.

Incline your ear, and come unto me: hear, and your soul shall live; and I will make an everlasting covenant with you, even the sure mercies of David.

Behold, I have given him for a witness to the people, a leader and commander to the people.

Behold, thou shalt call a nation that thou knowest not, and nations that knew not thee shall run unto thee, because of the Lord thy God, and for the Holy One of Israel; for he hath glorified thee.

Seek ye the Lord while he may be found, call ye upon him while he is near:

Let the wicked forsake his way, and the unrighteous man his thoughts: and let him return unto the Lord, and he will have mercy upon him; and to our God, for he will abundantly pardon.

For my thoughts are not your thoughts, neither are your ways my ways, saith the Lord.

For as the heavens are higher than the earth, so are my ways higher than your ways, and my thoughts than your thoughts.

For as the rain cometh down, and the snow from heaven, and returneth not thither, but watereth the earth, and maketh it bring forth and bud, that it may give seed to the sower, and bread to the eater:

So shall my word be that goeth forth out of my mouth: it shall not return unto me void, but it shall accomplish that which I please, and it shall prosper in the thing whereto I sent it.

For ye shall go out with joy, and be led forth with peace: the mountains and the hills shall break forth before you into singing, and all the trees of the field shall clap their hands.

Instead of the thorn shall come up the fir tree, and instead of the brier shall come up the myrtle tree:

And it shall be to the Lord for a name, for an everlasting sign that shall not be cut off. —Isa. 55:1-13

549 The Christian's Armor

Finally, my brethren, be strong in the Lord, and in the power of his might.

Put on the whole armour of God, that ye may be able to stand against the wiles of the devil.

For we wrestle not against flesh and blood, but against principalities, against powers, against the rulers of the darkness of this world, against spiritual wickedness in high places.

Wherefore take unto you the whole armour of God, that ye may be able to withstand in the evil day, and having done all, to stand.

Stand therefore, having your loins girt about with truth, and having on the breastplate of righteousness; and your feet shod with the preparation of the gospel of peace;

Above all, taking the shield of faith, wherewith ye shall be able to quench all the fiery darts of the wicked.

And take the helmet of salvation, and the sword of the Spirit, which is the word of God:

Praying always with all prayer and supplication in the Spirit, and watching thereunto with all perseverance and supplication for all saints.

—Eph. 6:10-18

550 Christ's Coming Again

When they therefore were come together, they asked of him, saying, Lord, wilt thou at this time restore again the kingdom to Israel?

And he said unto them, It is not for you to know the times or the seasons, which the Father hath put in his own power.

But ye shall receive power, after that the Holy Ghost is come upon you: and ye shall be witnesses unto me both in Jerusalem, and in all Judaea, and in Samaria, and unto the uttermost part of the earth.

And when he had spoken these things, while they beheld, he was taken up; and a cloud received him out of their sight.

And while they looked stedfastly toward heaven as he went up, behold, two men stood by them in white apparel;

Which also said, Ye men of Galilee, why stand ye gazing up into heaven? this same Jesus, which is taken up from you into heaven, shall so come in like manner as ye have seen him go into heaven. — Acts 1:6-11

For the grace of God that bringeth salvation hath appeared to all men, teaching us that, denying ungodliness and worldly lusts, we should live soberly, righteously, and godly, in this present world;

Looking for that blessed hope, and the glorious appearing of the great God and our Saviour Jesus Christ;

Who gave himself for us, that he might redeem us from all iniquity, and purify unto himself a peculiar people, zealous of good works. — Titus 2:11-14

Behold, I come quickly: hold that fast which thou hast, that no man take thy crown. — Rev. 3:11

551 World Missions

For Christ is the end of the law for righteousness to every one that believeth.

For Moses describeth the righteousness which is of the law, That the man which doeth those things shall live by them.

But the righteousness which is of faith speaketh on this wise, Say not in thine heart, Who shall ascend into heaven? (that is, to bring Christ down from above:)

Or, who shall descend into the deep? (that is, to bring up Christ again from the dead.)

But what saith it? The word is nigh thee, even in thy mouth, and in thy heart: that is, the word of faith, which we preach;

That if thou shalt confess with thy mouth the Lord Jesus, and shalt believe in thine heart that God hath raised him from the dead, thou shalt be saved.

For with the heart man believeth unto righteousness; and with the mouth confession is made unto salvation.

For the scripture saith, Whosoever believeth on him shall not be ashamed.

For there is no difference between the Jew and the Greek: for the same Lord over all is rich unto all that call upon him.

For whosoever shall call upon the name of the Lord shall be saved.

How then shall they call on him in whom they have not believed? and how shall they believe in him of whom they have not heard? and how shall they hear without a preacher?

And how shall they preach, except they be sent? as it is written, How beautiful are the feet of them that preach the gospel of peace, and bring glad tidings of good things! — Rom. 10:4-15

552 The Incarnate Word

Let not your heart be troubled: ye believe in God, believe also in me.

In my Father's house are many mansions: if it were not so, I would have told you. I go to prepare a place for you.

And if I go and prepare a place for you, I will come again, and receive you unto myself; that where I am, there ye may be also.

And whither I go ye know, and the way ye know.

Thomas saith unto him, Lord, we know not whither thou goest; and how can we know the way?

Jesus saith unto him, I am the way, the truth, and the life: no man cometh unto the Father, but by me.

If ye had known me, ye should have known my Father also: and from henceforth ye know him, and have seen him.

Philip saith unto him, Lord, shew us the Father, and it sufficeth us.

Jesus saith unto him, Have I been so long time with you, and yet hast thou not known me, Philip? he that hath seen me hath seen the Father; and how sayest thou then, Shew us the Father?

Believest thou not that I am in the Father, and the Father in me? the words that I speak unto you I speak not of myself: but the Father that dwelleth in me, he doeth the works.

Believe me that I am in the Father, and the Father in me: or else believe me for the very works' sake.

Verily, verily, I say unto you, He that believeth on me, the works that I do shall he do also; and greater works than these shall he do; because I go unto my Father.

Yet a little while, and the world seeth me no more; but ye see me: because I live, ye shall live also.

At that day ye shall know that I am in my Father, and ye in me, and I in you.

He that hath my commandments, and keepeth them, he it is that loveth me:

And he that loveth me shall be loved of my Father, and I will love him, and will manifest myself to him.
— John 14:1-12, 19-21

553 The Holy Scriptures

Search the scriptures; for in them ye think ye have eternal life: and they are they which testify of me. *— John 5:39*

We have also a more sure word of prophecy; whereunto ye do well that ye take heed, as unto a light that shineth in a dark place, until the day dawn, and the day star arise in your hearts:

Knowing this first, that no prophecy of the scripture is of any private interpretation.

For the prophecy came not in old time by the will of man: but holy men of God spake as they were moved by the Holy Ghost.
— II Pet. 1:19-21

But continue thou in the things which thou hast learned and hast been assured of, knowing of whom thou hast learned them;

And that from a child thou hast known the holy scriptures, which are able to make thee wise unto salvation, through faith which is in Christ Jesus.

All scripture is given by inspiration of God, and is profitable for doctrine, for reproof, for correction, for instruction in righteousness:

That the man of God may be perfect, throughly furnished unto all good works. *— II Tim. 3:14-17*

554 Our Witness to Christ

Whosoever shall confess me before men, him shall the Son of man also confess before the angels of God:

But he that denieth me before men shall be denied before the angels of God.

And whosoever shall speak a word against the Son of man, it shall be forgiven him: but unto him that blasphemeth against the Holy Ghost it shall not be forgiven.

And when they bring you unto the synagogues, and unto magistrates, and powers, take ye no thought of how or what thing ye shall answer, or what ye shall say: for the Holy Ghost shall teach you in the same hour what ye ought to say.

And seek not ye what ye shall eat, or what ye shall drink, neither be ye of doubtful mind.

For all these things do the nations of the world seek after: and your Father knoweth that ye have need of these things.

But rather seek ye the kingdom of God; and all these things shall be added unto you.

Fear not, little flock; for it is your Father's good pleasure to give you the kingdom.

Blessed are those servants, whom the lord when he cometh shall find watching: verily I say unto you, that he shall gird himself, and make them to sit down to meat, and will come forth and serve them.

And if he shall come in the second watch, or come in the third watch, and find them so, blessed are those servants.

And this know, that if the goodman of the house had known what hour the thief would come, he would have watched, and not have suffered his house to be broken through.

Be ye therefore ready also: for the Son of man cometh at an hour when ye think not. — *Luke 12:8-12, 29-32, 37-40*

555 Thanksgiving

Oh that men would praise the Lord for his goodness, and for his wonderful works to the children of men!

Let them exalt him also in the congregation of the people, and praise him in the assembly of the elders.

He turneth rivers into a wilderness, and the watersprings into dry ground;

A fruitful land into barrenness, for the wickedness of them that dwell therein.

He turneth the wilderness into a standing water, and dry ground into watersprings.

And there he maketh the hungry to dwell, that they may prepare a city for habitation; and sow the fields, and plant vineyards, which may yield fruits of increase.

He blesseth them also, so that they are multiplied greatly, and suffereth not their cattle to decrease.

Again, they are minished and brought low through oppression, affliction, and sorrow.

He poureth contempt upon princes, and causeth them to wander in the wilderness, where there is no way.

Yet setteth he the poor on high from affliction, and maketh him families like a flock.

The righteous shall see it, and rejoice: and all iniquity shall stop her mouth.

Whoso is wise, and will observe these things, even they shall understand the lovingkindness of the Lord.
— *Ps. 107:31-43*

556 The Suffering Servant

Who hath believed our report? and to whom is the arm of the Lord revealed?

For he shall grow up before him as a tender plant, and as a root out of a dry ground: he hath no form nor comeliness; and when we shall see him, there is no beauty that we should desire him.

He is despised and rejected of men; a man of sorrows, and acquainted with grief: and we hid as it were our faces from him; he was despised, and we esteemed him not.

Surely he hath borne our griefs, and carried our sorrows: yet we did esteem him stricken, smitten of God, and afflicted.

But he was wounded for our transgressions, he was bruised for our iniquities: the chastisement of our peace was upon him; and with his stripes we are healed.

All we like sheep have gone astray; we have turned every one to his own way; and the Lord hath laid on him the iniquity of us all.

He was oppressed, and he was afflicted, yet he opened not his mouth: he is brought as a lamb to the slaughter, and as a sheep before her shearers is dumb, so he openeth not his mouth.

He was taken from prison and from judgment: and who shall declare his generation? for he was cut off out of the land of the living: for the transgression of my people was he stricken.

And he made his grave with the wicked, and with the rich in his death; because he had done no violence, neither was any deceit in his mouth.

Yet it pleased the Lord to bruise him; he hath put him to grief:

When thou shalt make his soul an offering for sin, he shall see his seed, he shall prolong his days, and the pleasure of the Lord shall prosper in his hand.

He shall see of the travail of his soul, and shall be satisfied: by his knowledge shall my righteous servant justify many; for he shall bear their iniquities.

Therefore will I divide him a portion with the great, and he shall divide the spoil with the strong; because he hath poured out his soul unto death:

And he was numbered with the transgressors; and he bare the sins of many, and made intercession for the transgressors.   — Isaiah 53

557 The Godly Mother

Who can find a virtuous woman? for her price is far above rubies.

The heart of her husband doth safely trust in her, so that he shall have no need of spoil.

She will do him good and not evil all the days of her life.

Her husband is known in the gates, when he sitteth among the elders of the land.

She maketh fine linen, and selleth it; and delivereth girdles unto the merchant.

Strength and honour are her clothing; and she shall rejoice in time to come.

She openeth her mouth with wisdom; and in her tongue is the law of kindness.

She looketh well to the ways of her household, and eateth not the bread of idleness.

Her children arise up, and call her blessed; her husband also, and he praiseth her.

Many daughters have done virtuously, but thou excellest them all.

Favour is deceitful, and beauty is vain: but a woman that feareth the Lord, she shall be praised.

Give her of the fruit of her hands; and let her own works praise her in the gates.   — Prov. 31:10-12, 23-31

558 Renewal in Worship

The Lord is my light and my salvation; whom shall I fear? the Lord is the strength of my life; of whom shall I be afraid?

When the wicked, even mine enemies and my foes, came upon me to eat up my flesh, they stumbled and fell.

Though an host should encamp against me, my heart shall not fear: though war should rise against me, in this will I be confident.

One thing have I desired of the Lord, that will I seek after; that I may dwell in the house of the Lord all the days of my life, to behold the beauty of the Lord, and to inquire in his temple.

For in the time of trouble he shall hide me in his pavilion: in the secret of his tabernacle shall he hide me; he shall set me up upon a rock.

When thou saidst, Seek ye my face; my heart said unto thee, Thy face, Lord, will I seek.

Hide not thy face far from me; put not thy servant away in anger: thou hast been my help; leave me not, neither forsake me, O God of my salvation.

When my father and my mother forsake me, then the Lord will take me up.

Teach me thy way, O Lord, and lead me in a plain path, because of mine enemies.

Deliver me not over unto the will of mine enemies: for false witnesses are risen up against me, and such as breathe out cruelty.

I had fainted, unless I had believed to see the goodness of the Lord in the land of the living.

Wait on the Lord: be of good courage, and he shall strengthen thine heart: wait, I say, on the Lord. — *Ps. 27:1-5, 8-14*

559 Consecration

I beseech you therefore, brethren, by the mercies of God, that ye present your bodies a living sacrifice, holy, acceptable unto God, which is your reasonable service.

And be not conformed to this world: but be ye transformed by the renewing of your mind, that ye may prove what is that good, and acceptable, and perfect, will of God.

For I say, through the grace given unto me, to every man that is among you, not to think of himself more highly than he ought to think; but to think soberly, according as God hath dealt to every man the measure of faith.

Let love be without dissimulation. Abhor that which is evil; cleave to that which is good.

Be kindly affectioned one to another with brotherly love; in honour preferring one another;

Not slothful in business; fervent in spirit; serving the Lord;

Rejoicing in hope; patient in tribulation; continuing instant in prayer;

Distributing to the necessity of saints; given to hospitality.

Bless them which persecute you: bless, and curse not.

Rejoice with them that do rejoice, and weep with them that weep.

Be of the same mind one toward another.

Mind not high things, but condescend to men of low estate. Be not wise in your own conceits.

Recompense to no man evil for evil. Provide things honest in the sight of all men.

If it be possible, as much as lieth in you, live peaceably with all men. Be not overcome of evil, but overcome evil with good. — *Rom. 12:1-3, 9-18, 21*

560 The Christian Home

Be ye therefore followers of God, as dear children;

> And walk in love, as Christ also hath loved us, and hath given himself for us an offering and a sacrifice to God for a sweetsmelling savour.

Giving thanks always for all things unto God and the Father in the name of our Lord Jesus Christ;

> Submitting yourselves one to another in the fear of God.

Wives, submit yourselves unto your own husbands, as unto the Lord.

> For the husband is the head of the wife, even as Christ is the head of the church: and he is the saviour of the body.

Therefore as the church is subject unto Christ, so let the wives be to their own husbands in every thing.

> Husbands, love your wives, even as Christ also loved the church, and gave himself for it;

That he might sanctify and cleanse it with the washing of water by the word,

> That he might present it to himself a glorious church, not having spot, or wrinkle, or any such thing; but that it should be holy and without blemish.

So ought men to love their wives as their own bodies. He that loveth his wife loveth himself.

> For no man ever yet hated his own flesh; but nourisheth and cherisheth it, even as the Lord the church:

For we are members of his body, of his flesh, and of his bones.

> For this cause shall a man leave his father and mother, and shall be joined unto his wife, and they two shall be one flesh.

This is a great mystery: but I speak concerning Christ and the church.

Nevertheless let every one of you in particular so love his wife even as himself; and the wife see that she reverence her husband.

— Eph. 5:1-2, 20-33

561 Worship and Trust

How amiable are thy tabernacles, O Lord of hosts!

> My soul longeth, yea, even fainteth for the courts of the Lord: my heart and my flesh crieth out for the living God.

Yea, the sparrow hath found an house, and the swallow a nest for herself, where she may lay her young, even thine altars, O Lord of hosts, my King, and my God.

> Blessed are they that dwell in thy house: they will be still praising thee.

Blessed is the man whose strength is in thee; in whose heart are the ways of them.

> Who passing through the valley of Baca make it a well; the rain also filleth the pools.

They go from strength to strength, every one of them in Zion appeareth before God.

> O Lord God of hosts, hear my prayer: give ear, O God of Jacob.

Behold, O God our shield, and look upon the face of thine anointed.

> For a day in thy courts is better than a thousand. I had rather be a doorkeeper in the house of my God, than to dwell in the tents of wickedness.

For the Lord God is a sun and shield: the Lord will give grace and glory: no good thing will he withhold from them that walk uprightly.

> O Lord of hosts, blessed is the man that trusteth in thee. *— Psalms 84*

562 Doers of the Word

The disciple is not above his master: but every one that is perfect shall be as his master.

And why beholdest thou the mote that is in thy brother's eye, but perceivest not the beam that is in thine own eye?

Either how canst thou say to thy brother, Brother, let me pull out the mote that is in thine eye, when thou thyself beholdest not the beam that is in thine own eye?

Thou hypocrite, cast out first the beam out of thine own eye, and then shalt thou see clearly to pull out the mote that is in thy brother's eye.

For a good tree bringeth not forth corrupt fruit; neither doth a corrupt tree bring forth good fruit.

For every tree is known by his own fruit. For of thorns men do not gather figs, nor of a bramble bush gather they grapes.

A good man out of the good treasure of his heart, bringeth forth that which is good; and an evil man out of the evil treasure of his heart, bringeth forth that which is evil: for out of the abundance of the heart his mouth speaketh.

And why call ye me, Lord, Lord, and do not the things which I say?

Whosoever cometh to me, and heareth my sayings, and doeth them, I will shew you to whom he is like:

He is like a man which built an house, and digged deep, and laid the foundation on a rock:

And when the flood arose, the stream beat vehemently upon that house, and could not shake it: for it was founded upon a rock.

But he that heareth, and doeth not, is like a man that without a foundation built an house upon the earth; against which the stream did beat vehemently, and immediately it fell; and the ruin of that house was great.
—Luke 6:40-49

563 The Saviour's Birth

And there were in the same country shepherds abiding in the field, keeping watch over their flock by night.

And, lo, the angel of the Lord came upon them, and the glory of the Lord shone round about them: and they were sore afraid.

And the angel said unto them, Fear not: for, behold, I bring you good tidings of great joy, which shall be to all people.

For unto you is born this day in the city of David a Saviour, which is Christ the Lord.

And this shall be a sign unto you; Ye shall find the babe wrapped in swaddling clothes, lying in a manger.

And suddenly there was with the angel a multitude of the heavenly host praising God, and saying,

Glory to God in the highest, and on earth peace, good will toward men.

And it came to pass, as the angels were gone away from them into heaven, the shepherds said one to another, Let us now go even unto Bethlehem, and see this thing which is come to pass, which the Lord hath made known unto us.

And they came with haste, and found Mary, and Joseph, and the babe lying in a manger.

And when they had seen it, they made known abroad the saying which was told them concerning this child.

And all they that heard it wondered at those things which were told them by the shepherds.

But Mary kept all these things, and pondered them in her heart.
—Luke 2:8-19

564 The Will of God

Furthermore then we beseech you, brethren, and exhort you by the Lord Jesus, that as ye have received of us how ye ought to walk and to please God, so ye would abound more and more.

For ye know what commandments we gave you by the Lord Jesus.

For this is the will of God, even your sanctification, that ye should abstain from fornication:

That every one of you should know how to possess his vessel in sanctification and honour; not in the lust of concupiscence, even as the Gentiles which know not God:

That no man go beyond and defraud his brother in any matter: because that the Lord is the avenger of all such, as we also have forewarned you and testified.

For God hath not called us unto uncleanness, but unto holiness.

He therefore that despiseth, despiseth not man, but God, who hath also given unto us his holy Spirit.

But as touching brotherly love ye need not that I write unto you: for ye yourselves are taught of God to love one another. —*I Thess. 4:1-9*

565 Purity of Heart

Behold, what manner of love the Father hath bestowed upon us, that we should be called the sons of God:

Therefore the world knoweth us not, because it knew him not.

Beloved, now are we the sons of God, and it doth not yet appear what we shall be: but we know that, when he shall appear, we shall be like him; for we shall see him as he is.

And every man that hath this hope in him purifieth himself, even as he is pure.

Hereby perceive we the love of God, because he laid down his life for us: and we ought to lay down our lives for the brethren.

But whoso hath this world's good, and seeth his brother have need, and shutteth up his bowels of compassion from him, how dwelleth the love of God in him?

My little children, let us not love in word, neither in tongue, but in deed and in truth.

And hereby we know that we are of the truth, and shall assure our hearts before him.

For if our heart condemn us, God is greater than our heart, and knoweth all things.

Beloved, if our heart condemn us not, then have we confidence toward God. —*I John 3:1-3, 16-21*

566 Christlikeness

For even hereunto were ye called: because Christ also suffered for us, leaving us an example, that ye should follow his steps: who did no sin, neither was guile found in his mouth:

Who, when he was reviled, reviled not again; when he suffered, he threatened not; but committed himself to him that judgeth righteously:

Who his own self bare our sins in his own body on the tree, that we, being dead to sins, should live unto righteousness: by whose stripes ye were healed. —*I Pet. 2:21-24*

Be ye all of one mind, having compassion one of another, love as brethren, be pitiful, be courteous:

Not rendering evil for evil, or railing for railing; but contrariwise blessing; knowing that ye are thereunto called, that ye should inherit a blessing.

For he that will love life, and see good days, let him refrain his tongue from evil, and his lips that they speak no guile:

Let him eschew evil, and do good; let him seek peace, and ensue it.

For the eyes of the Lord are over the righteous, and his ears are open unto their prayers: but the face of the Lord is against them that do evil.

—*I Pet. 3:8-12*

567 Thirsting for God

As the hart panteth after the water brooks, so panteth my soul after thee, O God.

My soul thirsteth for God, for the living God: when shall I come and appear before God?

My tears have been my meat day and night, while they continually say unto me, Where is thy God?

When I remember these things, I pour out my soul in me: for I had gone with the multitude, I went with them to the house of God, with the voice of joy and praise, with a multitude that kept holyday.

Why art thou cast down, O my soul? and why art thou disquieted in me? hope thou in God: for I shall yet praise him for the help of his countenance.

Yet the Lord will command his lovingkindness in the daytime, and in the night his song shall be with me, and my prayer unto the God of my life.

I will say unto God my rock, Why hast thou forgotten me? why go I mourning because of the oppression of the enemy?

As with a sword in my bones, mine enemies reproach me; while they say daily unto me, Where is thy God?

Why art thou cast down, O my soul? and why art thou disquieted within me?

Hope thou in God: for I shall yet praise him, who is the health of my countenance, and my God.

—*Ps. 42:1-5, 8-11*

568 Achieving Faith

Now when he had ended all his sayings in the audience of the people, he entered into Capernaum.

And a certain centurion's servant, who was dear unto him, was sick, and ready to die.

And when he heard of Jesus, he sent unto him the elders of the Jews, beseeching him that he would come and heal his servant.

And when they came to Jesus, they besought him instantly, saying, That he was worthy for whom he should do this:

For he loveth our nation, and he hath built us a synagogue.

Then Jesus went with them. And when he was now not far from the house, the centurion sent friends to him, saying unto him, Lord, trouble not thyself: for I am not worthy that thou shouldest enter under my roof:

Wherefore neither thought I myself worthy to come unto thee: but say in a word, and my servant shall be healed.

For I also am a man set under authority, having under me soldiers, and I say unto one, Go, and he goeth; and to another, Come, and he cometh; and to my servant, Do this, and he doeth it.

When Jesus heard these things, he marvelled at him, and turned him about, and said unto the people that followed him, I say unto you, I have not found so great faith, no, not in Israel.

And they that were sent, returning to the house, found the servant whole that had been sick. —*Luke 7:1-10*

569 The Coming Kingdom

The wilderness and the solitary place shall be glad for them; and the desert shall rejoice, and blossom as the rose.

It shall blossom abundantly, and rejoice even with joy and singing: the glory of Lebanon shall be given unto it, the excellency of Carmel and Sharon, they shall see the glory of the Lord, and the excellency of our God.

Strengthen ye the weak hands, and confirm the feeble knees.

Say to them that are of a fearful heart, Be strong, fear not: behold, your God will come with vengeance, even God with a recompence, he will come and save you.

Then the eyes of the blind shall be opened, and the ears of the deaf shall be unstopped.

Then shall the lame man leap as an hart, and the tongue of the dumb sing: for in the wilderness shall waters break out, and streams in the desert.

And the parched ground shall become a pool, and the thirsty land springs of water: in the habitation of dragons, where each lay, shall be grass with reeds and rushes.

And an highway shall be there, and a way, and it shall be called The way of holiness; the unclean shall not pass over it; but it shall be for those: the wayfaring men, though fools, shall not err therein.

No lion shall be there, nor any ravenous beast shall go up thereon, it shall not be found there; but the redeemed shall walk there:

And the ransomed of the Lord shall return, and come to Zion with songs and everlasting joy upon their heads: they shall obtain joy and gladness, and sorrow and sighing shall flee away. — *Isaiah 35*

570 The Christian's Task

And Jesus went about all the cities and villages, teaching in their synagogues, and preaching the gospel of the kingdom, and healing every sickness and every disease among the people.

But when he saw the multitudes, he was moved with compassion on them, because they fainted, and were scattered abroad, as sheep having no shepherd.

Then saith he unto his disciples, The harvest truly is plenteous, but the labourers are few;

Pray ye therefore the Lord of the harvest, that he will send forth labourers into his harvest. — *Matt. 9:35-38*

Jesus saith unto them, My meat is to do the will of him that sent me, and to finish his work.

Say not ye, There are yet four months, and then cometh harvest? behold, I say unto you, Lift up your eyes, and look on the fields; for they are white already to harvest.

And he that reapeth receiveth wages, and gathereth fruit unto life eternal: that both he that soweth and he that reapeth may rejoice together. And herein is that saying true, One soweth, and another reapeth.

I sent you to reap that whereon ye bestowed no labour: other men laboured, and ye are entered into their labours. — *John 4:34-38*

Go ye therefore, and teach all nations, baptizing them in the name of the Father, and of the Son, and of the Holy Ghost:

Teaching them to observe all things whatsoever I have commanded you: and, lo, I am with you alway, even unto the end of the world.
— *Matt. 28:19-20*

571 The Church Triumphant

And I looked, and, lo, a Lamb stood on the mount Sion, and with him an hundred forty and four thousand, having his Father's name written in their foreheads.

And I heard a voice from heaven, as the voice of many waters, and as the voice of a great thunder: and I heard the voice of harpers harping with their harps:

And they sung as it were a new song before the throne, and before the four beasts, and the elders: and no man could learn that song but the hundred and forty and four thousand, which were redeemed from the earth.

These are they which are not defiled with women; for they are virgins. These are they which follow the Lamb whithersoever he goeth.

These were redeemed from among men, being the firstfruits unto God and to the Lamb.

And in their mouth was found no guile: for they are without fault before the throne of God.

And I saw another angel fly in the midst of heaven, having the everlasting gospel to preach unto them that dwell on the earth, and to every nation, and kindred, and tongue, and people,

Saying with a loud voice, Fear God, and give glory to him; for the hour of his judgment is come: and worship him that made heaven, and earth, and the sea, and the fountains of waters.

Here is the patience of the saints: here are they that keep the commandments of God, and the faith of Jesus.

And I heard a voice from heaven saying unto me, Write, Blessed are the dead which die in the Lord from henceforth: Yea, saith the Spirit, that they may rest from their labours.

— *Rev. 14:1-7, 12-13*

572 Church Growth

Therefore let all the house of Israel know assuredly, that God hath made that same Jesus, whom ye have crucified, both Lord and Christ.

Now when they heard this, they were pricked in their heart, and said unto Peter and to the rest of the apostles, Men and brethren, what shall we do?

Then Peter said unto them, Repent, and be baptized every one of you in the name of Jesus Christ for the remission of sins, and ye shall receive the gift of the Holy Ghost.

For the promise is unto you, and to your children, and to all that are afar off, even as many as the Lord our God shall call.

And with many other words did he testify and exhort, saying, Save yourselves from this untoward generation.

Then they that gladly received his word were baptized: and the same day there were added unto them about three thousand souls.

And they continued stedfastly in the apostles' doctrine and fellowship, and in breaking of bread, and in prayers.

And fear came upon every soul: and many wonders and signs were done by the apostles.

And all that believed were together, and had all things common;

And sold their possessions and goods, and parted them to all men, as every man had need.

And they, continuing daily with one accord in the temple, and breaking bread from house to house, did eat their meat with gladness and singleness of heart.

Praising God, and having favour with all the people. And the Lord added to the church daily such as should be saved.

— *Acts 2:36-47*

573 The Garden Prayer

And he came out, and went, as he was wont, to the mount of Olives; and his disciples also followed him.

And when he was at the place, he said unto them, Pray that ye enter not into temptation.

And he was withdrawn from them about a stone's cast, and kneeled down, and prayed,

Saying, Father, if thou be willing, remove this cup from me: nevertheless not my will, but thine, be done.

And there appeared an angel unto him from heaven, strengthening him.

And being in an agony he prayed more earnestly: and his sweat was as it were great drops of blood falling down to the ground.

And when he rose up from prayer, and was come to his disciples, he found them sleeping for sorrow,

And said unto them, Why sleep ye? rise and pray, lest ye enter into temptation. — *Luke 22:39-46*

574 The Resurrection

In the end of the sabbath, as it began to dawn toward the first day of the week, came Mary Magdalene and the other Mary to see the sepulchre.

And, behold, there was a great earthquake: for the angel of the Lord descended from heaven, and came and rolled back the stone from the door, and sat upon it.

His countenance was like lightning, and his raiment white as snow:

And for fear of him the keepers did shake, and became as dead men.

And the angel answered and said unto the women, Fear not ye: for I know that ye seek Jesus, which was crucified.

He is not here: for he is risen, as he said. Come, see the place where the Lord lay.

And go quickly, and tell his disciples that he is risen from the dead; and, behold, he goeth before you into Galilee; there shall ye see him: lo, I have told you.

And they departed quickly from the sepulchre with fear and great joy; and did run to bring his disciples word.

And as they went to tell his disciples, behold, Jesus met them, saying, All hail. And they came and held him by the feet, and worshipped him.

Then said Jesus unto them, Be not afraid: go tell my brethren that they go into Galilee, and there shall they see me. — *Matt. 28:1-10*

575 Christ's Care

When Jesus then lifted up his eyes, and saw a great company come unto him, he saith unto Philip, Whence shall we buy bread, that these may eat?

And this he said to prove him: for he himself knew what he would do.

Philip answered him, Two hundred pennyworth of bread is not sufficient for them, that every one of them may take a little.

One of his disciples, Andrew, Simon Peter's brother, saith unto him,

There is a lad here, which hath five barley loaves, and two small fishes: but what are they among so many?

And Jesus said, Make the men sit down. Now there was much grass in the place. So the men sat down, in number about five thousand.

And Jesus took the loaves; and when he had given thanks, he distributed to the disciples, and the disciples to them that were set down; and likewise of the fishes as much as they would.

When they were filled, he said unto his disciples, Gather up the fragments that remain, that nothing be lost.

Therefore they gathered them together, and filled twelve baskets with the fragments of the five barley loaves which remained over and above unto them that had eaten.

Then those men, when they had seen the miracle that Jesus did, said, This is of a truth that prophet that should come into the world.

— John 6:5-14

576 The Day of the Lord

But, beloved, be not ignorant of this one thing, that one day is with the Lord as a thousand years, and a thousand years as one day.

The Lord is not slack concerning his promise, as some men count slackness;

But is longsuffering to us-ward, not willing that any should perish, but that all should come to repentance.

But the day of the Lord will come as a thief in the night; in the which the heavens shall pass away with a great noise,

And the elements shall melt with fervent heat, the earth also and the works that are therein shall be burned up.

Seeing then that all these things shall be dissolved, what manner of persons ought ye to be in all holy conversation and godliness,

Looking for and hasting unto the coming of the day of God, wherein the heavens being on fire shall be dissolved, and the elements shall melt with fervent heat?

Nevertheless we, according to his promise, look for new heavens and a new earth, wherein dwelleth righteousness.

— II Pet. 3:8-13

577 Kingdom Priorities

No man can serve two masters: for either he will hate the one, and love the other; or else he will hold to the one, and despise the other.

Ye cannot serve God and mammon.

Therefore I say unto you, Take no thought for your life, what ye shall eat, or what ye shall drink; nor yet for your body, what ye shall put on. Is not the life more than meat, and the body than raiment?

Behold the fowls of the air: for they sow not, neither do they reap, nor gather into barns; yet your heavenly Father feedeth them. Are ye not much better than they?

Which of you by taking thought can add one cubit unto his stature?

And why take ye thought for raiment? Consider the lilies of the field, how they grow; they toil not, neither do they spin:

And yet I say unto you, That even Solomon in all his glory was not arrayed like one of these.

Wherefore, if God so clothe the grass of the field, which to day is, and to morrow is cast into the oven, shall he not much more clothe you, O ye of little faith?

Therefore take no thought, saying, What shall we eat? or, What shall we drink? or, Wherewithal shall we be clothed?

(For after all these things do the Gentiles seek:) for your heavenly Father knoweth that ye have need of all these things.

But seek ye first the kingdom of God, and his righteousness; and all these things shall be added unto you.

Take therefore no thought for the morrow; for the morrow shall take thought for the things of itself.

— Matt. 6:24-34

578 Praise to God

The heavens declare the glory of God; and the firmament sheweth his handywork.

Day unto day uttereth speech, and night unto night sheweth knowledge.

There is no speech nor language, where their voice is not heard.

Their line is gone out through all the earth, and their words to the end of the world. In them hath he set a tabernacle for the sun,

Which is as a bridegroom coming out of his chamber, and rejoiceth as a strong man to run a race.

His going forth is from the end of the heaven, and his circuit unto the ends of it: and there is nothing hid from the heat thereof.

The law of the Lord is perfect, converting the soul: the testimony of the Lord is sure, making wise the simple.

The statutes of the Lord are right, rejoicing the heart: the commandment of the Lord is pure, enlightening the eyes.

The fear of the Lord is clean, enduring for ever: the judgments of the Lord are true and righteous altogether.

More to be desired are they than gold, yea, than much fine gold: sweeter also than honey and the honeycomb.

Moreover by them is thy servant warned: and in keeping of them there is great reward.

Who can understand his errors? cleanse thou me from secret faults.

Keep back thy servant also from presumptuous sins; let them not have dominion over me: then shall I be upright, and I shall be innocent from the great transgression.

Let the words of my mouth, and the meditation of my heart, be accept- able in thy sight, O Lord, my strength, and my redeemer. —*Psalms 19*

579 The Future Life

All flesh is not the same flesh: but there is one kind of flesh of men, another flesh of beasts, another of fishes, and another of birds.

There are also celestial bodies, and bodies terrestrial: but the glory of the celestial is one, and the glory of the terrestrial is another.

There is one glory of the sun, and another glory of the moon, and another glory of the stars: for one star differeth from another star in glory.

So also is the resurrection of the dead. It is sown in corruption; it is raised in incorruption: it is sown in dishonour; it is raised in glory: it is sown in weakness; it is raised in power:

It is sown a natural body; it is raised a spiritual body. There is a natural body, and there is a spiritual body.

And so it is written, The first man Adam was made a living soul; the last Adam was made a quickening spirit.

Howbeit that was not first which is spiritual, but that which is natural; and afterward that which is spiritual.

The first man is of the earth, earthy: the second man is the Lord from heaven.

Behold, I shew you a mystery; We shall not all sleep, but we shall all be changed, in a moment, in the twinkling of an eye, at the last trump: for the trumpet shall sound, and the dead shall be raised incorruptible, and we shall be changed.

For this corruptible must put on incorruption, and this mortal must put on immortality. —*I Cor. 15:39-47, 51-53*

Moreover, brethren, I declare unto you the gospel which I preached unto you, which also ye have received, and wherein ye stand;

By which also ye are saved, if ye keep in memory what I preached unto you, unless ye have believed in vain.

For I delivered unto you first of all that which I also received, how that Christ died for our sins according to the scriptures;

And that he was buried, and that he rose again the third day according to the scriptures:

And that he was seen of Cephas, then of the twelve:

After that, he was seen of above five hundred brethren at once; of whom the greater part remain unto this present, but some are fallen asleep.

After that, he was seen of James; then of all the apostles.

And last of all he was seen of me also, as of one born out of due time.

For I am the least of the apostles, that am not meet to be called an apostle, because I persecuted the church of God.

But by the grace of God I am what I am: and his grace which was bestowed upon me was not in vain; but I laboured more abundantly than they all: yet not I, but the grace of God which was with me.

Therefore whether it were I or they, so we preach, and so ye believed.

But now is Christ risen from the dead, and become the firstfruits of them that slept.

For since by man came death, by man came also the resurrection of the dead.

For as in Adam all die, even so in Christ shall all be made alive.
—I Cor. 15:1-11, 20-22

Blessed are the poor in spirit: for theirs is the kingdom of heaven.

Blessed are they that mourn: for they shall be comforted.

Blessed are the meek: for they shall inherit the earth.

Blessed are they which do hunger and thirst after righteousness: for they shall be filled.

Blessed are the merciful: for they shall obtain mercy.

Blessed are the pure in heart: for they shall see God.

Blessed are the peacemakers: for they shall be called the children of God.

Blessed are they which are persecuted for righteousness' sake: for theirs is the kingdom of heaven.

Blessed are ye, when men shall revile you, and persecute you, and shall say all manner of evil against you falsely, for my sake.

Rejoice, and be exceeding glad: for great is your reward in heaven: for so persecuted they the prophets which were before you.

Ye are the salt of the earth: but if the salt have lost his savour, wherewith shall it be salted? it is thenceforth good for nothing, but to be cast out, and to be trodden under foot of men.

Ye are the light of the world. A city that is set on an hill cannot be hid.

Neither do men light a candle, and put it under a bushel, but on a candlestick; and it giveth light unto all that are in the house.

Let your light so shine before men, that they may see your good works, and glorify your Father which is in heaven.
—Matt. 5:3-16

582 Redemption

Therefore being justified by faith, we have peace with God through our Lord Jesus Christ:

By whom also we have access by faith into this grace wherein we stand, and rejoice in hope of the glory of God.

And not only so, but we glory in tribulations also: knowing that tribulation worketh patience; and patience, experience; and experience, hope:

And hope maketh not ashamed; because the love of God is shed abroad in our hearts by the Holy Ghost which is given unto us.

For when we were yet without strength, in due time Christ died for the ungodly.

For scarcely for a righteous man will one die: yet peradventure for a good man some would even dare to die.

But God commendeth his love toward us, in that, while we were yet sinners, Christ died for us.

Much more then, being now justified by his blood, we shall be saved from wrath through him.

For if, when we were enemies, we were reconciled to God by the death of his Son, much more, being reconciled, we shall be saved by his life.

And not only so, but we also joy in God through our Lord Jesus Christ, by whom we have now received the atonement.   — *Rom. 5:1-11*

583 Christian Baptism

Know ye not, that so many of us as were baptized into Jesus Christ were baptized into his death?

Therefore we are buried with him by baptism into death: that like as Christ was raised up from the dead by the glory of the Father, even so we also should walk in newness of life.

For if we have been planted together in the likeness of his death, we shall be also in the likeness of his resurrection:

Knowing this, that our old man is crucified with him, that the body of sin might be destroyed, that henceforth we should not serve sin.

For he that is dead is freed from sin.

Now if we be dead with Christ, we believe that we shall also live with him:

Knowing that Christ being raised from the dead dieth no more; death hath no more dominion over him.

For in that he died, he died unto sin once: but in that he liveth, he liveth unto God.

Likewise reckon ye also yourselves to be dead indeed unto sin, but alive unto God through Jesus Christ our Lord.

Let not sin therefore reign in your mortal body, that ye should obey it in the lusts thereof.

Neither yield ye your members as instruments of unrighteousness unto sin:

But yield yourselves unto God, as those that are alive from the dead, and your members as instruments of righteousness unto God.   — *Rom. 6:3-13*

584 Revival

Lord, thou hast been favourable unto thy land: thou hast brought back the captivity of Jacob.

Thou hast forgiven the iniquity of thy people, thou hast covered all their sin.

Thou hast taken away all thy wrath: thou hast turned thyself from the fierceness of thine anger.

Turn us, O God of our salvation, and cause thine anger toward us to cease.

Wilt thou be angry with us for ever? wilt thou draw out thine anger to all generations?

Wilt thou not revive us again: that thy people may rejoice in thee? Shew us thy mercy, O Lord, and grant us thy salvation.

I will hear what God the Lord will speak: for he will speak peace unto his people, and to his saints: but let them not turn again to folly.

Surely his salvation is nigh them that fear him; that glory may dwell in our land.

Mercy and truth are met together; righteousness and peace have kissed each other.

Truth shall spring out of the earth; and righteousness shall look down from heaven. — *Ps. 85:1-11*

585 The Church's Mission

Comfort ye, comfort ye my people, saith your God.

Speak ye comfortably to Jerusalem, and cry unto her, that her warfare is accomplished, that her iniquity is pardoned: for she hath received of the Lord's hand double for all her sins.

The voice of him that crieth in the wilderness, Prepare ye the way of the Lord, make straight in the desert a highway for our God.

Every valley shall be exalted, and every mountain and hill shall be made low: and the crooked shall be made straight, and the rough places plain:

And the glory of the Lord shall be revealed, and all flesh shall see it together: for the mouth of the Lord hath spoken it.

The voice said, Cry. And he said, What shall I cry? All flesh is grass, and all the goodliness thereof is as the flower of the field:

The grass withereth, the flower fadeth: because the spirit of the Lord bloweth upon it: surely the people is grass.

The grass withereth, the flower fadeth: but the word of our God shall stand for ever. — *Isa. 40:1-8*

586 Partakers of Christ

For this cause we also, since the day we heard it, do not cease to pray for you, and to desire that ye might be filled with the knowledge of his will in all wisdom and spiritual understanding;

That ye might walk worthy of the Lord unto all pleasing, being fruitful in every good work, and increasing in the knowledge of God;

Strengthened with all might, according to his glorious power, unto all patience and longsuffering with joyfulness;

Giving thanks unto the Father, which hath made us meet to be partakers of the inheritance of the saints in light:

Who hath delivered us from the power of darkness, and hath translated us into the kingdom of his dear Son:

In whom we have redemption through his blood, even the forgiveness of sins:

Who is the image of the invisible God, the firstborn of every creature:

For by him were all things created, that are in heaven, and that are in earth, visible and invisible, whether they be thrones, or dominions, or principalities, or powers: all things were created by him, and for him:

And he is before all things, and by him all things consist.

And he is the head of the body, the church: who is the beginning, the firstborn from the dead; that in all things he might have the preeminence. — *Col. 1:9-18*

587 God Ever Present

O Lord, thou hast searched me, and known me.

Thou knowest my downsitting and mine uprising, thou understandest my thought afar off.

Thou compassest my path and my lying down, and art acquainted with all my ways.

For there is not a word in my tongue, but, lo, O Lord, thou knowest it altogether.

Whither shall I go from thy spirit? or whither shall I flee from thy presence?

If I ascend up into heaven, thou art there: if I make my bed in hell, behold, thou art there.

If I take the wings of the morning, and dwell in the uttermost parts of the sea;

Even there shall thy hand lead me, and thy right hand shall hold me.

If I say, Surely the darkness shall cover me; even the night shall be light about me.

Yea, the darkness hideth not from thee; but the night shineth as the day: the darkness and the light are both alike to thee.   *— Ps. 139:1-4, 7-12*

588 The Christian Life

For God hath not appointed us to wrath, but to obtain salvation by our Lord Jesus Christ,

Who died for us, that, whether we wake or sleep, we should live together with him.

Wherefore comfort yourselves together, and edify one another, even as also ye do.

And we beseech you, brethren, to know them which labour among you, and are over you in the Lord, and admonish you;

And to esteem them very highly in love for their work's sake. And be at peace among yourselves.

Now we exhort you, brethren, warn them that are unruly, comfort the feebleminded, support the weak, be patient toward all men.

See that none render evil for evil unto any man; but ever follow that which is good, both among yourselves, and to all men.

Rejoice evermore. Pray without ceasing. In every thing give thanks: for this is the will of God in Christ Jesus concerning you.

Quench not the Spirit. Despise not prophesyings. Prove all things; hold fast that which is good.

Abstain from all appearance of evil.

And the very God of peace sanctify you wholly; and I pray God your whole spirit and soul and body be preserved blameless unto the coming of our Lord Jesus Christ.

Faithful is he that calleth you, who also will do it.   *— 1 Thess. 5:9-24*

589 The Living Word

In the beginning was the Word, and the Word was with God, and the Word was God.

The same was in the beginning with God.

All things were made by him; and without him was not any thing made that was made.

In him was life; and the life was the light of men.

And the light shineth in darkness; and the darkness comprehended it not.

There was a man sent from God, whose name was John.

The same came for a witness, to bear witness of the Light, that all men through him might believe.

He was not that Light, but was sent to bear witness of that Light.

That was the true Light, which lighteth every man that cometh into the world.

He was in the world, and the world was made by him, and the world knew him not.

He came unto his own, and his own received him not.

But as many as received him, to them gave he power to become the sons of God, even to them that believe on his name:

Which were born, not of blood, nor of the will of the flesh, nor of the will of man, but of God.

And the Word was made flesh, and dwelt among us, (and we beheld his glory, the glory as of the only begotten of the Father,) full of grace and truth. —John 1:1-14

590 Resurrection Faith

Blessed be the God and Father of our Lord Jesus Christ, which according to his abundant mercy hath begotten us again unto a lively hope, by the resurrection of Jesus Christ from the dead,

To an inheritance incorruptible, and undefiled, and that fadeth not away, reserved in heaven for you, who are kept by the power of God, through faith unto salvation, ready to be revealed in the last time.

Wherein ye greatly rejoice, though now for a season, if need be, ye are in heaviness through manifold temptations:

That the trial of your faith, being much more precious than of gold that perisheth, though it be tried with fire, might be found unto praise and honour and glory, at the appearing of Jesus Christ:

Whom having not seen, ye love; in whom, though now ye see him not, yet believing, ye rejoice with joy unspeakable and full of glory:

Receiving the end of your faith, even the salvation of your souls.
—I Pet. 1:3-9

591 God's Care

I will bless the Lord at all times: his praise shall continually be in my mouth.

My soul shall make her boast in the Lord: the humble shall hear thereof, and be glad.

O magnify the Lord with me, and let us exalt his name together.

I sought the Lord, and he heard me, and delivered me from all my fears.

They looked unto him, and were lightened: and their faces were not ashamed.

This poor man cried, and the Lord heard him, and saved him out of all his troubles.

The angel of the Lord encampeth round about them that fear him, and delivereth them.

O taste and see that the Lord is good: blessed is the man that trusteth in him.

O fear the Lord, ye his saints: for there is no want to them that fear him.

The young lions do lack, and suffer hunger: but they that seek the Lord shall not want any good thing.

The eyes of the Lord are upon the righteous, and his ears are open unto their cry.

The face of the Lord is against them that do evil, to cut off the remembrance of them from the earth.

The righteous cry, and the Lord heareth, and delivereth them out of all their troubles.

The Lord is nigh unto them that are of a broken heart; and saveth such as be of a contrite spirit. —Ps. 34:1-10, 15-18

592 Heroes of Faith

And what shall I more say? for the time would fail me to tell of Gedeon, and of Barak, and of Samson, and of Jephthae; of David also, and Samuel, and of the prophets:

Who through faith subdued kingdoms, wrought righteousness, obtained promises, stopped the mouths of lions,

Quenched the violence of fire, escaped the edge of the sword, out of weakness were made strong, waxed valiant in fight, turned to flight the armies of the aliens.

Women received their dead raised to life again: and others were tortured, not accepting deliverance; that they might obtain a better resurrection:

And others had trial of cruel mockings and scourgings, yea, moreover of bonds and imprisonment:

They were stoned, they were sawn asunder, were tempted, were slain with the sword: they wandered about in sheepskins and goatskins; being destitute, afflicted, tormented;

(Of whom the world was not worthy:) they wandered in deserts, and in mountains, and in dens and caves of the earth.

And these all, having obtained a good report through faith, received not the promise: God having provided some better thing for us, that they without us should not be made perfect.

Wherefore seeing we also are compassed about with so great a cloud of witnesses, let us lay aside every weight, and the sin which doth so easily beset us.

And let us run with patience the race that is set before us, looking unto Jesus the author and finisher of our faith;

Who for the joy that was set before him endured the cross, despising the shame, and is set down at the right hand of the throne of God.

Wherefore we receiving a kingdom which cannot be moved, let us have grace, whereby we may serve God acceptably with reverence and godly fear. —Heb. 11:32 – 12:2, 28

593 The Source of Help

I will lift up mine eyes unto the hills, from whence cometh my help.

My help cometh from the Lord, which made heaven and earth.

He will not suffer thy foot to be moved: he that keepeth thee will not slumber.

Behold, he that keepeth Israel shall neither slumber nor sleep.

The Lord is thy keeper: the Lord is thy shade upon thy right hand.

The sun shall not smite thee by day, nor the moon by night.

The Lord shall preserve thee from all evil: he shall preserve thy soul.

The Lord shall preserve thy going out and thy coming in from this time forth, and even for evermore.
—Psalms 121

Topical Index

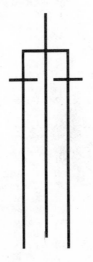

General Index

Titles and *First Lines*

Glory Be to the Father

GLORIA PATRI

Anonymous

Charles Meineke, 1782 - 1850

Glo - ry be to the Fa - ther, and to the Son, and to the Ho - ly Ghost; As it

was in the be - gin-ning, is now, and ev-er shall be, world without end. A-men. A-men.

Lord, Dismiss Us with Thy Blessing

SICILIAN MARINERS' HYMN

John Fawcett, 1740 - 1817, alt.

From a Sicilian melody

1. Lord, dis - miss us   with Thy bless-ing; Fill our hearts with   joy and peace.
2. Thanks we give and   ad - o - ra - tion For Thy gos - pel's   joy - ful sound.

Let   us   each, Thy   love pos-sess-ing, Tri - umph in re - deem-ing grace.
May   the fruits of   Thy   sal - va - tion In   our hearts and   lives a - bound;

Oh,   re-fresh us; oh, re-fresh us, Trav-'ling thro' this   wil - der - ness!
Ev - er faith-ful, ev-er faith-ful To the truth may   we be found.